MUD
4 00

D1226907

McGRAW-HILL PUBLICATIONS IN THE
AGRICULTURAL SCIENCES

LEON J. COLE, CONSULTING EDITOR

FIELD CROPS

*The quality of the material used in the manufacture
of this book is governed by continued postwar shortages.*

There are also the related series of McGraw-Hill Publications in the Botanical Sciences, of which Edmund W. Sinnott is Consulting Editor, and in the Zoological Sciences, of which A. Franklin Shull is Consulting Editor. Titles in the Agricultural Sciences were published in these series in the period 1917 to 1937.

Field Crops

BY

HOWARD C. RATHER

Professor and Head, Farm Crops Department,
Michigan State College;
Head, Farm Crops Section,
Michigan Agricultural Experiment Station

FIRST EDITION
NINTH IMPRESSION

McGRAW-HILL BOOK COMPANY, INC.
NEW YORK AND LONDON
1942

FIELD CROPS

COPYRIGHT, 1942, BY THE

McGRAW-HILL BOOK COMPANY, INC.

PRINTED IN THE UNITED STATES OF AMERICA

*All rights reserved. This book, or
parts thereof, may not be reproduced
in any form without permission of
the publishers.*

THE MAPLE PRESS COMPANY, YORK, PA.

To
The Memory of My Father
Henry Robert Rather
1861–1942

PREFACE

An introductory course in field crops is designed to provide a broad survey of agronomy for students who eventually choose this as their major work. It also must provide insight into agronomic problems for those whose specialty may be in other agricultural fields or in one of the basic sciences closely related to agriculture.

This book has been prepared to serve these broader needs. It deals with the theory and practice of crop production and management of the land. It is intended for use by college students taking their first and in many instances their only formal course in field crops. It should also prove useful to college short-course students who are primarily concerned with applications of agronomic principles to immediate farm practice. It is hoped that not a few farmers may find much of the material interesting and useful.

Questions and problems in various forms are provided at the end of each chapter to aid in reviewing and applying the subject material. References have been suggested from which closely related information may be secured, and it is expected that both students and instructors will find the publications of their own state colleges of agriculture exceedingly useful both in supplementing the discussion of principles and in making applications of local significance.

Acknowledgment is made of the published material quoted and duly credited in each instance and of the photographs and illustrations that others have contributed. Appreciation is also due the great numbers of workers who have contributed to general agronomic information and experience.

The author is particularly indebted to a colleague, Dr. Carter M. Harrison, for a most helpful critical examination of the entire manuscript.

HOWARD C. RATHER.

EAST LANSING, MICH.,
August, 1942.

CONTENTS

FIELD CROPS

CHAPTER I

THE SIGNIFICANCE OF FARM CROPS

HISTORICAL

Man's progress has been closely associated with the culture and care of crop plants. The primitive savage who hunted and fished for a living did not need a fixed home. Even the earliest livestock keepers could be more or less nomadic, following their herds and flocks from one grazing land to another. But when man started to grow plants, he had to "stay on the job." There were plantings to be made, weeds to be pulled, predators and enemies to be driven off, and harvests to be gathered. With the culture of plants, there developed the acquisition of property and the building of homes. Ownership of the land was first tribal and communal, later feudal, and finally private with all its stimulating effect on individual interest and initiative.

Civilization did not make its greatest advances in the humid tropics where food was plentiful and could be had for the taking. Such conditions bred indolence. Nor did it develop in the barrenness of the desert or in regions that were forever bleak and cold where only poverty could prevail. But in regions where man's ingenuity was tested and also rewarded, where nature, guided by man's effort, responded, where crops had to be cared for in seasons of productivity and stored and saved for seasons of adversity, there civilizations were born.

ORIGIN OF CROP PLANTS

The development of plants from their wild estate into the productive forms that feed and clothe the human race is a story that intrigues the imagination. But it is a story that for the most part is buried with a remote and unrecorded era. Even the tale a scientist might put together in his study of genes and chromosomes and genetic relationships is based on much conjecture, for the wild ancestors of many of our most common and most useful field crops have never been found.

The Story of Corn.—There is in point the story of maize, or Indian corn, the greatest contribution of the Western Hemisphere to world agriculture. Today corn is maturing somewhere in the world every month of the year. It is surpassed only by wheat as a source of human food. Yet white man first knew corn in 1492, when Spaniards who accompanied Columbus found it growing in the West Indies. Nor has white man for all his skill and knowledge made any fundamental genetic improvement in corn, at least, not until very recent years.

Every kind of corn—flour corn, popcorn, sweet corn, the early flints of the North, the great dents of the corn belt, the prolific varieties

Fig. 1.—Corn, the New World's greatest contribution to agriculture.

of the South—was known and grown by the Indians long before Columbus made his eventful voyage to a New World. By that time, corn had already played a leading role in the civilizations developed by the Incas of South America and the Mayas of Central America, both of which lay claim to its origination.

Mangelsdorf and Reeves[1] after exhaustive study believe corn to be of South American rather than Mexican origin. They visualize

[1] Mangelsdorf, P. C., and R. G. Reeves, The Origin of Indian Corn and Its Relatives, *Tex. Agr. Expt. Sta. Bul.* 574 (monograph), 1939.

maize as a wild pod corn originating from a remote andropogonaceous ancestor. Tripsacum, a coarse perennial grass of southwestern United States and South America, they believe, has a similar ancestor; and natural crosses, rare but possible between these remotely related species, gave rise to a new plant, teosinte. Evidence from chromosome and other genetic studies, which they present, indicates that back-crosses between teosinte and the original corn are probably responsible for some of the newer types such as the pointed popcorns, the dent corns, and the straight-rowed flint and flour corns grown by Central and North American Indians but still almost unknown in the Andean region where the first corn is believed to have evolved.

Old World Plants.—Possibly in some such fashion, at least the genetic history of some of our crop plants may be pieced together. In a general way, we know most of these crops to be of Old World origin. Wheat, barley, and alfalfa appear to have originated in southwestern Asia and wild ancestral forms of barley are still growing in the general region of the Red Sea. Oats, too, originated in western Asia or eastern Europe. Rye, much less remote in its beginnings, is apparently strictly a Russian plant.

Chinese scholars lay some claims to wheat as being an oriental species; and certainly wheat, rice, common millet, proso, and soybeans were cultivated in China in very ancient times.

Cotton belongs to both hemispheres. Centuries before the Christian Era, cotton culture had attained importance in India whence it spread into Egypt, Greece, Italy, and Spain. But cotton also was used by the ancient Incas, and Spanish explorers found it growing in the West Indies, Mexico, and Peru.

The use of sugar as an important human food is of modern origin. Honey, sweet fruits, and sirups satisfied the sweet tooth of the ancients, and sugar was supposed to be a medicine sold only by the apothecaries. The cane plant from which most of our sugar comes is of tropical origin, probably from New Guinea. Early Greek writers told of the sugar that comes from bamboos and mentioned it as a rare product. As late as 1482, sugar is said to have sold on the London market for $275 a 100 lb.; but within a few years the price was greatly reduced, and sugar became a food item.

A German chemist, Andreas Marggraf, first obtained sugar from the beet in 1747; and one of his students, Franz Karl Achard, perfected these methods so that they could be used commercially. He received financial support from Frederick the Great.

Beginnings of Forage Culture.—The culture and preservation of forage crops are largely a development of European agriculture.

Though grass, in its broadest sense, contributes to the livelihood of more people throughout the world than any other crop, it was the European farmer who cared for and domesticated most of the wild species used for forage and who developed hay curing and intensive pasture management to a high degree; and it was the European colonist who carried his ideas and methods of forage-crop culture to North and South America, South Africa, Australia, New Zealand, and elsewhere.

It is true that alfalfa and possibly red clover, our greatest legumes, were cultivated in southwestern Asia in ancient times. But red clover occurs naturally throughout most of Europe, and the spread of alfalfa to the New World was the result of European enterprise.

Timothy, greatest of American hay grasses, is a native of Europe, although it was first brought under cultivation in New Hampshire and, as a crop, was introduced into Europe from this country.

Kentucky and Canada bluegrass, so widely grown in North America as to appear native and be known by American names, are also of Old World origin. Possibly they came to this country in hayloft sweepings that the earliest colonists brought to this country for seeding purposes.

The fescues and reed canary grass are native to both North America and Europe. Bermuda grass, a southern perennial, is a native of India. Smooth brome, first cultivated in Hungary and Russia, was introduced into the United States by the California Experiment Station about 1880. Sudan grass was introduced by workers of the U.S. Department of Agriculture as recently as 1909.

Of the legumes, alfalfa, as an important crop, originated in Asia and was brought to this country by the Spaniards. Its significant culture in this country began in California in the gold-rush days. Red clover evidently originated in the same general Asiatic region but was brought to America by English colonists long familiar with its culture. White clover seems first to have been harvested in Holland; and alsike clover was found by Linnaeus, the great Swedish botanist, growing in the churchyard of a country parish not far from Stockholm. Lespedeza, a native of eastern Asia, has only recently come into prominence in this country and apparently never was cultivated in its native land.

Crops American in Origin.—Many horticultural crops, including pumpkins, squashes, tomatoes, peppers, pineapples, watermelons, cassava, bananas, strawberries, raspberries, and several kinds of nuts, originated in the Americas. The list of field crops of American origin is much smaller, but the crops are exceedingly important in world agriculture. They include Indian corn, potatoes, both sweet and Irish, tobacco, peanuts, sunflowers, Jerusalem artichokes, and certain kinds of beans and cotton.

Potatoes, despite their Irish name, are of Central or South American origin and were used at an early date as an important source of food. Sir Francis Drake, on a piratical expedition to the West Indies, is said to have picked up some potatoes and turned them over to his friend Sir Walter Raleigh, who had a large farm near Cork, Ireland. Their culture and use were learned in Europe, and today Europe grows 42 million of the world's 48 million acres.

LEADING WORLD CROP REGIONS

The leading crop-growing regions of the World are the United States and Canada in North America, Brazil and Argentina in South America, the European continent, and parts of Asiatic Russia, India, areas in both northern and southern Africa, and Australia.

Europe and Russia.—Russia with its broad expanses of land has never been fully exploited as an agricultural region. Millions of its acres are especially suitable for the small grains; and the U.S.S.R., according to 1925–1934 estimates, has been leading the world in the production of wheat, rye, oats, barley, and flaxseed. Russia also leads in potatoes and sugar beets and has an important cotton and fiber-flax acreage.

Europe proper is an intensive agricultural region, and crop growing has been fostered by the various countries in efforts to become self-sufficient. Potatoes are very important as a food crop. France, with an area comparable with that of Texas, grows as many acres of potatoes as does the entire United States. Germany grows nearly twice the acreage produced in the United States. Europe, as a whole, grows over 90 per cent of the world's potato crop. The intensive culture of this crop in Europe may be appreciated from the fact that average acre yields are more than twice as high there as in the United States. The crop has important industrial as well as food uses, and certain European varieties are grown especially for industry.

One of the most productive agricultural regions in Europe is the Danube River basin including Hungary, Yugoslavia, Bulgaria, and Rumania. This region is important in the production of all small grains, especially wheat; it is Europe's great corn-growing area; and Rumania, in particular, produces and exports a substantial quantity of dry beans.

Europe, outside of Russia, produces much of its sugar from sugar beets, Germany, Poland, and France leading the Continent with this crop.

The Orient.—Chief crops of the Orient are wheat, barley, rice, sugar cane, cotton, soybeans, corn, and tobacco. India, Burma, and French Indo-China produce most of the world's rice. India likewise leads in sugar production. India and China rank next to the United States in cotton and tobacco production. China, Manchuria, and Japan produce great quantities of soybeans for home use and export; and China ranks second in barley and India third of all countries in wheat.

South America.—The greatest agricultural countries of South America are Argentina and Brazil. Argentina, a great cattle country,

Fig. 2.—Miles of the world's richest crop land in the heart of the United States corn belt. (*J. C. Allen and Son.*)

fattens much of its beef on alfalfa pasture. Although the acreage is relatively low, Argentina is one of the chief exporters of wheat, oats, and flaxseed. Besides its great coffee industry, Brazil leads all countries in production of dry beans, and it has become an important cotton producer.

Canada.—One of the greatest of exporting countries is The Dominion of Canada. For the years 1925 to 1934, Canada exported two-thirds as much wheat as the combined total of its three nearest rivals, Argentina, the United States, and Australia. Canada ranks second in exports of oats and barley and grows a fair amount of corn and tobacco in Ontario and flaxseed in the western provinces. Exports of forage seeds to the United States including alfalfa, red clover, alsike, and brome grass are frequently of considerable volume.

Island Crops.—Some of the island countries have developed noteworthy crop enterprises. Cuba is exceeded only by India in production of cane sugar, most of it being exported to the United States. Java and the Philippine Islands are likewise leading sugar producers, as are Hawaii and Puerto Rico. The three latter are insular possessions of the United States. Cuba and American insular areas supply three-fourths the sugar consumed in continental United States.

The United States.—The United States of America, greatest of all agricultural regions, is our particular concern. Its crop enterprises form the basis for the discussions presented in this book.

THE SCIENCE OF CROP PRODUCTION (AGRONOMY)

Crop production as a science, or the science of agronomy, deals with both the theoretical and the applied aspects of growing the plants that have played so important a role in man's progress. In a large measure, it is a correlating science, concerned with bringing together and harmonizing the principles developed in the more specialized scientific fields.

Crop Botany.—Of all specialized sciences, none is more important to crop production than botany. Botany deals with the morphology and anatomy of plants and, in the case of crop plants, emphasizes the structures that man finds useful. It is concerned with how plants grow and a study of the functions and parts of the living plants. An important botanical phase of crop production is the study of the principles of plant nutrition and the development of practices that result in more adequately supplying crop plants with effective nutrient materials.

Effective crop production must deal with plant characters and also with principles of inheritance, the way in which these characters are passed on from generation to generation. Plant breeders who by exploration, by hybridization, and by selection have made available superior germ plasm, providing plants resistant to cold or to disease, more useful in structure, more desirable in quality, and more effective in productivity, have contributed remarkably to agronomic progress.

A study of crop ecology, the mutual relations between plants and their environment, the soil, the climate, and associated vegetation and other organisms, is an important phase of crop production. Of special interest is the effect on plant growth of light, temperature, water, humidity, and particularly such extreme weather influences as freezing and drought.

It is important that crop plants be properly classified not only as to their botanical relationships but also as to their functions in agriculture, the uses to which they are put, and the way in which they fit into a balanced scheme of farming operations.

Soils.—The soil provides the medium on which plants are grown. The soil and its effective management in the interests of human well-being are so vital that a vast comprehensive field of soil science has developed as a specialized branch of agronomy. This science concerns itself with the physical, chemical, and biological nature of soils. In its applied phases, it seeks to develop practicable systems of soil management and utilization.

The Control of Crop Enemies.—Crop production cannot be carried on without effective weapons to thwart the ravages of the enemies of plant growth. To this end, agronomy calls on the science of plant pathology for an understanding of the organisms that cause disease and on entomology for essential information about insects. Control measures have depended for their effectiveness not only on information acquired directly in the fields of plant pathology and entomology but also on chemistry for essential fungicides and insecticides and on plant breeding for the development of pest-resistant varieties.

Weeds, aptly defined as "plants out of place," are classed as crop enemies. Before they can be effectively controlled, they must be understood and their periods of weakness and strength determined. The whole technique of seedbed preparation and cultivation is directed to a very large extent toward controlling weeds. Here agricultural engineering makes a major contribution to agronomy as it does, too, in the development of equipment for planting, harvest, and transport.

Agronomy and Livestock Husbandry.—Most of the products of the field are not used directly by man but are the basic materials for production of dairy products, meat, eggs, wool, and power. In meeting the various feed requirements of farm animals, quantity production is but one consideration. Choice of crops and methods of culture have a profound effect on general quality and on such specific quality factors as chemical make-up, palatability and digestibility, and content of health-giving vitamins.

Harvesting and curing practices are of particular interest, for they influence the value of crops that are to be fed. In producing forage, for example, the time of cutting affects both its yield and its character as a feed. Alfalfa, if sun-cured, should be high in vitamin D and low in vitamin A, but high in vitamin A and low in vitamin D if it is artificially fire-dried. Hay thoroughly dried before it is stacked or put into a mow undergoes only mild respiration; but in the case of hay with too much moisture, respiration is vigorous, material is destroyed by oxidation, and a browned, less digestible product is left. In extreme cases, spontaneous combustion may result. Uncured hay may be stored under conditions where most of the air is excluded. Fermentation then takes place. If too much air is present, molds and spoilage result; if too little air is present, there is an undesirable type of fermentation; but if the balance is right, a fine quality of silage is preserved. These, as well as many other processes, must be understood and controlled in the successful production of feed crops.

Crop residues and animal manures provide one of the chief means of keeping soils in condition. Their return to the land helps to maintain the supply of nutrients essential to plant growth. Thus, in the farm-management scheme, we find another close link between agronomy and livestock husbandry.

The Concern for Food.—Of major importance to agronomy are the economic and social implications of crop production. The food of mankind comes directly or indirectly from plants. The importance of plants, especially cultivated plants, has had a powerful effect on the way of human life, on geographic distribution, on mode of government, and even on religion. A religious ceremony instituted by a Chinese emperor more than 2,000 years ago had to do with plowing and the planting of seeds of wheat, rice, proso, and soybeans. This ceremony is said to have been conducted year after year, even to modern times, on a mountaintop in the province of Shansi.

Malthus (1766–1834) was one of many who expressed concern over man's food supply. He held that population tends to increase faster than its means of subsistence can be made to increase. From his dismal viewpoint, when this occurs the poorer and the weaker classes must suffer from lack of food; and unless population be held in check by prudential restraint, poverty is inevitable. Some densely populated sections of the world that today know famine and want provide evidence to support the Malthusian theories.

Many have held that the depletion of soil fertility through cropping practices provides the limit to possible food production. With this in view, Lipman[1] has emphasized the need for a watchful inventory of the essential plant nutrients. He points out that the losses in phosphorus are almost ten times as much as is supplied in chemical fertilizers and that, in some countries, "Where the cumulative losses of basic materials have not been made up by liming, marling, etc., there has been a striking increase in soil acidity, a serious loss in phosphorus, and a marked shrinkage in the size of domestic animals." He further indicates the tremendous losses in nitrogen which, he points out, might

---

[1] LIPMAN, J. G., Preliminary Note on the Inventory and Balance Sheet of Plant Nutrients in the United States, *N.J. Agr. Expt. Sta. Bul.* 607, 1936.

be checked by such changes in soil and crop management as would reduce the water runoff, increase the water-holding capacity of the soil, increase the acreage of legumes, increase the nonsymbiotic nitrogen fixation, and decrease the oxidation of organic matter.

Soil Conservation.—Unquestionably, soil erosion has played an important part in reducing the potential food production of vast areas. In a nationwide survey of the agricultural lands of the United States, made in 1937, one of the conclusions was:

The present cropland area of the United States (1935 census of agriculture) is 415,334,931 acres. Of this, practically 61 per cent—about 253,000,000

Fig. 3.—Over half of the United States crop land is in need of good soil-conservation practices to prevent serious damage. (*Courtesy of U.S. Dept. Agr. Soil Conservation Service.*)

acres—is either subject to continued erosion or is of such poor quality as not to return a satisfactory income to farmers . . . (at a price level equal to that for the period 1921–1936). To continue present practices on the part of this land subject to erosion is to mine it and progressively destroy it. Over half of it is in need of good soil conservation practices to prevent serious damage.[1]

The Surplus Problem.—In 1898, Sir William Crookes,[2] an English economist, predicted that by 1930 all available wheat lands in the United States would be in use and that the United States would be

---

[1] "Soils and Men," *U.S. Dept. Agr. Yearbook of Agriculture*, p. 6, 1938.

[2] CROOKES, SIR WILLIAM, The Wheat Problem, *Brit. Assoc. Adv. Sci. Rpt.* 68, pp. 8–9, 1898.

driven to import and would be struggling with Great Britain for a lion's share of the world's wheat supply.

In 1930, however, the United States held a major share of one of the world's greatest wheat surpluses. During the late 1920's and the 1930's, serious economic difficulties resulted in many countries from the production of an excess of crops, which could not be marketed at remunerative prices.

The crops-surplus problem in the United States has been responsible for much economic planning, which has had a direct bearing on agronomy. To many the most obvious solution of a surplus, whether it be in the field of industry, labor, or agriculture, has been curtailment of production. This gave rise to an "economy of scarcity," based on the unusual principle that all may have more if each produces less.

Efforts to achieve a curtailed production of such important agricultural commodities as wheat, corn, and cotton have met with serious difficulties, due, at least in part, to the problem of providing practical usage for land thus relieved of its customary functions. Campaigns that sought to secure voluntary reduction in the planting of crops troubled by burdensome surpluses failed to alleviate the surplus condition. In 1933, under direction of the Agricultural Adjustment Administration, a program for the control of crop surpluses was carried on that involved Federal payments to cooperating farmers to compensate them for making the necessary adjustments. Plans were changed from time to time and in some instances amounted essentially to compulsion.

In the case of wheat, representative of the crops for which reduction of acreage was on a voluntary basis, the planted acreage for the crop of 1934 was reduced by 7 per cent as compared with that of 1933, a normal fluctuation. The acreage was increased each year thereafter until 1937 when the planted acreage amounted to 81,072,000, an all-time high for the United States.

However, the harvested acreage and the total production dropped materially in 1934, 1935, and 1936, owing in part to unusually severe droughts. In 1938, wheat production in the United States was 930,800,000 bushels, nearly a record crop.

In the case of corn, cotton, and tobacco, some reduction in acreage evidently resulted from control measures, much more stringent for cotton and tobacco than for wheat, until 1941, when compulsory control measures were adopted with the support of a grower referendum.

In 1936, the Supreme Court of the United States declared unconstitutional the production-control features of the Agricultural Adjustment Act. Later that same year, Congress passed an amendment to the Soil Conservation Act, providing for the Agricultural Conservation Program.   Under this act, payments were made to cooperating farmers on the basis of the planting of increasing percentages of crops that were classed as soil conserving rather than soil depleting and for the carrying on of specified soil-conserving practices. The work done under this program has undoubtedly quickened interest in the land and stimulated the planting of sod-forming grasses and legumes that reduce erosion and improve the character of the soil.

The production of agricultural commodities in excess of the effective market demand in the United States went hand in hand with general economic depression which left "one-third of the nation ill-housed, ill-clad, and ill-fed." The difficulties of the times not only involved agriculture but carried broad social and economic implications equally pertinent to industry, labor, and commerce as well as to agriculture.

TABLE 1.—RELATION OF SUGAR-BEET YIELDS IN MICHIGAN TO PRODUCTION COSTS AND NET RETURNS*

Item	Yield group			
	Low	Medium low	Medium high	High
Number of farms	59	84	78	58
Average yield an acre, tons	6.6	8.9	10.8	13.2
Average cost an acre	$49.96	$52.51	$56.16	$60.98
Returns with sugar beets at $5.63† a ton				
Average acre value	$37.16	$50.11	$60.80	$74.32
Net acre returns	−12.80	−2.40	4.64	13.34
Returns with sugar beets at $8† a ton				
Average acre value	$52.80	$71.20	$86.40	$105.60
Net acre returns	2.84	18.69	30.24	44.62

* WRIGHT, K. T., Sugar Beet Costs and Returns in Michigan, *Mich. Agr. Expt. Sta. Bul.* 305, 1940.

† During the 10-year period 1930–1939, the lowest returns a ton that Michigan sugar-beet growers received was $5.63; the highest, $8.

The Need for Producing Well.—Although agriculture is subject to the same play of economic forces as is the rest of society, forces that have brought both periods of difficulty and periods of well-being, it is well to remember that the welfare of agriculture under any circumstances is closely linked with the soil. Fine farm homes and well-kept farm communities go with productive land. Though many farm problems are of general interest, the successful operation of a farm is a highly individualistic enterprise. Adjustments to a changing economic environment are always necessary, for the economic environment is one of constant change. But such adjustments are not in conflict with the need for producing well. A fertile soil and high acre yields are basic to successful crop production. In connection with this principle, it has been well said that "There is both more satisfaction and more profit in the production of 300 bushels of potatoes off 1 acre than there is in the production of 400 bushels of potatoes off 4 acres."

Enterprise cost studies have inevitably emphasized the important part that high acre yields play in profitable crop production. This principle, true for crop production in general, is illustrated in Table 1, which presents data adapted from studies of sugar-beet costs and returns, made in Michigan.

Although acre costs were somewhat higher for the higher sugar-beet yields, the costs for a ton of beets, the market unit, were materially lower because of these higher yields. The net returns from an enterprise are governed by the costs per market unit, the selling price, and the volume of business. High acre yields are important because, within wide limits, they reduce the cost of production and they increase the volume of sales. Likewise, high acre yields often are attended by superior quality, which may advantageously influence the price.

Review Questions

1. What American crop enters most largely into world commerce?
2. What is the relationship of the corn plant to teosinte?
3. Name five important crops of Asiatic origin.
4. Under what climatic conditions is the production of sugar cane carried on?
5. Where was grassland agriculture first developed on the most intensive basis?
6. In what section of the United States did alfalfa growing first assume importance? Why?
7. Name four important field crops that originated in the New World.
8. Why are potatoes called *Irish* potatoes?
9. What section of Europe is highly important in grain production?
10. What are the chief crops of South America that enter into world commerce?
11. What led to the development of the beet-sugar industry in Europe?
12. What basic sciences contribute materially to effective methods of crop production?
13. Are Federal measures for soil conservation and crop control in harmony? Explain your answer.
14. Why is it sound economy for farmers to strive for high acre yields?

Problems

1. Make a table showing the trend in wheat exports from the four chief exporting countries of the world.

2. Prepare a brief summary of the measures taken by leading European countries to become self-sufficient in respect to wheat prior to the outbreak of the Second World War in 1939.

3. Explain the conditions that make Canada one of the world's greater crop-exporting countries.

4. Look up reference material and prepare a short report on the origin and history of one of the leading special crops of your state, for example, potatoes, soybeans, sugar beets, tobacco.

5. Prepare a table showing the planted and harvested acreage and total production of wheat, corn, cotton, and tobacco for the United States for 8 years prior to and 8 years following the advent of the Agricultural Adjustment Administration in 1933.

6. Secure from your farm-management or agricultural-economics department the cost of production figures, by yield groups, of some crop in which you are especially interested, and note the effect of yield on net return in the case of this crop.

References

BENNETT, HUGH HAMMOND: "Soil Conservation," McGraw-Hill Book Company, Inc., New York, 1939.

CARLETON, M. A.: "The Small Grains," The Macmillan Company, New York, 1924.

CARRIER, LYMAN: "The Beginnings of Agriculture in America," McGraw-Hill Book Company, Inc., New York, 1923.

MANGELSDORF, P. C., and R. G. REEVES: The Origin of Indian Corn and Its Relatives, *Tex. Agr. Expt. Sta. Bul.* 574 (monograph), 1939.

PIPER, C. V.: "Forage Plants and Their Culture," The Macmillan Company, New York, 1924.

U.S. Dept. Agr. Agricultural Statistics, Superintendent of Documents, Government Printing Office, Washington, D.C., current issue.

CHAPTER II

CLASSIFICATION OF FARM CROPS

The seed balls growing on the top of a potato plant are very similar to young green tomatoes. Not only are these two very useful plants alike in many respects, but they also have much in common with such apparently dissimilar plants as tobacco, the brightly flowered petunia, the annoying horse nettle, and the drug-producing belladonna. Their flowers have the same leaf arrangement, the same number of stamens, and the same kind of single compound pistil. The fruit may be large as is that of the tomato and eggplant or a mere capsule as in petunia. The leaves are alternately placed along the stem, and both stems and leaves are characterized by a similar star-shaped pubescence. Thus the structure and arrangement of these plants, their flowers, and fruits provide the basis for grouping them into one botanical family called *Solanaceae* or, more commonly, the nightshade or potato family. The same principles are used in the botanical classification of all plants.

BOTANICAL CLASSIFICATION

One of the first effective systems for classifying plants was devised by Linnaeus, an eminent Swedish naturalist of the eighteenth century. Linnaeus's gardens are still maintained as a memorial at Uppsala, Sweden. He introduced the natural system of classification, modified and improved since his day, which seeks to arrange groupings on the basis of natural affinities and evolutionary tendencies rather than on mere similarities in appearance. Botanists have found that, in the evolutionary process, reproductive structures, the flowers, fruits, and seeds, have changed far less under the influence of diverse environmental conditions and natural selection than have the roots, stems, and leaves. These reproductive structures therefore are of greater value in showing the true relationships among plants, and they provide a more adequate basis for botanical classification.

Plant Groupings.—One-celled organisms are the simplest forms of living matter. Filterable viruses, which cause so many destructive plant and animal diseases, appear to fill the gap between nonliving matter and the lowest unicellular forms of life. A pure strain of the virus causing tobacco mosaic has been crystallized. Its molecule, one

15

of the largest known, has been photographed; but this was possible only with the aid of the electron microscope, fifty times more powerful than the best light microscopes. These apparently lifeless molecules have the lifelike power of reproducing themselves. The lowest forms of plant life appear to be the algae, represented by the green scums that gather on the surface of stagnant water, and the fungi, which include the highly important bacteria, molds, and mildews and the rusts and smuts of small grains.

Mosses and ferns represent two broad classes of plant life intermediate between the algae and fungi forms and the most complex group of all, the seed-bearing plants. The pines, firs, hemlocks, cedars, and spruces are cone bearers (coniferous) and are grouped in a class called *Gymnosperms*, whereas the common field, orchard, and garden plants belong to another class of seed producers called *Angiosperms*. Group arrangements include the subclass, order, family, genus, species, and a final division, which vitally concerns the farmer as he chooses plants most suited to local conditions of environment, the variety.

Plant Names.—Plants are universal; language is extremely provincial. Field bindweed has a dozen "common" names that are not common at all but purely local in usage. The creeping Charlie of one community is the feminine creeping Jennie of another. It is hedge bells in one place, lap-love in another. And these descriptive appellations are by no means confined to the English language. Undoubtedly the French, the Germans, the Russians, and the Danes have excellent examples in their own mother tongues.

The common names of plants make up a veritable babel of terms, with many names applied to a single species on the one hand and with several distinct species going by the same name on the other. Because Latin has been more widely studied than any other language, it has been used to provide the universal plant nomenclature. In this binomial system the scientific name of each plant is composed of two words. Thus, the bindweed, wild morning-glory, hedge bells, or creeping Jennie of a dozen localities becomes *Convolvulus arvensis* throughout the botanical world. The first word, *Convolvulus*, is the name of the genus to which this particular bindweed belongs; the second word, *arvensis*, is the name of the species. The *L.* or *Linn.*, which often follows the scientific name denotes that this species was first named and described by the botanist Linnaeus.

THE GRASS FAMILY (GRAMINEAE)

A rich green pasture, the forage in a meadow, the herbage of an almost limitless range, a well-kept lawn or golf course—these mean grass to the layman. However, many of the plants found useful in lawns, pastures, and meadows are not grasses at all in the botanical sense, and true grasses have many more uses than are ordinarily associated with grass farming. The grass family does include many lawn, pasture, hay, marsh, and range grasses, but it also takes in the common grain crops, corn, wheat, oats, rye, barley, and rice. It numbers many weeds partly or entirely unusable in agriculture. Its members range in size from the low-growing, fine-leaved bent grasses to the giant bamboo, which has a woody stem and stretches up 100 ft. or more.

Grasses develop a fibrous root system without the tendency toward a strong central taproot such as is found in the beet, dandelion, sweet clover, or alfalfa plant. More often than not the root system is fairly shallow, but some grass species readily develop roots extending to a depth of 6 or 7 ft.

Grass Stems.—The farmer is much more concerned with grass stems than the botanist. Grass stems, to the botanist, are elongated cylindrical structures which he calls *culms*. The enlarged solid joints from which the leaves diverge are the *nodes*, and the stem structure between these joints makes up the *internodes*. The internodes may be filled with pith as in corn, but they are usually hollow at maturity as in common wheat.

To the farmer, grass stems and their leaves (the leafier the better) represent feed for his cattle and bedding for his stables. He is concerned with their strength, their fineness, the readiness with which animals consume them, and their feeding value.

When stems bend or break over (lodging), harvest of the crop becomes more difficult and yields are curtailed. The farmer has learned that some grasses are more susceptible to lodging than others, that there are varietal as well as species differences in this respect, and also that under conditions of extreme mechanical pressure as with violent winds and driving rains even the most sturdy of the grasses goes down. He has found that, when lodging occurs fairly early in the development of a crop, the plants may come back to their erect position and little damage results. But there is gloom at the farmstead when a wheat crop or other small grain is flattened by a storm just as the seed is beginning to form; for the grain will be light and of inferior quality, and the yield will be low. This is because in the bent, broken, and uprooted grain there is gross interference with root absorption, food manufacture, and translocation.

Tillering.—When a single grass seed germinates and develops successfully, there arises, not one single stem but two, three, or possibly a score of them, depending on the species.　This development of more than one stem, or culm, on a single plant is called *tillering* or *stooling*. The tillers are in fact branches developing from near the base of the primary stem.　The first branches, or tillers, may in turn produce other tillers, and so on, until a large number have developed from growth originating from one seed.

Tillering is influenced by heredity.　Spartan barley inherently produces more tillers than the Oderbrucker variety when the two are grown in the same environment.　(Tillering is also enhanced by relatively wide spacing of plants, early seeding, high soil fertility, a large amount of reserve food in the seed, and generally favorable growing conditions with respect to temperature and moisture.)

Rhizomes and Stolons.—In perennial grasses a portion of the stem tissue may develop extensive underground growth which serves as an effective place for storage of reserve food and provides for vegetative extension of the plant.　Quack grass (*Agropyron repens*) is a very persistent weed because of the spreading character of its underground stems, or *rhizomes*, and because of the effective conservation of reserve food in them.　Rhizomes are differentiated from true roots by the presence of buds and scalelike leaves.　Both roots and erect annual stems may develop from the nodes on the rhizomes.

In orchard grass (*Dactylis glomerata*) the rhizomes are short and the aboveground stems grow in close clumps, giving a branching habit of growth.　Bunch grasses once supported the great buffalo herds of the plains country.　They are among the more common range grasses of the West.

Some grasses develop stems that grow in a horizontal position above the ground.　At each node, under favorable conditions, roots and erect stems may be produced.　Such stems are called *stolons*.　The bents commonly used on the greens of golf courses are stoloniferous, in fact are propagated commercially by means of stolons.

Leaves.—Grass leaves make up one of nature's great assets. Although grass stems are eaten by livestock, the highly nutritious leaves are far more important.　Green leaves are rich in health-giving vitamins, and they also provide carbohydrates, proteins, and minerals in forms desirable for all farm animals.　As in all green plants the grass leaves contain the chlorophyll which, with energy from the sun, carries on photosynthesis to convert carbon dioxide and water into plant structure.　This is nature's way of storing energy.

Grass leaves develop at each node in alternate arrangement as one follows along the stem.　Later, the buds in the axils of the leaves may elongate to form new leaves.　The leaf base forms a tube or sheath around the stem, with the broader flattened blade growing away from the stem.

Seeds.—More than 200 million acres of United States farm land is used to grow the seed of several grass species. With such members of the grass family as corn, the small grains, and the grain sorghums, seed is the goal of harvest. The head that develops at the end of a stem, as in wheat, barley, or rye, is first a group of flowers, self-pollinated in wheat and barley, cross-fertilized in rye. Each fertile flower bears a single seed. The wheat head is an unbranched spike; in common oats or Kentucky bluegrass, the head is a branched, open panicle.

◄——— LEGUMES (LEGUMINOSAE) ———►

Legumes are next in importance to grasses as commercial crops, and they are even more important with respect to their effects on the

Fig. 4.—A mixture of alfalfa and smooth brome grass. The nitrogen fixed in excess of the needs of the legume plants is readily taken up by the grasses so often grown in association with them.

soil and on other plants. The most noteworthy characteristic of legumes is the association with them, in nodules or tubercles growing on the roots, of symbiotic bacteria which have the power to fix the free nitrogen from the air into forms that can be utilized by the plant.

Because both the seeds and the leaves of legumes are characteristically high in nitrogen, this family of plants has an important place in livestock feeding.   The nitrogen fixed in excess of the needs of legume plants is readily taken up by grasses so often grown in association with them, and the plowed-under legume makes soil richer in nitrogen, higher in organic matter, and better in physical structure. Beans, peas, soybeans, and peanuts are legumes that, with some others of lesser importance, provide economical and very nutritious human food.

Some Legume Characteristics.—The legumes used in agriculture are for the most part low-growing herbs like bush beans, clover, and alfalfa.   Vetches grow on vines that are approached in type by some kinds of peas and beans.   The locust, largest of legumes, is a tree. Legume flowers are usually arranged in typical racemes like those of the pea; in a spikelike raceme as with alfalfa; or in a head like clover. The fruit is most commonly a pod, and the pod itself is called a *legume.* The term is derived from the Latin *legere* which means "to gather." It originated from the fact that these fruits might be gathered without cutting the plants.   This is still a not uncommon harvest practice with such crops as green peas, string beans, and edible green soybeans.

Legume seeds usually have little or no endosperm, the storage tissue so important in the starchy-seeded grains.   But the legume seeds do provide for storage of food in the thick cotyledons which are a part of the embryo, or germ.   Beans are illustrative of those leguminous species which, on germinating, push the cotyledons through the soil.   The cotyledons provide the seedling with food until green leaves develop and photosynthesis is started.   In the case of peas the cotyledons remain underground during germination.

FAMILIES OF OTHER CROP PLANTS

No attempt will be made here to present a detailed botanical classification of crop plants, but it is of interest to note a few of the family associations of some of the commercially important crops. That of potatoes with tomatoes and tobacco has already been mentioned.   Here are three important farm crops belonging to the same botanical family, each grown for a different part of its structure, the potato for its tuberous stem tissue, the tomato for its fruit, and tobacco for its leaves.   Sweet potatoes are of the same family as the notorious field bindweed as well as the more pleasing porch-climbing morning-glory.   Sugar beets, red beets, mangel-wurzels, spinach, and Swiss chard are all members of the goosefoot family (Chenopodiaceae), as is Russian thistle.   Cotton, the world's greatest fiber plant, belongs to the mallow family (Malvaceae) along with such ornamental plants as the hollyhock and hibiscus.

CLASSIFICATION AS TO GROWTH HABIT

The adaptation, time of planting, stand management, and harvest of most crops is modified and regulated by the growth habits of the plants.

Annuals.—The corn plant is planted in the spring and harvested in the autumn. Even though not harvested, its life cycle is completed in one season. It is a typical annual as are spring-sown wheat, oats and barley, peas, beans, and many others.

Some plants, like winter wheat, start growth in the autumn of one season, live through the winter, and complete it the following summer. Such plants are known as *winter annuals.*

Biennials.—Plants that require two seasons to attain full development, mature seed, and die are biennials. Common sweet clover and most strains of red clover are typical biennials. Although a sugar-beet grower plants his seed in the spring and harvests the roots that autumn, the beet does not produce seed in a single season. It develops stalk growth, flowers, and seeds the second season after planting; therefore, it, too, is a biennial.

Perennials.—Some plants live for several years. They may produce seed each year, but they do not die with seed production. Variable types of storage organs provide food reserves which in turn provide energy to start the plants off to new growth each season. Such plants are perennials. Trees, of course, are perennials. So are many crop plants, especially among forages, including alfalfa, alsike, and white clover of the legumes and timothy, smooth brome grass, the bluegrasses, and a host of others of the grass family. Chicory, though harvested for its roots the season it is sown, is in fact a perennial.

The scientific name, botanical family, and growth duration of several field-crop plants are given in Table 2.

AGRICULTURAL CLASSIFICATION

The botanical classification of plants is based on their natural relationships. However, there are other groupings in which the farmer catalogues plants. His first classification may be broad and inclusive, merely differentiating between the plants he finds useful, his crops, and those which are out of place and troublesome, the weeds. Those which he sells are *cash crops;* those marketed through livestock, *feed crops.* On farms and in businesses closely associated with agriculture field crops are classified in accordance with their use.

Cereals.—Corn, wheat, oats, barley, rye, and rice are grown because of the value of their seeds as human food and as feed for livestock.

TABLE 2.—THE NAMES, FAMILY, AND GROWTH DURATION OF SOME CROP PLANTS

Common name	Scientific name	Growth duration
Family Gramineae		
Barley:		
Six-row, nodding..........	*Hordeum vulgare*	Annual, winter annual
Six-row, erect.............	*H. hexastichum*	Annual, winter annual
Two-row.................	*H. distichum*	Annual, winter annual
Bermuda grass.............	*Cynodon dactylon*	Perennial
Bluegrass:		
Kentucky...............	*Poa pratensis*	Perennial
Canada.................	*P. compressa*	Perennial
Brome grass, smooth........	*Bromus inermis*	Perennial
Corn......................	*Zea mays*	Annual
Crested wheat grass........	*Agropyron cristatum*	Perennial
Fescue:		
Meadow................	*Festuca elatior*	Perennial
Red and Chewings........	*F. rubra*	Perennial
Sheep..................	*F. ovina*	Perennial
Johnson grass..............	*Sorghum halepense*	Perennial
Millet:		
Barnyard grass..........	*Echinochloa crusgalli*	Annual
Foxtail.................	*Setaria italica*	Annual
Proso..................	*Panicum miliaceum*	Annual
Pearl..................	*Pennisetum glaucum*	Annual
Oats:		
Common................	*Avena sativa*	Annual, winter annual
Side...................	*A. orientalis*	Annual
Hull-less...............	*A. nuda*	Annual
Red...................	*A. byzantina*	Annual, winter annual
Orchard grass..............	*Dactylis glomerata*	Perennial
Quack grass................	*Agropyron repens*	Perennial
Reed canary grass...........	*Phalaris arundinacea*	Perennial
Redtop....................	*Agrostis alba*	Perennial
Rice......................	*Oryza sativa*	Annual
Rye......................	*Secale cereale*	Winter annual, annual
Rye grass:		
Italian.................	*Lolium multiflorum*	Perennial (short-lived)
Perennial...............	*L. perenne*	Perennial
Sorghum..................	*Sorghum vulgare*	Annual
Sudan grass...............	*S. vulgare var. sudanense*	Annual
Sugar cane...............	*Saccharum officinarum*	Perennial
Timothy..................	*Phleum pratense*	Perennial
Wheat:		
Common................	*Triticum vulgare*	Annual, winter annual
Club...................	*T. compactum*	Annual, winter annual
Durum.................	*T. durum*	Annual
Emmer.................	*T. dicoccum*	Annual, winter annual
Spelt..................	*T. spelta*	Annual, winter annual

TABLE 2.—THE NAMES, FAMILY, AND GROWTH DURATION OF SOME CROP PLANTS.
(*Continued*)

Common name	Scientific name	Growth duration
Family Leguminosae		
Alfalfa:		
Common..............	*Medicago sativa*	Perennial
Sickle..............	*M. falcata*	Perennial
Bean:		
Pea and kidney..........	*Phaseolus vulgaris*	Annual
Lima..............	*P. lunatus*	Annual
Bur clover..............	*Medicago arabica*	Annual
Clover:		
Alsike..............	*Trifolium hybridum*	Perennial
Crimson..............	*T. incarnatum*	Annual, winter annual
Red, mammoth..........	*T. pratense*	Biennial, perennial
White, Ladino..........	*T. repens*	Perennial
Cowpea..............	*Vigna sinensis*	Annual
Crotalaria..............	*Crotalaria striata*	Perennial
Lespedeza, common........	*Lespedeza striata*	Annual
Lespedeza, Korean........	*L. stipulacea*	Annual
Lespedeza, sericea..........	*L. sericea*	Perennial
Pea..............	*Pisum sativum*	Annual
Peanut..............	*Arachis hypogaea*	Annual
Sainfoin..............	*Onobrychis vulgaris*	Perennial
Serradella..............	*Ornithopus sativus*	Annual
Soybean..............	*Soja max*	Annual
Sweet clover:		
White..............	*Melilotus alba*	Biennial, annual
Yellow..............	*M. officinalis*	Biennial, annual
Trefoil:		
Bird's-foot..............	*Lotus corniculatus*	Perennial
Yellow..............	*Medicago lupulina*	Annual, perennial
Family Chenopodiaceae		
Sugar beet..............	*Beta vulgaris*	Biennial
Family Convolvulaceae		
Sweet potato..............	*Ipomoea batatus*	Perennial
Family Cichoriaceae		
Chicory..............	*Cichorium intybus*	Perennial
Family Carduaceae		
Jerusalem artichoke........	*Helianthus tuberosus*	Perennial
Family Compositae		
Sunflower..............	*Helianthus annuus*	Annual

TABLE 2.—THE NAMES, FAMILY, AND GROWTH DURATION OF SOME CROP PLANTS.
(*Continued*)

Common name	Scientific name	Growth duration
Family Cruciferae		
Rape.....................	*Brassica napus*	Biennial
Rutabaga.................	*B. campestris*	Biennial
Turnip....................	*B. rapa*	Biennial
Family Linaceae		
Flax......................	*Linum usitatissimum*	Annual
Family Malvaceae		
Cotton:		
Upland.................	*Gossypium hirsutum*	Annual
Sea island...............	*G. barbadense*	Annual
Family Moraceae		
Hop.......................	*Humulus lupulus*	Perennial
Family Polygonaceae		
Buckwheat.................	*Fagopyrum vulgare*	Annual
Family Solanaceae		
Potato....................	*Solanum tuberosum*	Perennial
Tobacco..................	*Nicotiana tabacum*	Annual
Tomato...................	*Lycopersicum esculentum*	Annual

Botanically they are grasses, but in agriculture and commerce they are the grain crops, or cereals. Several varieties of sorghum, grown for their seed, are called *grain sorghums* to differentiate them from sorghum varieties grown primarily for forage. More than two million acres of flax are grown in the United States for the seed; this provides the linseed oil of commerce and a by-product, linseed meal, which is a high-protein livestock feed.

Large-seeded Legumes.—Field beans, peas, soybeans, cowpeas, and peanuts are large-seeded legumes. These legume seeds are all grown for human food; and all are used, at least to some extent, in the feeding of livestock. Soybean seed has found an important place in industry, providing raw material for a host of industrial products ranging from oil used in paints and varnishes to plastics.

Seeds for Reproduction.—Most farm crops are propagated by means of seed. Although the primary commercial interest may center in some other portion of the plant, seed production in itself becomes an important enterprise for some farmers. Thus, growing the seed of alfalfa, clover, timothy, and Kentucky bluegrass is important as a source of income for some farmers though fundamentally these crops are grown for their stems and leaves which provide hay and pasture. Sugar beets are grown for the sucrose contained in their roots, and the production of sugar-beet seed is a distinct and separate industry carried on to a considerable extent in areas that do not grow beets for sugar at all. Potatoes are propagated vegetatively by means of tubers, and true seed is important only as a means of varietal improvement through breeding and seedling selection. The production of potato tubers having special merit for the propagation of vigorous table stock crops relatively free from potato diseases has become a 10- to 15-million-bushel certified "seed" enterprise.

Forage Crops.—In the United States, over 150 million acres of plowland are used for the production of plants the stems and leaves of which are consumed by livestock. These are *forage crops.* Hay is dried forage. Normally it is dried by the sun and wind. However, artificial dehydrating of some superior kinds of forage, especially alfalfa, has been developed on an extensive commercial basis. Pastures are made up of forage plants, the aboveground portions of which are consumed by livestock directly from the growing plants. An essential feature of a good pasture plant is the ability to make a rapid recovery growth after much of the leaf and stem tissue has been grazed. *Silage* is forage preserved in succulent condition by a process of natural fermentation or by acidification. A *soiling crop* is one cut while still green and fed at once to livestock.

Fiber Crops.—Several plants are grown for their fiber. The fiber may be part of the stem tissue as it is in flax and hemp. The cotton boll, on the other hand, is the enlarged and developed pistil of a cotton flower.

Cotton is by far the most important fiber crop, the agriculture and commerce of a great portion of the southeastern United States being closely integrated with the production and marketing of this commodity. Cotton is inexpensive and durable. Its uses in textiles and clothing are almost universal. Chemically the cotton fiber is almost pure cellulose.

Fiber flax and hemp have been grown to a very limited extent in the United States. The best flax fibers are used in fine linens; the coarser material, produced under less favorable climatic conditions, may merely provide upholstery tow. Hemp fiber is used in ropes and twines.

Sisal and henequen are tropical plants of the genus *Agave* that yield fiber used in binder twine, general-purpose ropes, and similar coarse materials. Ramie, an Asiatic plant, produces a fiber with a luster that is capable of being spun and woven into fine fabrics. Cellulose is also an important by-product of some crops, for example, the building material made from sugar-cane stalks after the sugar-containing juice has been extracted.

Sugar Crops.—Sugar cane and sugar beets are the two great sources of sugar throughout the world. Both produce sucrose; and, in pure form, the sucrose from these two crops is chemically identical. Dextrose, or corn sugar, is secured in quantity from corn; the sweet sorghums provide sirup; levulose, sweetest of sugars, may be secured from the tubers of the Jerusalem artichoke, the roots of chicory, or the tubers of the dahlia plant.

Stimulants and Medicinal Crops.—Tobacco is classed as a stimulant and is the chief crop of this class in the United States. The grain crops, particularly corn, barley, rye, and rice, are stimulant-producing crops to the extent that they are used in the brewing and distilling of alcoholic beverages.

Tea and coffee are not produced in the United States. But the roots of chicory when dried, roasted, and ground are used as an adjunct to coffee.

The mint crop, an important one on certain muck soils, provides a valuable oil used for flavoring and for medicinal purposes. There are a number of plants that produce drugs of medicinal value; but their culture is a special enterprise, and hardly any of them can be classed as field crops in the usual sense.

The hemp plant produces an alkaloid from which is derived the dangerous and illicit drug, marijuana.

Crops for Special Farm Uses.—Farmers themselves have many special uses for certain of the crops they grow.

Emergency crops are quick-growing annuals sown in the place of earlier planted crops that have failed.

Companion crops are crops grown together on the same land area. It is a common practice to make forage seedings in association with small grains. In this case the grain is often called a *nurse crop*. The use of the term is unfortunate in that it implies an advantage contributed by the grain whereas, for the most part, the grain is a severe competitor of the forage seeding. The sowing of grain with the forage seeding is justified as a means of cheapening the cost of establishing the forage provided that the soil is capable of doing two things at one time, producing a grain crop and successfully starting a forage seeding. For this reason, grain crops with which a forage seeding has been made will be classified in this text as companion rather than as nurse crops.

A *green manure* is a crop grown to be plowed under for its beneficial effect on the soil.

Cover crops are those grown primarily to protect the soil from leaching or from the destructive effects of wind and water erosion during periods when the land might otherwise lie bare.

Review Questions

1. Why are plants belonging to the legume family so important both in livestock and in soil management?

2. What is the difference between a culm, a rhizome, and a stolon?

3. A potato tuber is representative of what form of plant structure?

4. What is the economic significance of the perennial nature of so many of the leading forage crops?

5. In what structure is reserve food largely stored in the case of the following plants: quack grass; smooth brome; wheat; sugar beet; potato; Jerusalem artichoke?

6. Why is quack grass so much more difficult to control than Kentucky bluegrass?

7. Differentiate between a soiling crop, a cover crop, and a green manure.

References

CARLETON, M. A.: "The Small Grains," The Macmillan Company, New York, 1924.

DARLINGTON, H. T., E. A. BESSEY, and C. R. MEGEE: Some Important Michigan Weeds, *Mich. Expt. Sta. Spec. Bul.* 304, 1940.

HITCHCOCK, A. A.: Manual of the Grasses of the United States, *U.S. Dept. Agr. Misc. Pub.* 200, 1935.

PIPER, CHARLES V.: "Forage Plants and Their Culture," The Macmillan Company, New York, 1917.

ROBBINS, W. W.: "The Botany of Crop Plants," The Blakiston Company, Philadelphia, 1924.

—— and FRANCIS RAMALEY: "Plants Useful to Man," The Blakiston Company, Philadelphia, 1937.

ROBINSON, B. L., and M. L. FERNALD: "Gray's New Manual of Botany," 7th ed. American Book Company, New York, 1908.

CHAPTER III

FIELD CROPS IN RELATION TO FARM MANAGEMENT

Farming has often been called a *way of life*. The designation has merit. There are health and vitality in the sunshine and fresh air of the open country. There is beauty in a wooded hillside, in the green

Fig. 5.—An Iowa farmstead. Farming provides the home and the way of living for one-quarter of the American people; it is also their business. (*J. C. Allen and Son.*)

expanse of a meadow, in the changing tints and shadows of billowing grain. There is artistry in a well-turned furrow, a gracefully capped wheat shock, a brightly yellowed ear of corn. There is anticipation in sowing, satisfaction in reaping.

But farming is more than this. It is capital, and labor, and finance. It is gambling with the winds and rains, with blighting disease and ravaging insect. It is providing food, clothing, and shelter, tools and machinery, conveniences for the household, and a few things called luxuries. Farming provides the home and the way of living for one-

28

quarter of the American people, but it is also their business. Upon its success as a business depends in no small measure its attainment as a satisfactory way of life.

WHY WE GROW CROPS

For the most part, farming is a means of getting the value or usefulness out of a natural environment. It is true that some farms are essentially factories that, by virtue of location, can purchase raw-feed materials and market them profitably at a convenient industrial center as finished dairy, poultry, and livestock products. But most farms develop their own resources of soil and climate. They are producers, not processors. And the first step in production is the growing of crops.

Cash Crops.—Many crops are sold off the farm in the essential form in which they are produced. Wheat, cotton, tobacco, potatoes, and sugar beets are almost solely cash crops. Some wheat is fed to livestock, but only a little as compared with the great quantity produced each year. These and similar crops are grown to be sold, potatoes reaching the consumer in the same form as that in which they leave the farm, the others to be processed into forms suitable for consumption. Many other crops such as corn, barley, and soybeans are grown sometimes to be fed on the farm producing them, sometimes to be sold for cash. They have important industrial uses and also enter the feed- and seed-trade channels. To the farmer who sells them they, too, are cash crops.

Feed Crops.—Corn, oats, and barley have a far greater importance as feed for livestock than they have in industry. For the most part, they are fed to livestock on the farm that produces them. These grains, along with hay, silage, and pasture, are grown primarily to be converted into marketable products through livestock. Pasture can be marketed only in this way; for the method of harvest is by direct livestock consumption, an important consideration in any program of grassland improvement. Some feed crops can be marketed only through livestock. With others, if the feeding enterprise is to be successful, the value of the crops as feed must materially exceed their value if sold directly for cash.

Soil-improving Crops.—Any crop or portion of a crop removed from the land that produced it takes something from the soil. Not only do some crops remove certain constituents from the soil, especially those grown in rows; but the effect of growing them, with the consequent cultivation, is to hasten soil depletion through the effects of leaching, decomposition of organic matter, and erosion.

The effect on the soil of the different crops varies widely. Some leguminous crops, even though removed from the land, may leave the soil in good physical condition, actually enhance its supply of nitrogen, and leave a deficit only of certain minerals, most notably calcium, phosphorus, and potassium. All sod-forming crops greatly reduce and may almost completely eliminate the destructive effects of leaching and erosion. Their root systems have beneficial physical effects on the soil.

Gradually there is developing a greater appreciation of the fact that some crops may be profitably fed to other crops as well as to livestock. In intensive farming systems the use of green manures is becoming increasingly important. Effective green manures may have the property of using relatively unavailable forms of plant food and converting them into forms readily usable by less vigorous feeders. If legumes, they add to the soil's nitrogen from the inexhaustible supply in the atmosphere; they improve water, physical, and biological relationships. They are definitely a part of sound land management.

WHAT FARM MANAGEMENT HAS TAUGHT

In an earlier chapter (page 12) it was pointed out that enterprise-cost studies have inevitably emphasized the important part that high acre yields play in profitable crop production. For successful farming, the attainment of high acre yields must be associated with a wise selection of crops, the availability of good markets, an efficient utilization of labor and equipment, and a suitable system of farming.

The Need for Productive Soil. The first consideration in the producing of high acre yields is a fertile soil. The valley of the Nile, the Danube River basin, the corn belt of the United States, all famous food-producing regions, are characterized first of all by the natural productivity of their soil. The fine farm homes we see in any prosperous agricultural community are built on productive land. The tumble-down shack, the eroded hillside, the barren sands, the parched dry lands, and other evidences of hopelessness indicate that such land always has been or through deterioration has become incapable of effective production.

Good management will prolong the productivity of good soil indefinitely. It may even lift marginal land into effective production. But poor management is a destructive force, providing livelihood only at low levels and leaving nature's handiwork scarred and beaten as a problem for generations to come.

Crops Must Be Adapted.—The soil and soil management cannot alone accomplish effective production. The successful farmer chooses crops adapted both to his soil and to his climate. The broader divisions with respect to adaptation are obvious. Cotton demands warm weather and either liberal rainfall or irrigation. Corn thrives on rich soil in fairly warm humid weather. It is true that some corns are grown where the weather is cool and the season short, but these are small, early types not nearly so productive as the vigorous varieties of the corn belt.

Potatoes can be grown in the South during the cooler seasons; but the crop is essentially a northern one, with Aroostook County in northern Maine the most noted of all potato-producing centers. Wheat does fairly well under conditions of limited rainfall in the Great Plains largely because the region is adapted to large farms and efficient extensive cultural operations. The sorghums are particularly adapted to subhumid areas.

The adaptation of a crop is frequently more than a species consideration and becomes a matter of variety. Essentially only spring wheats are grown in North Dakota because of the severity of the winters there. In milder Kansas and Nebraska winter wheats predominate. Hairy Peruvian alfalfa is superior in Arizona and New Mexico where winter hardiness is not a problem; but it is valueless in the North where such cold-resistant strains as Grimm, Hardigan, and Ladak must be chosen. A midseason oat is most productive in the North; but earlier maturing varieties are needed in the heart of the corn belt, to mature before the advent of extremely hot weather. In the South, winter oat varieties are entirely feasible, whereas in northern areas these varieties completely freeze out.

With respect to soil, potatoes are productive and of good quality on sandy soils, preferably well supplied with organic matter. On heavy high-lime soils, such as are preferred for sugar beets, potatoes are generally ill-shaped and scabby. Alfalfa needs a well-drained soil and plenty of lime, for it is a high calcium feeder. Alsike will grow on a wet soil and also contains only slightly more than half as much calcium as alfalfa; hence, the soil need not be so well supplied with lime for alsike as for alfalfa.

Soil as well as climate has a profound effect on varietal adaptation in many instances. A stiff-strawed small grain is much more essential on a fertile soil with abundant moisture than on an infertile one; where the growing season is limited much earlier corns are required on muck than on uplands; the soft white wheats grown in Michigan and New York tend to follow the heavy, moisture-retentive soils. In the case of corn the narrowly bred hybrids are more restricted in their adaptation than open-pollinated varieties.[1]   Thus, farmers must give full consideration to adaptation in choosing not only the crops they grow but also the specific varieties of these crops.

Importance of Good Markets.—A most important consideration in successful farming is the marketing of farm products at remunerative prices.   Individual growers cannot influence market trends, nor can they anticipate market fluctuations with any degree of accuracy. Nevertheless, they can take advantage of many market opportunities.

The nearness of large centers of population that provide a fluid milk market has caused the agriculture of such states as New York, Michigan, and Wisconsin to emphasize dairying and the type of crop production that supports the dairy industry.   The production of truck crops is always intensified on high-value land near cities.

Price History and Prospects.—The current price of a given commodity offers a most uncertain basis for crop selection.   High prices tend to attract marginal growers, with a consequent increase in production that often results in abnormally low prices for the next crop. But the long-time price history furnishes a reasonably reliable guide as to what the farmer may expect in the way of prices over a period of years.

A grower choosing the potato crop in 1930, on the basis of the 1920–1929 prices of $1.05 a bushel or of the abnormal war years 1916–1919 of $1.48 a bushel, would have been doomed to disappointment, for the 1930–1939 farm price averaged but $0.65 a bushel. However, had he considered the longer price history of the crop, his price of $0.65 would have compared very favorably with that of 1900–1916, when potato prices averaged $0.61.

The wheat grower cannot plan on $1 a bushel for his crop, for the price history of wheat shows many more years when wheat returned less than $1 than years when the price was above this figure.   Drought caused a temporary shortage of barley in 1936, and the average price that year was $0.78 a bushel.   The long-time price history of the crop indicates, however, that barley usually brings much less than $0.78, the 1920–1939 average being $0.53.   Not only must the grower consider the long-time price average in his plans, but he must also recognize the likelihood of seasons when the price will be materially below average.

A study of the current situation sometimes makes possible temporary adjustments in cropping plans in relation to price prospects. Each year the U.S. Department of Agriculture and cooperating col-

[1] ROBERTS, L. M., and D. F. JONES: Ensilage Corn Trials at Mt. Carmel, Connecticut, 1940, *Conn. Agr. Expt. Sta. Mimeographed Prog. Rpt.*

leges of agriculture issue an *outlook report*, which presents the situation with reference to current supplies, potential demand, international trade, and the general economic situation, all of which have a bearing on prices. For many farmers, however, season-to-season adjustment of crop acreages is difficult; in general, plans must be made on a long-time basis.

Quality and Price.—The individual grower can often enhance the price of his crops and most certainly can avoid profit-reducing discounts by careful attention to quality. A current price sheet issued by a large milling company discounts smutty wheat by $0.01 to $0.10 a bushel depending on how badly the grain is smutted. With beans at $3 a hundred-weight, 100 lb. of beans containing 2 per cent culls would return a farmer $2.80. If the lot contained 8 per cent culls, the farm return would be but $2.20. Barley suitable for malting often brings $0.05 to $0.15 a bushel more than feeding barley. Thus, with each crop, quality has a definite bearing on price.

Special Enterprises.—There is a limited opportunity for qualified growers to enhance the price of their commodities by taking advantage of special crops or special markets. More than 10 million bushels of high-quality certified seed potatoes are produced annually in the United States by skillful growers who take special precautions to keep their seed as free as possible from disease. Normally such seed brings 35 to 40 cents a bushel more than table stock potatoes.

A special industry for the production of hybrid-seed corn has been developing rapidly. The market is a continuous one, for users of hybrid seed must purchase new seed each year. The production of sugar-beet seed has been developed extensively in the West. Production of forage-crop seed such as alfalfa, red clover, alsike, Ladino, brome grass, timothy, and Kentucky bluegrass may well be classed with the more specialized enterprises.

Feeding as a Market for Crops.—The most important means of marketing farm crops is to feed them to livestock. The production from some 65 million acres of tame and wild hay land as well as that from over 500 million acres of pasture land of one kind or another is essentially all marketed by means of livestock. Most of the corn, oats, and barley produced in the United States is fed; so are substantial quantities of the bread grains wheat and rye. The sorghums provide large quantities of livestock feed in subhumid areas. Soybeans are far more important as a livestock feed than as a raw product for industry.

The fundamental principle of feeding is that many farm crops can be marketed at higher prices if fed to livestock than if sold directly for cash. Some crops, pastures, for example, can be marketed effectively only through livestock; and many of the farm by-products and roughages have no material sales value but can be used in the feeding of livestock. Livestock enterprises provide the farmer with an opportunity to market labor as well as feed.

Crop production and livestock husbandry are closely related enterprises. The curing of hay, the making of silage, the development of a superior corn hybrid, the management of a pasture are merely a few representatives of the vast number of projects of mutual concern to both the crop and the livestock industries.

Crops and Farm Labor.—A farm and all its equipment represent a substantial capital investment upon which returns are to be made. The well-managed farm also provides the farmer, his family, and frequently some hired help with remunerative employment. In choosing his crop enterprises the farmer must consider labor, its cost, its availability, and its distribution.

One of the great troubles with the one-crop farm, found most commonly in the wheat country and cotton belt, is that the labor is concentrated into two or three short periods of time. That farm which grows only wheat has the labor of seedbed preparation and seeding and the labor of harvest. Months are left in which such a farm provides no remunerative employment. This factor alone is an important contributor to the distressed conditions associated with the culture of these two crops.

The farm that provides opportunity for diversification of crop enterprises, if these enterprises be well chosen and coordinated, provides also plenty of work to be done and distributes it as evenly as possible throughout the season. Add to such a farm effective livestock enterprises, and work is distributed throughout the entire season. Management studies indicate that even a small farm must provide a minimum of around 400 days of remunerative employment in a year. This, of course, involves the work of more than one individual. Greater success is likely if the farm can provide 500 to 600 or even more days of labor to the farmer and the helpers he employs. A succession of crops and the kind of livestock and equipment that can utilize this labor most efficiently are essential.

Land Values and Crop Selection.—Where land is low-priced, farm acreages can be large and the volume of business can be attained by extensive handling of large acreages. Cash grain production and range-land grazing are illustrative of the sort of enterprises demanding large acreages to secure a remunerative volume of business. In 1939, it took 6.2 acres of wheat to produce as much gross farm income as 1 acre of sugar beets and nearly 15 acres of wheat to equal the gross returned by 1 acre of tobacco. In the case of tobacco, volume of business is attained by intensive culture and considerable hand labor on relatively small acreages. Where the chief reliance is on wheat, the volume is secured by the handling of large acreages with, to a considerable extent, machinery. The sugar-beet crop is intermediate. Crops of high acre value are necessary to pay returns on high-value land.

Farming Systems.—Broadly speaking, there are three types of farming systems, each with almost numberless ramifications. These

Fig. 6.—A diversified family farm. Note the silo and barns for livestock, the apple storage (left rear), and the well-capped shocks of wheat. (*Courtesy of Garfield Farley.*)

are embodied in the family farm, the tenant farm, and the corporate farm.

The *family farm* has been regarded as a stabilizing feature in American agriculture. A major advantage lies in the fact that much of the family well-being in the way of food, shelter, and sometimes fuel and clothing is provided directly by the farm. The owner-operator of a farm finds it to his interest to choose a cropping system that not only provides immediate income but assures the continued productivity of his land.

Tenant farms have a double burden. Not only must such farms support the tenant and his family, but they must contribute to the support of the landowner as well. Tenancy is far more likely to prove successful on a productive soil. All too frequently the concern is with immediate returns, and cropping enterprises that are soil exhaustive in character may gradually ruin the land. Tenant-owner agreements that provide for maintenance of buildings and fences and that require good management practices and adequate seedings of crops beneficial to the land tend to alleviate some of the objectionable features of tenancy. Short-time leases make the arrangements for such desirable soil-maintenance features more difficult.

Many of the difficulties encountered in the management of farms under the tenancy system are likewise evident with farms carrying a heavy debt burden. Here, too, emphasis on immediate cash returns perforce delays desirable investments in land improvement which are essential to a permanently effective system of management.

The *corporate farm* is normally a large holding or a number of farms under one management. Its advantages lie in the efficient use of the more costly kinds of equipment and in the opportunity to employ trained skillful management. Such "bonanza" enterprises generally suffer most in periods of depression but may prove highly successful financially in periods of satisfactory prices. Improved facilities for transportation of crops and mechanized operations in culture and harvesting have made corporate farming more feasible. The system lacks the inspirational and often stabilizing influence of ownership of home and land characteristic of the well-run family farm.

Personal Considerations.—Of the fact that personal preferences strongly influence the selection of farming enterprises and consequently the choice of crops there can be no doubt. The farmer who chooses dairying must produce feeds and forages. But if he does not like the dairy business and its stern demands for labor and supervision 365 days of the year, then his choice of crops will be entirely different. There will be less emphasis on protein-rich hays, silage crops, and intensively managed pastures, for no system of farming markets such crops so effectively as dairying.

The efficient grower of potatoes must be willing to study something of pathology and entomology if he is successfully to recognize and combat the diseases and insects that may plague his crop. The sugar-beet grower must be a skillful manager of labor. The farm utilizing much mechanical equipment demands an operator with considerable mechanical skill. The producer of a special crop such as certified seed will find salesmanship ability a great asset.

Most men probably have sufficient adaptability to adjust their preferences and skills to a wide range of enterprises. Nevertheless, personal preferences and personal aptitude have a noteworthy bearing on the choice of enterprises and on the attainment of success.

Review Questions

1. Make a list of the most important cash crops grown in your state, together with the average gross acre value of each.

2. Look up the price history of the leading cash crop in your state, and try to account for years of unusually high and unusually low prices.

3. What notable differences would there be in your choice of crops if your farm is to emphasize hog raising rather than dairying?

4. What plans should you make for maintenance of soil fertility on a strictly cash-crop farm in your locality?

5. How does the sugar-beet crop differ from the potato crop in labor and equipment requirements?

6. What variety of alfalfa is recommended for your locality? Why?

7. Why are the grain sorghums grown to so large an extent in Texas, Oklahoma, and Kansas?

8. Wisconsin leads all other states in the number of silos. Why?

9. How may the price discount for smutty wheat be avoided?

10. How are farms raising beef cattle likely to differ from those engaged in the dairy business?

11. Make a list of the advantages and disadvantages of tenant farming.

12. How do land values influence the choice of crops?

Problems

1. Consult the current agricultural-outlook report published by your college of agriculture or the U.S. Department of Agriculture, and prepare a brief statement with reference to the prospects for the leading cash crop of your state.

2. You have a medium sandy loam farm and wish to grow a small grain for feed and use the straw for bedding. Which grain crop will you grow? Give your reasons.

3. The estimated cost of growing an acre of corn (see *U.S. Dept. Agr. Agricultural Statistics*) is substantially higher in Iowa and Illinois than in Missouri and Nebraska. However, the estimated cost per bushel of corn is lower in Iowa and Illinois. Explain these differences.

4. Prepare a short article explaining the marked increase in soybean production in the United States, telling where the increase has occurred and what crop or crops soybeans apparently has supplanted.

References

ADAMS, R. L.: "Farm Management," McGraw-Hill Book Company, Inc., New York, 1921.

Cox, J. F., and L. E. JACKSON: "Crop Management and Soil Conservation," John Wiley & Sons, Inc., New York, 1937.

FORESTER, G. W.: "Farm Organization and Management," Prentice-Hall, Inc., New York, 1938.

SANDERSON, DWIGHT, *et al.:* "Farm Income and Farm Life," University of Chicago Press, for The American Country Life Association, New York, 1927.

U. S. Dept. Agr. Agricultural Statistics, Superintendent of Documents, Government Printing Office, Washington, D. C.

CHAPTER IV

SOIL CONSERVATION AND MANAGEMENT

The earth is the mother of us all—plants, animals, and men. The phosphorus and calcium of the earth build our skeletons and nervous systems. Everything else our bodies need except air and sun comes from the earth.

Nature treats the earth kindly. Man treats her harshly. He overplows the cropland, overgrazes the pasture land, and overcuts the timberland. He destroys millions of acres completely. He pours fertility year after year into the cities, which in turn pour what they do not use down the sewers into the rivers and the ocean. The flood problem insofar as it is man-made is chiefly the result of overplowing, overgrazing, and overcutting of timber.
. . .

We know what can be done, and we are beginning to do it. As individuals we are beginning to do the necessary things. As a nation, we are beginning to do them. The public is waking up, and just in time. In another 30 years it might have been too late.

The social lesson of soil waste is that no man has the right to destroy soil even if he does own it in fee simple. The soil requires a duty of man which we have been slow to recognize.[1]

Thus, in 1938, did the United States Secretary of Agriculture state the problem of soil conservation.

THE NATURE OF SOIL LOSSES

Soil being used for agricultural purposes does not necessarily deteriorate in productive capacity. Good farming systems that provide adequate crop rotations, protection of the soil from the destructive effects of erosion, and replacement of necessary plant nutrients through the use of manure and commercial fertilizers are most likely to prove remunerative to the farmer and, at the same time, permit maintenance of or even improvement in the productivity of the soil.

However, many soils, because of improper management, have become less productive, often seriously so.

Erosion.—Most damaging of soil losses is that occasioned by erosion. Some erosion occurs wherever there are losses of water through runoff, the losses tending to increase with the degree of slope. Wind

---

[1] WALLACE, HENRY A., "Soils and Men (foreword)," *U.S. Dept. Agr. Yearbook of Agriculture*, 1938.

erosion may occur regardless of slope. Losses due to erosion are intensified by tillage of the land which removes its protective cover of vegetation and hastens the decomposition of its organic matter.

Erosion losses are not fully represented by the tons of soil lost from each acre of land. Some plant-food constituents, calcium, potassium, and magnesium, may even be present in greater quantity below the first foot of soil than in the plow layer itself. The amount of nitrogen, however, normally decreases with the depth of the soil, and the availability of phosphorus depends to an appreciable degree on the humus, most of which is in the plow layer.

Frequently of greater importance than the loss of plant nutrients is the unfavorable structure of much of the soil after the top has been removed by erosion. Productive soil, with its porous and granular structure, has been built up through the years by decaying vegetation or the dense root growth of covering grasses. This condition, once destroyed, cannot quickly be restored. Clay or silt soil from which the organic matter has been lost is heavy and often soggy and lifeless. Such soil is hard to till and difficult to drain. The mere addition of nitrogen, phosphorus, potassium, and calcium by no means restores its productivity. In this connection, E. J. Utz and associates[1] tell of an experiment at Tyler, Tex., in which desurfaced plots, treated with an annual application of 400 lb. per acre of 4-12-4 fertilizer and a green-manure crop plowed under annually, produced only 61 per cent as much cotton as normal plots without either fertilizer or green manure.

The gullies caused by water erosion make future working of the land difficult and, in extreme cases, may force the abandonment of the land for cropping purposes.

Leaching.—As rain water passes through the surface soil, it picks up readily soluble plant nutrients and carries them away in the drainage. Nitrogen and calcium are readily lost by this process of leaching, potassium and magnesium moderately so, and phosphorus scarcely at all. It is a fact particularly important to good management that losses of nitrogen by leaching are far greater on bare tilled soil than on that covered by grass or farmed with a good crop rotation. On the lighter soils, most subject to the effects of leaching, nitrogen losses can be greatly reduced by use of cover crops which use and hold the nitrogen and return it to the soil when they are plowed under.

Removal of Plant Food by Crops.—The 14 elements generally recognized as being essential for plant growth are given in Table 3. The nutrients of major consideration are nitrogen, phosphorus, potas-

[1] Utz, E. J., *et al.*, The Problem: The Nation as a Whole, "Soils and Men," *U.S. Dept. Agr. Yearbook of Agriculture*, **1938**.

sium, and calcium. Occasionally some of the others, the so-called *minor* or *secondary* elements, may be deficient; and their lack will be reflected in plant abnormalities and deficiencies. Generally speaking, the losses of the four major elements named above are most likely to prove critical.

TABLE 3.—CHEMICAL ELEMENTS CONSIDERED ESSENTIAL FOR NORMAL PLANT DEVELOPMENT

Carbon	Magnesium
Oxygen	Iron
Hydrogen	Sulphur
Nitrogen	Boron
Calcium	Manganese
Phosphorus	Copper
Potassium	Zinc

Carbon, oxygen, and hydrogen come from the air and water. The other elements are obtained by the plant from the soil, although atmospheric nitrogen may be made suitable for plant use by the activities of nitrogen-fixing bacteria.

Soils are by no means uniform with respect to their content of these plant nutrients, nor do the different crops act alike with respect to their removal.   Nitrogen may come from decaying organic matter in the soil or from the air owing to the activities of nitrogen-fixing bacteria growing on the roots of leguminous crops; a little is brought into the soil by rain; and some is the result of the work of free-living nitrogen-fixing organisms represented by Azotobacter and other groups. Phosphorus, potassium, and calcium sufficient for productive crop growth must be in the soil, or they must be added.

Obviously, the larger the yield of a crop, the more plant food it removes from the soil.   There can be no legitimate argument against high yields, but the fact that larger yields do remove more nutrients must be dealt with by the farmer in his soil-management practices.

A crop of alfalfa contains far more nitrogen than a crop of wheat. But its nitrogen is normally secured from the air, and so the growing of alfalfa leaves the soil with more nitrogen, whereas the smaller nitrogen content of wheat all comes from the soil and removal of the wheat crop reduces the soil's nitrogen supply.

But though alfalfa may enrich the soil with respect to nitrogen, it is a heavy user of calcium and potassium.   A 3-ton crop of alfalfa hay contains about 120 lb. of potassium, compared with only 8 or 10 lb. in 50 bu. of shelled corn.   The 3 tons of alfalfa hay also contains about 85 lb. of calcium, whereas the amount in 50 bu. of corn would be less than 1 lb.

The chemical analysis of a plant does not show with accuracy what the plant actually requires from the soil, for the same crop will vary widely in percentage composition of the different constituents with variations in culture, precipitation, sunlight, and the soil itself. However, such analyses, on the average, make possible a general estimate of the quantity of nutrients that a given weight of the various crops removes from the soil.

Tables showing the average percentages of the different fertilizing constituents found in a large number of plants and feeds are given in "Feeds and Feeding" by Morrison[1] and "Fertilizers and Crop Production" by Van Slyke.[2]

Extent of Soil Deterioration.—Agronomists generally agree that the net effect of erosion, leaching, crop removal, and organic nitrogen decomposition has been a gradual lowering of the productivity of American farm land despite the wide adoption of many improved cultural practices. After enumerating many of these improved methods such as better drainage, more productive varieties, greater use of lime and fertilizers, growing legumes in the rotation, improved tillage machinery, more timely planting and harvesting, and more effective control of insects and diseases, Salter, Lewis, and Slipher state, "There can be but one explanation for the stubbornness with which acre yields have resisted the farmer's efforts to improve them. The natural productive capacity of the land has been deteriorating at a rate almost fast enough to offset all of these improvements in soil and crop management. With every step ahead we have slipped back almost if not quite as far."[3]

HOW SOIL PRODUCTIVITY CAN BE MAINTAINED

The management of soils is a science in itself, in fact a group of sciences including soil classification, soil chemistry, soil physics, and soil microbiology. It is possible here to suggest only some of the major management considerations most directly related to the growing of crops.

Erosion Control.—To a very large degree the control of erosion is an agronomic problem. The use of erosible land too constantly for the production of small grains and more especially row crops increases

---

[1] MORRISON, F. B.: "Feeds and Feeding," 20th ed., The Morrison Publishing Co., Ithaca, N.Y., 1936.

[2] VAN SLYKE, L. L.: "Fertilizers and Crop Production," Orange Judd Publishing Co., Inc., New York, 1932.

[3] SALTER, R. M., R. D. LEWIS, and J. A. SLIPHER: Our Heritage, the Soil, *Ohio Ext. Bul.* 175, 1936.

erosion hazards, as does extremely close grazing of pasture lands. The maintenance of a high content of organic matter in the soil is important in reducing both wind and water erosion. Good grass cover is in itself the most effective erosion barrier. Where sufficient moisture is available to produce legumes, a mixture of grasses and legumes has marked advantages. The grasses, both from the standpoint of the more dense cover they provide and because of the granular structure of the soil that their roots produce, are more effective in erosion prevention, but the legumes supply extra nitrogen which contributes directly to the plant-nutrient supply and makes for effective decomposition of car-

FIG. 7.—Erosion control by means of a grass waterway in corn strips. Strip cropping is being practiced in the background. (*Courtesy of U.S. Dept. Agr. Soil Conservation Service.*)

bonaceous organic matter. A more extensive use of grass cover and crop rotations involving the increased growing of sod-forming grasses or grass-legume mixtures is the first essential in reducing erosion losses. This involves a system of farming whereby grass production may be effectively utilized by livestock to convert the products of the land into something marketable.

Contour Planting and Strip Cropping.—In glaciated regions the contours of hilly land are often exceedingly irregular and broken, and grass cover may be the only practical means of checking the erosion of cropland. Where contours are longer, planting the crops in rows on the contour or strip cropping may be feasible. Strip cropping consists in the planting of strips, of variable width, to sod-forming grasses and legumes alternated between strips of row crops, grains, or other crops requiring considerable tillage. The strips, 4 or 5 to as much as 10 rods wide, follow the contours. The alternating sod crops reduce runoff and increase penetration of water into the soil.

Strips of taller growing crops planted broadside to the direction of prevailing winds reduce wind erosion. On many soils and especially on muck the planting of tree windbreaks is resorted to.

The mechanics of erosion control also provide for grass-covered channels by which excess water can escape without creating destructive gullies.

Terracing.—A terrace is an earth ridge with a channel above, constructed so as to follow the contour of a slope. Its function is to intercept water so that it may be either absorbed or conducted slowly from the area. Nichols and Chambers state:

> Terracing must be correlated with land-use practices, and future uses of the land should be considered. Land to be retired to pasture or other close-growing crops will seldom require the additional protection of mechanical control. Only where the soil has been damaged by erosion to such an extent that it will not support a protective vegetal cover, or on exceptionally erodible soils that require mechanical protection during the interim necessary to produce a cover, will such measures be necessary. . . .
>
> Population density and economic conditions will sometimes dictate land-use practices and produce situations where cultivation is necessary on severely eroded land that should normally be retired, or on slopes too steep for tillage. In these situations, construction of terraces may be necessary even though the cost will be high and their effectiveness will be impaired.[1]

Tree Planting.—Tree planting may be used as a means of erosion control on soils too steep for or otherwise unsuited to crop production. They may also be used as windbreaks. In both instances, they may aid in the protection of more valuable land adjacent to the plantings by preventing coverage of good land with undesirable eroded soil and by reducing wind erosion. Well-kept wooded areas have aesthetic value, provide wild-life food and cover, and may make some contribution economically as a source of posts, firewood, Christmas trees, and decorative shrubbery in addition to their erosion-prevention value.

MAINTAINING ORGANIC MATTER

Organic matter is the basis of soil productivity. Plants can be grown in the greenhouse in quartz sand by constantly supplying them with nutrients in a solution. But, under field conditions, the soil itself must contain plant food; it must hold water and yet be well

[1] NICHOLS, M. L., and T. B. CHAMBERS: Mechanical Measures of Erosion Control, "Soils and Men," *U.S. Dept. Agr. Yearbook of Agriculture*, 1938.

drained; it must contain bacteria to cause decomposition of organic material and release plant foods; it must be well aerated. Not only is organic matter a source of nitrogen, but it provides a means by which undue loss of nitrogen through leaching and volatilization is prevented. It lightens heavy soils and holds lighter soils together. It imparts a darker color to soil, thereby making for the absorbing of heat on bright days with a resultant rise in the soil's temperature.

Sources of Organic Matter.—Plants are the original source of organic matter. Organic matter in wooded areas has been built up from decaying leaves and the rotting roots and tops of trees and other

Fig. 8.—Bankrupting the soil. Crop residues not otherwise profitably used should go back to the land to help maintain its content of organic matter. (*Courtesy of E. E. Patton.**)

vegetation that has fallen back on the soil. In treeless regions the prairie grasses have built up an accumulation of organic material. On cropped land the crop residues in the form of roots, straw, stalks, and leaves not otherwise used are returned to the land to provide its organic content. Commonly, many of these crop residues are used for feed and bedding, and considerable organic material is eventually returned to the soil in the form of farm manures.

Coarse sands and gravel soils may contain less than 1 per cent of organic matter, a good mineral soil 3 to 6 per cent, and peat 90 per cent or more.

Carbon-Nitrogen Ratio.—The number of pounds of carbon in 100 lb. of organic material divided by the number of pounds of nitrogen in 100 lb. of the material gives the carbon-nitrogen (C:N) ratio. Soil

* E. E. Patton is photographer for the Farmers' and Manufacturers' Beet Sugar Association, Saginaw, Mich.

organic matter has a C:N ratio of about 10:1 although in some soils it may be as high as 12:1. The legumes, naturally high nitrogen plants, have a relatively narrow C:N ratio whereas the ratio is high for small-grain straw, cornstalks, and similar materials.

Materials having a high C:N ratio decay slowly. Because of this the plowing under of such materials may cause a temporary lowering of the soil's productivity. The organisms that cause the decay of this carbonaceous material require nitrogen. If there is not enough in the material itself, they take it from the soil, causing a temporary shortage. When the process of decay is completed, the nitrogen again becomes available for plant use.

In the plowing under of legumes or immature grasses there is little likelihood of this nitrogen shortage. If straw, cornstalks, or large quantities of other carbonaceous material are to be plowed under, the addition of a nitrogen fertilizer will supply the organisms causing decay with needed nitrogen, decomposition of the material will be hastened, and the temporary depression in the soil's productivity will be prevented.

Organic Matter from Legumes.—Leguminous crops are an ideal source of nitrogen and organic matter. These crops obtain nitrogen from the air by the activities of symbiotic nitrogen-fixing bacteria growing in nodules on their roots. Part of this nitrogen makes for protein-rich feed; part is left in the soil. Alfalfa is one of the most effective of all in nitrogen fixation. According to Gustafson[1] a fixation of 80 to 100 lb. an acre annually for red and alsike clover, or mixtures of them, and 150 to 200 lb. for alfalfa may be regarded as highly satisfactory. Such crops are our soil builders. Their decomposition is rapid, and they exert a marked beneficial effect on crops that follow.

Lyon[2] in a study of the effect of legumes and combinations of legumes and cereals on the yields of succeeding cereal crops secured the results reported in Table 4. Legumes such as peas, field beans, and soybeans do not exert the same beneficial effect on the soil produced by the close-growing clovers and alfalfa. (1) They do not fix so much nitrogen. (2) They do not leave nearly so much residue in the soil. (3) Tillage practices, especially when they are grown in rows as is customary with field beans and common with soybeans, are conducive to organic-matter destruction and loss of nitrogen through leaching and volatilization.

[1] GUSTAFSON, A. F., "Soils and Soil Management," McGraw-Hill Book Company, Inc., New York, 1941.
[2] LYON, T. L., The Residual Effects of Some Leguminous Crops, *Cornell Univ. Agr. Expt. Sta. Bul.* 645, 1936.

TABLE 4.—TEN-YEAR AVERAGE ANNUAL YIELDS OF CEREAL CROPS FOLLOWING
EACH LEGUME OR MIXTURE OF LEGUME AND CEREAL

Crop Preceding Cereal	Yield of Cereal Following Legume or Mixture of Legume and Cereal, Pounds per Acre of Grain and Straw
Red clover	5,144
Alsike clover	5,126
Alfalfa	6,068
Sweet clover	5,119
Vetch and wheat	2,805
Red clover and alsike clover	5,243
Sweet clover and vetch	4,951
Soybeans	2,953
Peas and oats	2,907
Field beans	2,760
Cereals only	2,214

Green Manures.—The excellent yields of potatoes secured in Aroostook County, Maine, may be attributed in no small degree to the extensive use of green-manure crops, especially crimson clover. In the field-bean-growing sections of Michigan, it is a common practice to seed sweet clover in small grain and plow it under in early May of the next season for beans. Hairy vetch, crimson clover, and bur clover are frequently grown as green-manure crops in the South. Occasionally alfalfa, red clover, soybeans, and cowpeas are grown strictly as green manures.

Of the nonleguminous crops, rye and buckwheat are most commonly used to add organic matter to the soil. Both can be grown on relatively poor land. Buckwheat is a quick-growing annual and can make a substantial growth when planted later than most crops, and rye is extremely winter hardy and can be planted after the harvest of various other crops in the autumn.

The chief function of a green manure is to supply organic matter and improve the physical condition and moisture relationship in the soil. In the case of legumes, the nitrogen added from the air is also a prime consideration. Far more nitrogen is added to the soil by the turning under of a leguminous green manure than is customarily added by commercial fertilizer, and at a much lower cost. The turning under of 1 ton of dry matter in sweet clover involves approximately 60 lb. of nitrogen in the tops alone, and another 55 or 60 lb. in the roots. If sulphate of ammonia carrying 20 per cent nitrogen were selling at $40 a ton, 120 lb. of nitrogen, or 600 lb. of the fertilizer, would cost $12. Because the sweet-clover nitrogen becomes available more gradually, much less loss of nitrogen by leaching and otherwise would be incurred with the green manure. However, large losses are incurred if no crop is planted within a reasonably short time after the sweet clover is plowed under.

The turning under of an unusually large growth of a green-manure crop is not always beneficial. Coarse stiff material such as ripe or nearly ripe rye or sweet clover may make the soil too loose. Also, by letting rye, sweet clover, and similar "growthy" crops grow too long

Fig. 9.—Rye sown in corn stubble the previous fall can provide soil-protecting cover during the winter, pasture and organic matter in early spring. (*Courtesy of E. E. Patton.*)

in the spring, a tremendous amount of soil water is used and, should the season be dry, the results may be most unfavorable.

Pettigrove and Millar[1] plowed sweet clover under for beans in November of the year the sweet clover was seeded and on May 1, 15, and 30 the following spring. Results secured with the autumn and with the May 1 and 15 plowings, when the sweet clover was relatively small, were satisfactory. The late May plowings with sweet clover 3 to 4 ft. high greatly reduced the bean yields in dry seasons and were no advantage over plowings when the sweet clover was small in the wet seasons. One dry spring, beans planted after the May 30 plowing did not come up for 20 days, whereas beans on the other

[1] PETTIGROVE, H. R., and C. E. MILLAR, *Mich. Agr. Expt. Sta.*, work unpublished.

plots were well up in a week. The big sweet clover had used the available moisture well below plow depth.

The economy of using green manures depends upon many local factors such as seed, climate, system of farming, and the particular crops grown. Livestock farming permits utilization of forages as feed, and considerable organic matter from feed wastes and bedding is returned to the soil as manure. But unless the livestock farmer purchases considerable feed, there will still be a soil-fertility deficit produced by constituents being sold off the farm as livestock products. Besides, there is waste in the storage and handling of manures. Thus, many livestock farms may find green-manure practices of value, especially when the green manure can be grown between crops, without loss of land use, as with companion or winter cover crops. For the strictly cash-crop farm, the necessity for keeping up the soil with green manures is obvious.

Farm Manure.—There is no question of the value of farm manures as sources both of organic matter and of plant-food constituents. The manure varies in quality with the material fed, the material used for bedding, the kind of livestock, and the care with which the manure has been handled. In general, it is high in nitrogen and potash and relatively low in phosphoric acid. On the average, the quantity of plant nutrients in a ton of manure is similar to that in 100 lb. of 10-5-10 fertilizer.

Not only does manure benefit the immediate crop, but it has a marked residual effect, particularly if large amounts are used on the heavier soils. This is due in part to the fact that manure is more than a source of plant food. On this basis alone, average manure normally has a fertilizing value of around $2 a ton. But many of the benefits of manure are indirect. As a source of humus and organic matter, it improves the physical condition of the soil, its water-holding capacity, aeration, and temperature relationships. It favors the activities of soil organisms that make nutrients available to plants. In addition, certain of its organic constituents may have definite value in promoting plant growth and stimulating root development.

Manure is most effective if supplemented with sufficient superphosphate to make up for its phosphoric acid deficiency. Moderate applications over wider areas bring more profitable returns than unusually heavy applications, a common rate of use being 8 tons per acre.

Because poor soils are particularly responsive to manure, it is common to apply it to less productive portions of the farm. Because it is a bulky material in proportion to its value, the fields nearest the barn are almost certain to get the heaviest applications. This is good economy provided that the fertility of the more remote fields is maintained by a judicious use of green manure and commercial fertilizers.

Fertilizers.—Commercial fertilizers are materials used to supply nitrogen, phosphorus, and potassium either singly or in combination. Those containing all three constituents are known as *complete* fertilizers. Their analysis is expressed by formulas that represent the percentage nitrogen, percentage available phosphoric acid, and percentage water-soluble potash that they contain. Thus a 4-16-4 fertilizer contains 4 per cent nitrogen, 16 per cent available phosphoric acid, and 4 per cent water-soluble potash.

Nitrogen.—Nitrogen as a plant food in commercial fertilizers comes in several different forms. In nitrate of soda the nitrogen is in the nitrate form, and in this condition it is very soluble in water and becomes quickly available to plants upon being applied to the soil. However, nitrate nitrogen, unless immediately used by plants, can also be quickly lost by leaching.

In sulphate of ammonia the nitrogen is combined in the form of ammonia or its compounds. This form of nitrogen is also quickly soluble in water but is less readily lost from the soil than nitrate nitrogen because it is more readily fixed by certain other soil constituents.

Organic nitrogens come from vegetable or animal materials such as soybean or cottonseed meal and animal tankage. These nitrogenous compounds are complex, and the nitrogen in them becomes available more slowly. Such nitrogenous materials as urea and cyanamide are organic in character, but the nitrogen is combined in simpler amide form as compared with the more complex proteins of cottonseed meal and tankage.

To be used by plants the nitrogen in the more complex forms is changed by bacterial action into the nitrate form or into ammonia.

Effects of Nitrogen.—Nitrogen is particularly effective in stimulating the vegetative growth of plants. In the case of small grains, too much nitrogen results in excessive straw growth; and the ultimate effect may be lodging of the straw, development of shriveled, light-weight kernels, and lower yields. A deficiency of nitrogen is associated with a stunted growth of the plants and a yellowed appearance. The rich green color noted in the leaves of plants adequately supplied with nitrogen is due to the stimulating effect this constituent has on chlorophyll development.

Nitrogen is markedly effective as a grass nutrient. Wherever the growing of legumes in association with grass forage or pasture crops is feasible, the nitrogen supplied by the legume is the most economical means of ensuring a vigorous growth of grass. Otherwise, it may be necessary to supply it in the more costly way by means of commercial fertilizer.

Where large quantities of carbonaceous material are plowed under, decomposition is hastened by applications of nitrogenous fertilizer with the material. The practice is becoming increasingly important where high-value crops follow such treatments.

Nitrogen is commonly used in small quantities in complete fertilizers to hasten initial growth and aid in the early development of a strong vigorous plant.

Phosphorus.—A great many soils are inadequately supplied with phosphorus. The deficiency tends to become increasingly acute with both livestock and grain farming. Phosphorus is an essential constituent of both plants and animals. Forage legumes and grasses both remove substantial quantities of phosphorus from the soil, as do the cereal grains. The seeds of large-seeded legumes such as field beans and soybeans carry even more phosphorus. It is likewise an important constituent of animal bones, historically the original source of phosphorus as a fertilizing material. Because so much phosphorus is sold off the land in the form of animals and animal products, cereal grains, and legume seeds and because it cannot be replenished from the atmosphere, as can nitrogen, its replacement in the land in a phosphate-carrying fertilizer becomes essential.

Most of the phosphate used in the United States is in the form of *superphosphate*, resulting from the treatment of phosphate rock with sulphuric acid. The phosphate value of such a fertilizer is determined by its amount of phosphoric acid soluble in water plus that soluble in ammonium citrate. The total is called the *available* phosphoric acid. Superphosphate contains 14 to 20 per cent available phosphoric acid. By treating phosphate rock with liquid phosphoric acid rather than sulphuric acid, a very concentrated fertilizer containing 40 to 50 per cent available phosphoric acid is formed. This is the *treble superphosphate* of the fertilizer industry.

Metaphosphate as manufactured by the Tennessee Valley Authority contains approximately 63 per cent of phosphoric acid. Ground to a suitable fineness the material is in good condition for drilling, and in numerous trials it has produced satisfactory results as a plant fertilizer.

Ammonium phosphate contains nitrogen as well as phosphorus. The *monoammonium phosphate* contains approximately 11 per cent nitrogen and 48 per cent phosphoric acid. Bone meal, both raw and steamed, basic slag, a phosphatic by-product of the steel industry, and finely ground phosphate rock, though not very suitable for mixed fertilizers, are used to some extent for direct application to the soil.

Potassium.—Potassium is absorbed by plants in the form of water-soluble potash. It is most lacking in the lighter sandy soils and in mucks and peats. The total potassium in heavier soils is abundant, but only a small fraction is readily available. Thus, continued cropping even of heavy soils may eventually result in a deficiency of potassium which plants actually can use.

Fig. 10.—It is important that a farming system shall provide that plant food be supplied as economically as possible to crops most likely to pay for returning to the soil those elements necessary to keep the soil productive. The smaller rows of sugar beets in the center of this picture were unfertilized; the balance of the field was treated with a complete fertilizer. (*Courtesy of E. E. Patton.*)

Considerable potash is returned to the soil in farm manures and many crop residues. For example, sugar-beet tops are high in potash; but this potash originally came from the soil, and it provides for only partial, not complete, replacement.

Muriate of potash (potassium chloride) is a chief source of potassium for fertilizer. Other sources include potassium sulphate, potassium nitrate (saltpeter), nitrate of soda-potash, manure salts, seaweed, and wood ashes.

Where soils are deficient in potash, crops generally respond in increased growth and vigor to applications of a potash-carrying fertilizer. Such prodigious potash users as alfalfa require liberal applications when grown on the sandier soils, and it is generally customary to use some potash in a mixed fertilizer for corn, small grains, sugar beets, potatoes, and tobacco. Potash is by far the most important fertilizing constituent for the growing of crops on muck.

Effects of Fertilizing Constituents.—Very little has been said here of any specific effects of the individual fertilizing constituents on plant reactions. It has often been stated that nitrogen delays maturity, phosphorus hastens maturity and stimulates root growth, and potash, in common with nitrogen, delays maturity. Under many conditions, this is doubtless true, but much depends upon circumstances. There are numerous instances where a reasonable application of nitrogen has tended to hasten rather than to delay maturity or where applications of phosphorus have had no effect in hastening maturity or stimulating root growth. There are many instances where a fertilizing constituent applied singly had no marked effect on production but applied with other constituents proved exceedingly effective. To the farmer it is highly important that plants be nourished liberally, not with one or two, but with all fertilizing constituents, that the rations be balanced for his plants as well as his animals, and that his system of operations be such that plant food is supplied as economically as possible to crops most likely to pay for the returning to the soil of those elements necessary to keep that soil productive. No system of farming can endure that constantly removes these vital constituents from the soil without providing for their effective return.

Fertilizer Placement.—For small grain and with broadcast forage seedings the commercial fertilizer used is broadcast, usually by means of a fertilizer attachment to a grain drill or with a regular fertilizer drill. In the case of row crops the response for the particular amount of fertilizer used is better if the fertilizer is concentrated in rows near the seed. In view of the fact that direct contact of fertilizer with the seed is often injurious, some seeds being particularly sensitive to fertilizer injury, equipment has been developed that will plant the fertilizer in bands close to but not in direct contact with the seed. In general, the desirable placement for row fertilizer applications appears to be in bands to the side and slightly below the seed level, with 1 to 2 in. of fertilizer-free soil between the seed and the fertilizer.

Lime.—Lime is both a plant food and a soil amendment. However, nearly all the stress with respect to its use has been placed on its function of correcting soil acidity. Alfalfa and sugar beets are among the field crops most sensitive to soil acidity, with red clover and sweet clover scarcely less so. Of the legumes, alsike, crimson clover, and vetch are fairly tolerant to an acid condition, and lespedeza is very tolerant. The fact that alfalfa and red clover, most useful of legumes and likewise most effective of plants in respect to soil improvement, have a high lime requirement is one of the important reasons for giving full consideration to the lime needs of the soil.

How Soil Acidity Is Expressed.—An ion is one of the small electrified particles into which molecules of a substance may be broken. When the concentration of hydrogen (H) ions is greater than that of hydroxyl

FIG. 11.—Refuse lime from a Michigan sugar company being hauled away for soil improvement. (*Courtesy of E. E. Patton.*)

(OH) ions, the solution is acid. The opposite condition constitutes alkalinity. In absolute pure water (H_2O), the H ions and OH ions are in balance, and the solution is neutral. Acidity is expressed in pH units, with pH7 representing neutrality. If a solution has a pH number of less than 7, it is acid; if its pH number is more than 7, it is alkaline. The change from one unit to another is in geometric progression; a solution of pH5 is 10 times as acid as one of pH6, and a solution of pH4 is 100 times as acid as one of pH6. The pH number of soils may vary from below 4 to about 10, anything above pH7.5 being very strongly alkaline and anything below pH5 being very strongly acid. A range in pH of 5 to 7 is common in humid regions.

Effects of Lime.—The relation of soil acidity to the growth of plants is exceedingly complex. It involves the physical condition of the soil, the activity of soil organisms, the availability of essential plant foods, the prevalence of plant diseases, and other important considerations.

A lack of lime in a heavy soil is associated with absence of the desirable granular structure necessary to good aeration, drainage, and conditions favorable to desirable chemical and biological activity. In a sandy soil the presence of sufficient lime tends to aid in holding soil particles together.

With respect to plant nutrients, phosphorus in particular is more available when sufficient lime is present to keep the soil reaction neutral or nearly so. Calcium and magnesium become less available as their supply diminishes in an increasingly acid soil. Soil organisms that cause the breakdown of organic matter find acid conditions unfavorable; hence, such acidity affects the supply of available nitrogen and other elements liberated by decomposition.

One reason why potato growing has been widely practiced on fairly acid soils is that the organism causing potato scab is supposedly inhibited when the pH number of the soil is below 5.3. In the absence of scab the potato plant does well in soils only slightly acid to neutral, but the crop is also tolerant of acidity to a marked degree.

Liming Specific Crops.—From the standpoint of sound economy the logical time for the application of lime, if needed, is in advance of the sowing of such legumes as alfalfa, sweet clover, and red clover. These crops are exceedingly responsive to lime applications, and their increased growth not only pays for the lime but creates soil conditions favorable to the growth of other crops for years to come.

A typical illustration of how liming an acid soil for a legume affects the entire rotation is given by Millar and Grantham in reporting the results of an experiment conducted on an Isabella sandy-loam soil in Kent County, Michigan (see Table 5).

Quantities of Lime Required.—The amount of lime that should be applied to a given soil depends upon the degree of acidity of the soil. Some soils are not acid and need no application of lime. Numerous quick field tests to determine approximately the degree of acidity in the soil have been devised. An acid, heavy soil will require much more lime to neutralize its acidity than will a sandy soil of the same acidity. Where soils are medium to strongly acid, applications of 2 to 5 tons of ground limestone to the acre or the chemical equivalent in some other product such as marl, refuse lime, or hydrated lime are indicated. An application of this amount should be adequate for 8 or 10 years.

TABLE 5.—YIELD RESULTS FOLLOWING THE LIMING OF AN ACID SOIL*

Treatment	First-year, clover, pounds	Second year, corn, bushels	Third year, oats, bushels	Fourth year, barley, bushels
Limed soil..............	6,854	63.0	31.8	20.7
Unlimed soil...........	3,158	54.6	16.6	16.0

* MILLAR, C. E., and G. M. GRANTHAM, Lime for Sour Soils, *Mich. Agr. Expt. Sta. Spec. Bul.* 91, 1932.

Lighter applications are sometimes preferable. For example, where it is desired to grow potatoes in rotation with alfalfa or some other legume with a high lime requirement, lighter lime applications close to the seed may give fair results with the legume and avoid providing conditions too favorable for the development of the potato-scab organisms.

CROP ROTATIONS

A crop rotation is a sequence of crops grown in recurring succession on the same area of land. It provides for the growing of different crops rather than continuous culture to one crop and for the growing of these different crops in systematic order rather than in haphazard fashion. The mere fact that crops are grown in systematic rotation does not necessarily ensure either good farming or good soil management, for rotations may be bad as well as good. But the rotation of crops does provide the opportunity for effective land-management and soil-conservation practices. In fact, the major benefits to be derived from a well-planned crop rotation accrue to the land.

Benefits of Crop Rotation.—The benefits to be derived from desirable crop rotations may be classed as follows:

1. Because differences in feeding habits are advantageous and because of other considerations, most crops yield better following other crops than they do following themselves or crops of similar feeding habits.

2. Crop rotations provide an opportunity to restore organic matter to the soil.

3. In a rotation, plant nutrients may be returned to the soil as manure and commercial fertilizer applied to the crops most likely to respond with paying returns.

4. Crop rotations can be so planned as to curtail greatly losses caused by erosion.

5. A series of feed and cash crops diversifies the sources of farm income.

6. The growing of crops with different seasonal requirements distributes labor and makes possible more effective farm management.

7. Crop rotations make possible the reduction of losses caused by certain weeds, insects, and plant diseases.

Crop-sequence Effects.—Salter and Lill[1] report on a crop-sequence project in which corn, sugar beets, oats, soybean hay, and soybean seed were grown in a series of arrangements wherein each crop followed itself as well as each other crop in the group. The soybeans were not significantly influenced by the crop sequence; but corn, sugar beets, and oats showed marked differences in this respect. Both corn and sugar beets gave poorest yields when following themselves; oats yielded least when following itself or corn. Best yields of each followed soybean hay, the advantages over following itself in the sequence being 1.24 tons for sugar beets, 18.7 bu. for corn, and 11.5 bu. for oats, as a 4-year average. Oats yielded better after sugar beets than after corn, corn yielded better after sugar beets than after oats, and sugar beets yielded better after corn or oats than after sugar beets.

The experiment reported above did not include a desirable rotation, for any arrangement of the five crops included would probably result in soil depletion at a fairly rapid rate. What it does illustrate is the general principle that many crops do not yield so well following themselves as they do after some other crop, particularly if the other crop has a distinctly different effect on the soil.

Irrespective of provisions for returning plant nutrients to the soil, crop rotations, properly arranged, tend to increase yields by providing changes in the location of the feeding range of the roots, altering physical conditions in the soil, and counteracting the possible development of toxic substances.

Restoring Fertility with Rotations.—If rotations merely altered the feeding range of crops, their eventual effect would be soil depleting in character, probably more depleting than continuous cropping to a single crop because of the increased removal of nutrients. But a rotation worthy of the name should be soil conserving or, even better, soil building in character. This is made possible in two ways, (1) by the inclusion of sod-forming leguminous crops and (2) by providing for effective applications of manure and fertilizer. The benefits of

[1] SALTER, R. M., and J. G. LILL, Crop Sequence Studies in Northwestern Ohio, *Jour. Amer. Soc. Agron.*, Vol. 32, No. 8, 1940.

grass roots in bringing about a desirable granular condition of the soil, of legumes in adding atmospheric nitrogen, and of both in supplying organic matter have already been discussed. So has the use of manure and of commercial fertilizer. Not only does the well-managed cropping system provide for rehabilitating the soil in respect to organic content and plant nutrients, but it provides for such restoration at times and for such crops as will most effectively give a paying response.

To supply an abundance of organic matter just previous to the planting of oats will, in humid regions at least, result in excessive straw growth, lodging, poorly filled grain, and reduced yields. To supply this organic matter just prior to the planting of a crop of corn, potatoes, tobacco, or cotton will result in a more thrifty crop and greater returns.

Not only is the application of commercial fertilizer intended to return nitrogen, phosphoric acid, and potash to the soil, but it is supposed to be paid for in profitable yield increases of the crops that follow. This obviously indicates the necessity of making manure and fertilizer applications to the higher value crops in a rotation. Considering 1930–1939 United States averages, a 20 per cent increase in the yield of oats would have been worth but $1.67, on an acre basis, and that would not pay for much fertilizer. A 20 per cent increase in corn would have been worth $2.75 an acre; in field beans, $4.97; in sugar beets, $12.63; in potatoes, $14.67; and in tobacco, $27.04. Little wonder that sugar beets, potatoes, and tobacco are among the field crops that receive and pay for the heaviest fertilizer applications, whereas less high value crops in the rotation must receive their benefits from the residual effects of manures, green manures, and fertilizers.

Some rotations do not have unusually high value cash crops. Under such circumstances the soil-improving treatments may precede the more valuable feed crops, or particular emphasis may be directed to the establishment of a vigorous legume. The oat crop alone may not pay for much fertilizer, but it may be sound business to apply fertilizer liberally with oats grown as a companion crop for a seeding of alfalfa. The increased yield of oats will help pay for the fertilizer, but the main consideration is the establishment of a good seeding of alfalfa which not only will give additional returns due to fertilization but, when plowed under, will make for better corn or whatever other crops may follow in the rotation.

The results of a Michigan experiment serve to illustrate the effectiveness of fertilizing alfalfa seeded in small grain where such fertilization is conducted in accordance with specific needs (see Table 6). In this trial, alfalfa was seeded in barley on a Miami silt-loam soil that had been well-manured rather frequently. In this situation, available potash in the soil was adequate for alfalfa, the legume supplied its own nitrogen, but phosphorus was lacking.

TABLE 6.—THE EFFECT OF FERTILIZERS APPLIED FOR BARLEY ON THE YIELD OF THE FOLLOWING ALFALFA CROP, MIAMI SILT-LOAM SOIL*

Treatment	Dry Hay per Acre, Pounds
0-16-0 at 250 lb	4,920
None	2,768
4-16-8 at 250 lb	4,864

* *Mich. Agr. Expt. Sta. Cir. Bul.* 154, 1936.

Importance of Legumes in Rotation.—The restoration of organic matter and nitrogen to the soil is most effectively accomplished by inclusion in the crop rotation of the close-growing legumes or mixtures of legumes and grasses. The long-time rotation experiments in Ohio, Illinois, Pennsylvania, and Missouri have all emphasized this consideration, as have a great many experiments of shorter duration as well as the common experiences of farmers in general. Table 7 presents data from the Ohio experiments showing the greater organic-matter and nitrogen content of soils cropped with a legume in the rotation as compared with that in soils continuously cropped with grain.

Work at Cornell University, previously described (see page 45), showed that alfalfa is even more beneficial than clover in maintaining productivity.

TABLE 7.—ORGANIC-MATTER AND NITROGEN CONTENT OF UNFERTILIZED PLOTS AT WOOSTER, OHIO*

Crop rotation	Begun, year	Analyzed, year	Organic matter, pounds per acre	Nitrogen, pounds per acre
Corn, oats, wheat, clover, timothy	1894	1894	35,050	2,176
Corn, oats, wheat, clover, timothy	1894	1925	26,700	1,546
Continuous corn	1894	1925	12,730	840
Continuous oats	1894	1925	22,800	1,425
Continuous wheat	1894	1925	22,050	1,315
Corn, wheat, clover	1897	1925	29,500	1,780

* SALTER, R. M., R. D. LEWIS, and J. A. SLIPHER, Our Heritage, the Soil, *Ohio Ext. Bul.* 175, 1936.

In many farming systems a legume can be economically worked into the rotation strictly for green-manuring purposes.

In the South, winter legumes are advantageous in the rotation as green manures. Summer legumes such as cowpeas and soybeans can be used; but the expense is greater in that they occupy the land for an entire crop season or they must be seeded as a companion crop, *i.e.,* cowpeas in corn.   Hairy vetch seeded in early fall is ready to be plowed under by next Apr. 10 for cotton or a little later for corn.   Crimson clover and bur clover are also grown as winter legumes.   Rye or rye and vetch are sometimes seeded for winter cover in the North.   If seeded by mid-September, they normally stand the winter well and

Fig. 12.—Where sweet-clover seedings can be secured readily this crop often is seeded in small grains and plowed under early the next spring for corn, field beans, and other row crops.   (*Courtesy of E. E. Patton.*)

make a vigorous spring growth in good condition to be plowed under in early May.

Rotations That Control Erosion.—Obviously, rotations that provide sod-forming crops and winter cover and that maintain a high organic-matter content in the soil are material aids in reducing losses caused by erosion.   In the corn, wheat, clover rotation so commonly used in Ohio, the wheat provides winter cover one year, the clover the next. Another rotation sometimes used in the corn belt, made up of corn, corn, soybeans, wheat, and clover is subject to severe erosion.

Louis Allais, farming very rolling sandy land in Van Buren County, Michigan, has been successful in controlling erosion and maintaining good yields by making legume seedings in corn. The success of the seedings on this land is based on making them in very clean corn by the time the corn is not over knee-high. His rotation is as follows: first year, corn for grain seeded to sweet clover; second year, corn for silage seeded to alfalfa and smooth brome. The alfalfa-smooth-brome mixture is used for hay and pasture for 2 to 5 years. His major source of income is from dairying. The land is well manured, and fertilization for the corn and seedings is high in both phosphorus and potassium to ensure a vigorous growth of the legumes. The land is never bare over winter.

Diversification of Sources of Income.—The one-crop farmer plays a gambler's game. He stakes all against the weather, disease, insect, and market hazards threatening his single crop. A rotation of crops diversifies the sources of income. Corn may be a cash crop or feed for livestock. Wheat is primarily a cash crop, and most oats and barley crops are fed. Forages presuppose livestock as a source of revenue. Thus, a corn, oats, wheat, clover rotation provides feed for livestock from two or three sources and a direct cash-crop income from at least one.

An interesting example of diversification is found in Michigan's fertile Thumb district where the cropping system frequently includes corn, oats, barley, wheat, beans, sugar beets, and alfalfa. The rotations are not fixed for the farm nor are all crops grown in equal acreages, but the long-time history of a given field might read: corn, barley seeded to sweet clover, beans, wheat, alfalfa, alfalfa, corn, sugar beets, oats, alfalfa, alfalfa. Beans, sugar beets, wheat, and frequently barley are sold for cash; the corn, oats, and alfalfa are marketed through livestock.

Distribution of Labor.—Seasonal distribution of labor is one of the major considerations in planning a suitable rotation. Crops that conflict in respect to labor requirements, for example, corn and soybeans, build up labor peaks. Some of the less valuable crops in a rotation, such as oats, find their place because planting time and harvest time are interspersed between the peak labor loads for more valuable crops like corn, sugar beets, beans, and potatoes. A full year's work for labor and equipment distributed as evenly as possible is one of the essentials of good land management.

Pest Control.—Row crops involving intertillage tend to keep down weeds. Many annuals that go to seed in grainfields are destroyed by cultivation in row crops. On the other hand, some of the perennial pests are checked when the land is in meadow. The repeated cutting of alfalfa and the rapidity with which this crop recovers are death to the Canada thistle which thrives in grain and is hard to eliminate by ordinary cultivation. Repeated cropping with winter rye or winter wheat, with summer fallowing between crops, is one of the most effective and economical means of controlling bindweed.

A number of plant diseases are greatly reduced in seriousness if a proper sequence of crops is followed. Alfalfa wilt usually does not become serious during the first 2 years, and losses that it causes may be checked by rotations that are planned to shorten the duration of the stand. Scab affects wheat, barley, corn, and rye. The disease is carried not only in the seed but in crop refuse. It may be intensified by growing susceptible crops in succession but reduced by interspersing resistant or immune crops such as oats, flax, soybeans, alfalfa, or clover. The Diplodia disease of corn, anthracnose and blight of beans, wilt of potatoes, root rot of cotton, damping-off and leaf blight of sugar beets, and several diseases of tobacco are at least reduced in seriousness by crop-rotation procedures. If disease spores are carried by the wind as in the case of cereal rusts, late blight of potatoes, and many others, no rotation is effective in controlling them.

Plowing, together with other cultural practices used in a complete crop rotation, is destructive to wireworms, white grubs, the European corn borer, sod webworms, and many other kinds of insects.

Setting Up the Rotation.—In a general way, crop rotations consist of row crops, small grains, and sod crops. Summer fallowing, such as is often practiced under semiarid conditions, may be classed with the intertilled row crops.

The 3-year rotation—row crop, corn; small grain, wheat; sod crop, clover—illustrates the use of the three different types of crops. However, crop rotations are flexible and may be adjusted to meet the requirements of different fields, different farms, and different markets and the emergencies of different seasons. In principle the 3-year rotation

Row crop	Corn
Small grain	Wheat
Sod crop	Clover

is the same as the 5-year rotation

Row crops	Corn, sugar beets
Small grain	Barley
Sod crops	Alfalfa, alfalfa

The row crop should use to advantage the fertility restored by turning under a grass-legume sod. The grain normally provides a cheap and convenient means of reestablishing the forage seeding. On droughty sands, it often is necessary to seed legumes without any companion crop, to prevent disastrous competition for moisture. The greater expense involved in this procedure is reduced, insofar as annual charges go, by using a long-lived legume like alfalfa and holding the stand 5 to 7 years.

A farmer may use short, intensive rotations for his level fields and keep his rolling land covered with sod crops for several years in succession. The important consideration is an appreciation of the principles involved in maintaining the productivity of the soil and in securing an adequate income and the application of those principles to a given problem with good judgment.

Some of the major rotations in actual use will be given in later chapters, with the discussion of individual crops.

Review Questions

1. A cubic foot of clay-loam soil that has grown several crops of corn is heavier than a cubic foot of the same kind of soil that has been growing grass. Why?

2. What are the different effects that erosion may have on the productivity of the soil?

3. Why are losses of nitrogen greater on bare tilled soil than on that covered by grass or farmed according to a good rotation?

4. What are the different ways by which a soil's supply of nitrogen is replenished?

5. Under what conditions may strip cropping be used advantageously as a means of erosion control?

6. What factors determine the width of strips to be used in a strip-cropping system?

7. How may the organic-matter content of cropped land be maintained?

8. Why does the plowing under of a large quantity of straw sometimes have a depressing influence on the yield of the crop that immediately follows, and how may this depressing effect be overcome?

9. Why is farm manure alone inadequate as a means of maintaining the productivity of the soil?

10. Why are applications of potash on a sandy soil more likely to result in profitable crop-yield responses than on a silt or clay loam?

11. What effect has soil acidity on the availability of phosphorus?

12. How can determinations be made as to the amount of lime that should be applied to a given soil for the growing of alfalfa?

13. List the benefits to be derived from a well-planned crop rotation.

14. How may a crop rotation bring about the more efficient management of farm labor?

Problems

1. A field of barley was seeded with sweet clover last year. This spring it is to be planted to field beans sometime between June 1 and 10. When will you plow the sweet clover? Why?

2. Make a list of green-manure crops that can be used in your locality without loss of use of the land for regular crop production. What is the current cost for enough seed of each for 1 acre?

3. Draw up a crop rotation for the most important crops in your community, and indicate what your manure and commercial-fertilizer practices would be in connection with this rotation.

4. You wish to sell alfalfa hay off a given field. At current fertilizer prices, how much will it cost you to replace the phosphorus and potassium sold off the field in each ton of hay?

References

BEAR, F. E.: "Theory and Practice in the Use of Fertilizers," 2d ed., John Wiley & Sons, Inc., New York, 1938.

GUSTAFSON, A. F.: "Soils and Soil Management," McGraw-Hill Book Company, Inc., New York, 1941.

PIETERS, A. J.: "Green Manuring, Principles and Practices," John Wiley & Sons, Inc., New York, 1927.

"Soils and Men," *U.S. Dept. Agr. Yearbook of Agriculture*, 1938.

CHAPTER V

TILLAGE AND CULTIVATION

Ever since man started the culture and care of plants rather than depending solely on what nature provided without his guidance, he has tilled the soil. His first implements were crude tools of wood. Today, in the most advanced agricultural regions, the tools are power-drawn implements of finest steel. Still the fundamental objectives of tillage have remained unchanged—to destroy weeds and vegetation; to incorporate organic matter into and make it a part of the soil; to prepare a bed of earth in which a tiny seed can find warmth, air, and moisture so that it may germinate and the resulting plant may find nourishment for growth and fruition. Tillage owes much to science, but it also is an art demanding both skill and experienced judgment from the farmer.

Plowing.—Ordinarily the first operation in fitting a seedbed is plowing although there are circumstances under which plowing may be dispensed with. Where the land is in sod or where considerable vegetation, dead or alive, is on the surface, plowing is essential, for it incorporates this material with the soil where it is broken down by bacterial action until it becomes an integral part of the soil. Hard soils must be broken up, loosened, and aerated; plowing accomplishes this. Not only does the curved moldboard tend to crumble the soil as it is sheared off into a furrow slice, but it tips the soil over, facilitating the coverage of trash.

Several attachments aid in trash coverage. The rolling colter and the jointer used on the plow beam cut the edge of the furrow cleanly and work trash toward or into the furrow where it is more readily covered. If the material to be covered is bulky, trash guards or wires can be used to drag it to the furrow and hold it there until it is covered by the furrow slice as the plow moves along. The wider plows are more effective in covering heavy trash. Horse-drawn plows are as narrow as 8 in. but more commonly cut a 12-in. furrow; tractor plows are most often 14-in. wide and are usually pulled in gangs of two or more, depending on the power. The general range in plow width is up to 18 in. for regular tillage, but some special-purpose breaking or ditching plows are much wider.

64

The disk plow is used in dry, hard soils, in sticky soils in which moldboards do not readily scour, or on new land with its roots and

Figs. 13 and 14.—Plowing, ordinarily the first step in seedbed preparation, was formerly a horse-powered job. Now tractors, usually pulling two or more plows, do the same work with greater efficiency.

bushes. The action of the disk plow is similar to that of the disk harrow; but the disks are larger in diameter, ranging up to 30 in., and thus they can be set for deep as well as for ordinary work. On dry land, complete coverage of straw may not be desirable. If a considerable amount of this material is merely partly worked into the surface, it tends to reduce blowing.

Middlebusters and listers have the appearance of two plows, one right-handed and the other left-handed, set back to back. They are used largely in semiarid regions for the preparation of beds and ridges to hold moisture and reduce wind erosion. Corn, the grain sorghums, and wheat may be drilled in the furrow left by a lister-planter combination. The furrows range in width from 8 to 14 in., a 20-in. size being used for making furrows in which to plant sugar cane.

Time of Plowing.—The proper time to plow is not strictly an agronomic consideration. In many instances the chief factor may be distribution of labor. In the rush of work in preparation for spring planting, plowing is a relatively slow job. If it can be got out of the way in the fall, it effectively hastens spring-planting operations. In most cases the greatest advantage of fall plowing is the convenience in effecting a more advantageous distribution of labor.

However, fall plowing, under some conditions, has other definite benefits. In heavy gumbolike soils, spring plowing, at least in time for crops that are planted relatively early, is often next to impossible. If such soils are plowed in the fall, time is saved and the freezing and thawing of winter and spring bring about a more granular condition, especially in the presence of a reasonable content of organic matter. On the heavier soil types, plowing or otherwise tilling the land when it is too wet may ruin the physical condition of the soil for several seasons. Wet, heavy soils are packed or puddled by tillage operations and upon drying are cemented into dense lumps almost as hard as a brick. These can be broken up and got into condition for proper aeration and moisture retention only after much time and tillage effort. This undesirable condition is most often brought about by spring plowing, but the tillage of heavy soils when they are too wet should be avoided in any season. Sandy soils are not similarly affected.

When a tough, heavy grass sod is to be plowed for a spring-planted crop, its effective decomposition is hastened by fall plowing. Furthermore, the settling that occurs during the winter helps eliminate air pockets. A plowed surface left in the rough over winter is more receptive of moisture from rains and snows. The first spring tillage on fall-plowed land hastens drying of the surface and often permits earlier planting than is possible if spring tillage must await the drying out of the land until conditions are suitable for spring plowing.

Fall plowing is not suitable for rolling land subject to erosion. If such land is left without vegetation over winter, excessive washing and gullying often take place, especially if the land is deficient in organic matter. Sandy soils if fall-plowed may be injured by wind erosion whether the land is sloping or level.

Usually, crop yields are as good after spring plowing as after fall plowing if the spring plowing is done early enough and subsequent tillage is sufficiently thorough to refine the seedbed, destroy air pockets, and establish good tilth. Plowing 3 or 4 weeks in advance of planting time usually permits adequate tillage. Alfalfa, sweet clover, and clover sods disintegrate rapidly and can be effectively spring-plowed for crops that do not demand extremely early planting. Sugar beets, which should be planted in early May in the eastern humid area, are usually favored by fall rather than by spring plowing. They are generally grown on heavy, level soil.

Where wheat follows wheat or another stubble crop, early summer plowing is highly desirable. The sooner plowing may follow harvest, the better from the standpoint of conservation of summer rainfall. Cole and Mathews[1] state that at Hays, Kans., if winter wheat is grown following winter wheat the yields obtained by beginning cultivation immediately after harvest may be as much as 50 per cent greater than if cultivation is delayed until near seeding time. Farther west in Kansas where summer rainfall is not heavy enough to provide for storage in the soil, the benefits of early tillage are greatly reduced.

Depth of Plowing.—Plows are supposed to work to best advantage when set to run at a depth equal to or slightly greater than one-half their width. Thus, a 12-in. plow would be set for a depth of 6 or 7 in., a 14-in. plow for 7 or 8 in. Plowing to a depth of 5 in. or less is considered shallow. Usually, though not under all conditions, shallow plowing does not result in as high crop yields as that done at 6 to 8 in.

In numerous experiments, plowing to greater depths, such as 10 in., or using subsoiling or deep-tillage equipment, which stirs or breaks up the soil as deep as 14 in., has seldom shown any advantages. The power cost for deep tillage is markedly greater.

Some variation in depth of plowing heavy soil is advisable from time to time to avoid development of an impervious plow pan. If a soil has normally been plowed shallow, the change to deeper plowing should be made gradually to avoid bringing up too much raw subsoil at one time.

Disking vs. Plowing.—If grain follows a row crop—as wheat after corn, soybeans, or field beans; oats or barley after corn, potatoes, beans, or sugar beets—plowing is not necessary and the first tillage

[1] COLE, JOHN S., and O. R. MATHEWS, Tillage, "Soils and Men," *U.S. Dept. Agr. Yearbook of Agriculture*, 1938.

operation in preparation for the grain is a thorough disking of the seed-bed. The spring-tooth harrow or the field cultivator may also be used for this first operation. Usually the grain yield following such tillage is as good as that following plowing, or the difference is not great enough to warrant the extra cost of plowing.

In dry-land areas even stubble land is often disked rather than plowed in order to leave enough straw and stubble at the surface to reduce blowing. If rye has been seeded as a winter cover, it may be

Fig. 15.—A double-disk harrow. Where grain follows a row crop plowing often is unnecessary and the first tillage may be with a disk harrow, a spring-tooth harrow, or a field cultivator. (*Courtesy of E. E. Patton.*)

disked into the surface in the spring rather than plowed under, if tillage is done when the rye is not over 12 or 14 in. high and the job is thorough enough to kill essentially all the rye plants. Lighter soils are often disked rather than plowed, for it is comparatively easy to work considerable trash into these soils with a disk.

At least one exception to the disking of land previously growing a row crop must be made. If corn has been infested with the European corn borer, either the crop must be cut extremely short or the corn stubble and refuse should be plowed under. The borer overwinters as a larva in cornstalks, stubble, or large-stalked weeds. If plowed under, most of the larvae will be destroyed provided that a clean job of plowing is accomplished. If corn stubble and -stalks are merely disked or if a considerable amount of such material is left on the surface, even though the land has been plowed, the larvae find shelter in this surface refuse and eventually emerge as moths to establish a new infestation.

Fitting the Seedbed.—Preparation of the seedbed is more than a mechanical operation. One of its main objectives is to destroy potential weed competition. Conceivably certain implements such as rotary tillers or a succession of implements hitched to one power unit might establish desirable mechanical tilth in the soil in one operation. How-

Fig. 16.—Refining a seedbed with a double disk followed by a spring-tooth harrow. (*Courtesy of E. E. Patton.*)

ever, one operation is not nearly so effective in destroying weeds as several carried on at intervals. If between each disking or harrowing enough time elapses to permit weed seeds to germinate, the next tillage operation destroys these seedlings. A succession of such operations, spaced as to time, makes for cleaner seedbeds, less competition for the crop, and less need for subsequent and more costly row cultivation of intertilled crops. In carrying on such tillage, consideration must be given to the proper time for sowing or planting the crop.

The disk harrow works deeply, cutting and breaking lumps and clods, aerating the soil, destroying vegetation, and eliminating large air spaces. Disking or double disking is the first operation after spring plowing, the first spring operation after fall plowing, or the first tillage operation of all in case plowing is not done.

The spring-tooth harrow is effective in refining the soil, loosening the surface, and destroying weeds. Whereas the disk may be ineffective in stony ground, the spring-tooth harrow with its flexible teeth encounters little difficulty under such conditions. The ordinary spring-tooth tends to spread stolons or rhizomes of some of the perennial noxious weeds, but a special type of this implement that digs deeply with little tendency to drag the material around is useful in bringing the underground portions of such weeds to the surface where they may be destroyed by desiccation and exposure. These field cultivators may have either duckfoot shovels or spring teeth. Their timely and thorough use is particularly effective against quack grass.

Fig. 17.—Firming the seedbed with a Cultipacker just before drilling in the seed.

The spike tooth is a smoothing harrow. It destroys weed seedlings that are not thoroughly rooted and may even be used for cultivation after a crop is planted but before it has attained any considerable growth. It is a good implement for putting the finishing touches to a seedbed for small grain, corn, and seeds of similar size.

Rollers crush lumps and firm the soil. The corrugated rollers or Cultipackers are particularly effective in this respect; their use is highly desirable, especially on lighter soils, to finish a seedbed for small hard seeds that must be planted near the surface. They are also effective if used immediately after plowing provided that the soil is dry enough to crumble under their impact.

The firming of medium loams to sandy soils is highly important when alfalfa, the clovers, and the small-seeded grasses are to be sown.

Many a farmer has found his alfalfa starting rapidly where the wheels of the drill or the horses' feet have packed the soil. Sometimes these are the only places where the plants get a start. All seeds must have moisture if they are to germinate. Small seeds, for which deep planting is not advisable, must have this moisture near the surface. A seedbed in which capillarity has been established by firming so that moist soil can be scuffed up almost at the surface is highly desirable. Final preparation of the lighter soils with a Cultipacker is very effective. In fact, this implement is often used to cover surface-sown seed. If run at right angles to a slope or to the direction of the prevailing winds, the ridging effect the Cultipacker has on the soil tends to reduce erosion.

On heavy soils the chief use of the roller or the Cultipacker is for breaking lumps or clods. Extreme fineness of such soil at planting time may be objectionable because a downpour of rain is more likely to cause puddling or form a crust on excessively refined, heavy soil. However, a certain amount of breaking up of clods and lumps is necessary in the earlier stages of seedbed preparation, and so rollers and Cultipackers are useful on heavy as well as on light soils. They are doubly essential to lend firmness to mucks and peats. In fact, unusually heavy rollers are built for these organic soils.

CULTIVATION

The small grains are good weed competitors. Their seedlings grow rapidly, soon shade the ground, and use much of the available moisture, thus holding in check most of the annual and some of the perennial weeds. They are not without weed troubles, of course; for weeds with similar growth characteristics, as chess in winter wheat or wild oats and wild buckwheat in spring-planted grain, may compete effectively with the crop. Such persistent perennials as the Canada thistle are likewise grainfield pests. Nevertheless, the grains normally can hold weed competition in check, and therefore cultivation after planting is not practiced. Consequently, the grains are either sown broadcast or drilled in close rows (7 in.), which for all practical purposes amounts to a broadcast seeding, drilling having an advantage in uniformity of depth and coverage.

Many of the forage crops start slowly from seed but are biennial or perennial in character. In their harvest years these crops start rapidly from stolons, crowns, or rhizomes; and they often form a close sod. Thus, they, too, compete successfully with most weeds, especially the annual ones; and they are seldom grown in cultivated rows except in a minor way for seed production.

Several other crops if drilled in close rows or broadcast could not compete at all with weeds. Also, much larger plants, which can be more conveniently handled and which yield better, are secured if spaced at fairly wide intervals. These are the row crops of agriculture. They include corn, field beans, often soybeans, cotton, tobacco, potatoes, sugar beets, and sorghum. Row crops involve interrow cultivation if good yields are to be secured.

Fig. 18.—Cultivating sugar beets. The purpose of cultivating row crops is to control weeds. Usually two or more cultivations are required to attain effective weed control economically. (*Courtesy of E. E. Patton.*)

Why Cultivate?—The main reason for cultivation of row crops, and in the vast majority of cases the only reason, is to control weeds. Weeds steal moisture. This often is their chief offense, although they also compete for plant food. They may be objectionable for many other reasons whether growing in competition with a row crop or otherwise. Thus, they crowd crop plants; often they grow faster and tend to shade or "smother" the crop; they may harbor insects and diseases that affect commercial crops; they may produce undesirable flavors, as wild onion in wheat; their spines or burs may be irritating; some are poisonous, for example, water hemlock; and a few are parasitic, like dodder which draws its nourishment directly from the clover or alfalfa plant rather than from the soil.

To control weeds effectively by tillage requires (1) a thorough preparation of the seedbed, with tillage operations spaced as to time so as to kill off as many weeds as possible before the crop seed is planted; (2) in the case of row crops, careful interrow cultivation; and (3) in some cases, hand hoeing or pulling.

If weeds are not controlled, their presence greatly reduces crop yields, in extreme cases to the point of complete crop failure. Investigators have studied this problem by means of scores of experiments dealing with every row crop. The results have invariably emphasized the absolute necessity of controlling weeds. To cite one typical result, the Nebraska Agricultural Experiment Station[1] reports a 6-year trial in which corn without cultivation and consequently without weed control yielded only 19 per cent as much as corn with four normal cultivations and effective weed control.

Whether cultivation has any beneficial effect beyond the control of weeds is debatable; at least the question provides the incentive for almost unending argument. There are those who contend that the soil mulch created by cultivation is effective as a means of moisture conservation. Again, numerous experiments have been conducted to test this possibility. In these experiments, weeds were controlled by hand pulling or scraping them out with a hoe without establishing a soil mulch; the results were compared with those following control by cultivation and the creation of a soil mulch, varying in depth. For the most part, crop yields were as good and soil moisture as high when the weeds were scraped or pulled as they were when a soil mulch was developed by cultivation.[2]

In one sense the question of whether or not cultivation of row crops has any beneficial effect beyond that of controlling weeds is academic; for weeds must be controlled, cultivation is the only practical way in which to control weeds, and the elimination of weeds does conserve moisture for the growing crop. The question ceases to be academic when cultivation of a weed-free crop is still continued. Such cultivation is an added expense. It can be justified only by increased crop yields. Most experimental results indicate that cultivation beyond the needs of weed control is not profitable except on

---

[1] KIESSELBACH, T. A., ARTHUR ANDERSON, and W. E. LYNESS, Cultural Practices in Corn Production, *Nebr. Agr. Expt. Sta. Bul.* 293, 1935.

[2] The results of a large number of such experiments have been summarized by Hughes and Henson. See H. D. Hughes and E. R. Henson, "Crop Production," Chap. XI, The Macmillan Company, New York, 1930.

certain heavy clay and gumbo soils where cultivation provides aeration and prevents some moisture loss from undue cracking of the soil. It is often possible to reduce the number of cultivations necessary for weed control by effective tillage of the land prior to the planting of the crop.

Depth of Cultivation.—The number of times a given row crop is cultivated is of little importance in itself. The important consideration is to eliminate weeds, whether this takes one cultivation or six. The depth of cultivation in the process of securing weed control may have a marked effect on the yield of the crop. When plants are small, a cultivator, with shields to prevent throwing soil on the seedlings, can be run fairly deep and close to the row. But roots grow and spread rapidly. The roots of two adjacent rows of corn soon intermingle, and even shallow cultivation cuts many of them off. The principle holds for other row crops. Deep cultivation is a serious root-pruning process and, especially in dry seasons, causes wilting of the plants and reduced yields. Repeated cultivation to a depth of 4 in. is almost always injurious. Cultivator blades that run shallow (about 1½ in.) are much to be preferred to deeply set shovels. The best cultivation for any crop is just deep enough to control weeds and shallow enough to prevent, insofar as possible, any serious root injury.

Early Cultivation.—When crop plants are small, many weeds can be eliminated with implements that work all the ground rather than only that between rows. The spike-tooth harrow, the weeder, and the rotary hoe are designed for this purpose. To be effective the rotary hoe must be used on fairly loose soil free from stones and when weed seeds are just sprouting and before they have taken root. The spike-tooth harrow tends to remove some crop plants; but if the stand is thick, this should not be serious and this implement is effective in destroying young weeds. Any damaging effects may be reduced by setting the teeth with a backward slant. The weeder has longer teeth with more spring to them. It can be used for corn up to 18 in. tall. It is least effective on heavy soils. These implements are best used after the early morning turgidity has left the plants and they become less susceptible to injury.

Weeders are made with seeder attachments, and they cover forage seedings nicely at a shallow depth. They can be used not only for regular seedings but provide an effective way of making seedings in corn when the corn is about 18 to 20 in. high.

Summer Fallowing.—Summer fallowing consists in keeping land free of vegetation during the summer months. It is widely used as a means of moisture conservation in semiarid regions. It brings about this moisture conservation largely because of the elimination of moisture-consuming plants. The harrowed surface may also be somewhat more receptive of moisture than an untilled hard surface.

Summer tillage does more than conserve moisture. The stirring and aeration of the soil create conditions favorable for the activities of nitrogen-fixing bacteria at the season when temperatures are most favorable to nitrification. Thus fallowing, in dry areas where leaching is not important, effects an accumulation of nitrates for use by the subsequent crop, usually wheat. The stimulation of nitrification by

FIG. 19.—A rotary hoe. The rotary hoe, spike-tooth harrow, and weeder are used to control weeds when the weeds are very small. (*Courtesy of E. E. Patton.*)

fallowing if carried on in regions of plentiful rainfall tends to stimulate loss of nitrogen by leaching.

Principles of Weed Control.—Annual and biennial weeds can be controlled by preventing seed production. This statement oversimplifies the problem, for in the case of many weeds it is not easy to prevent seed production if the crop with which they compete is to be allowed to mature. Furthermore, many weed seeds are hard-coated and long-lived. Once such seed is in the soil, it may furnish a source of infestation for many years. Nevertheless, prevention of seed production and avoidance of seed dissemination by planting clean crop seed are the control measures that must be pressed with vigor and thoroughness in order to reduce competition from weeds of this character.

Perennial weeds present a different problem. Once started, these long-lived invaders renew their growth year after year from organic foods stored in their roots, rhizomes, or other underground portions. Prevention of seed production and dissemination is important for perennial weeds as for annuals and biennials, but this alone is not sufficient. The plants themselves must be destroyed, or they will live to produce seed another year. Annuals and the less persistent perennials and biennials are destroyed by plowing and normal tillage operations, including intertillage of row crops. Crop rotation, therefore, with its variable, recurrent tillage practices is effective in holding many weeds within bounds.

In more permanent meadows and pastures, weed infestations follow conditions unfavorable to the crop species. Field sorrel (*Rumex acetosella* L.) persists in meadows on acid sandy soils. When these soils are properly limed and fertilized and a vigorous growth of alfalfa is secured, the sorrel can no longer compete and practically disappears. An Oscoda County, Michigan, farmer had a bluegrass pasture, on a moisture-retentive heavy soil, that developed an almost solid infestation of orange hawkweed (*Hieracium aurantiacum* L.). He fertilized the field heavily with superphosphate, which stimulated wild white clover and a better grass growth, and the orange hawkweed vanished almost completely in a single season. Crab grass persists in poorly nourished lawns where close cutting and frequent light watering are practiced. It can be controlled by proper fertilization and watering and the setting of the mower to cut $1\frac{1}{2}$ to 2 in. high, thereby providing conditions which enable the lawn grass successfully to compete with this weed.

Some perennials are unusually persistent, and control measures are aimed at depleting the reserve organic foods which they store and by means of which they are able to survive ordinary tillage practices. Control practices for three of these noxious invaders will be described.

Canada Thistle.—The Canada thistle (*Cirsium arvense*) is a noxious perennial plant with a deep, horizontal, wide-spreading, white root system, from any part of which rosettes of leaves and new stems may originate. The reserve of food material stored in these roots is lowest just before the plants bloom; and mowing at this time, followed persistently by cutting off the new shoots when they appear, will clean up heavy infestations. In fields where alfalfa can be made to thrive, the most economical way to eradicate the Canada thistle is to sow the field to alfalfa and cut it for hay. The repeated cutting of the alfalfa and the rapidity with which new alfalfa growth comes on serve effectively to starve out this weed. In tillage the sweep types of cultivator blades are more effective against Canada thistles than are disks, spring teeth, or shovels.

Field Bindweed.—Field bindweed (*Convolvulus arvensis*) is also called *small-flowered morning-glory*, *small bindweed*, and *creeping Jennie*. It is one of the most persistent of perennial noxious weeds, reproducing both by seeds and by creeping roots. It is particularly bad in row crops, none of which appears able to offer it much competition. The roots cannot all be reached with tillage equipment; for many of them will be several feet underground, still carrying sufficient organic food reserves to send shoots to the surface. In the North, the surface roots are killed by freezing, and new growth comes from the deep unfrozen roots; hence, this new growth does not appear until late in the spring.

One effective method of greatly reducing bindweed in a badly infested field is to grow winter wheat or rye 3 years in succession or more. The small grain makes its start before the new shoots of bindweed reach the surface and therefore has a marked advantage in competition for plant food, moisture, and light. After grain harvest the field is summer-fallowed to keep down all aboveground growth of the bindweed and in the early autumn is again seeded to grain. This method may take 5 or 6 years to obtain anything approaching complete eradication but has the advantage of providing for a crop each year. It is most effective in humid, fertile areas where wheat or rye makes a tall dense growth very rapidly. Bindweed is very sensitive to this shading.

A modification of the above system is to crop the land only in alternate years and to keep it in fallow the rest of the time. By this system, either fall- or spring-sown crops may be used as competitors. Sudan grass, broadcast sorghum, and millet, where adapted, are spring- or summer-sown crops that have a strong chance of competing successfully with the bindweed. Biennial sweet clover is another excellent competitor. Because a longer time for tillage is permitted by the alternate fallow season, this method, according to Kephart,[1] can be expected almost completely to eradicate bindweed in 4 years. In semiarid regions, the sorghums are effective competitors, taking nearly all available moisture before the bindweed has a chance.

The most rapid means of controlling this pest where it has become established is to practice very thorough fallow tillage for two full seasons. Whether fallow is practiced as the sole measure of control or alternated with competitive crops, tillage must be repeated about every 2 weeks during the fallow season and tillage equipment must be so designed as to cut off bindweed roots to a depth of 4 in. Any roots

[1] KEPHART, L. W., Bindweed or Wild Morning Glory, *U.S. Dept. Agr. Mimeographed Leaflet*, 1940.

that escape will respread the infestation. The field cultivator equipped with blades or duckfoot shovels that overlap by 3 in. is the one type of implement that can effectively sever all plants. With almost any system of control a few plants escape. These can be treated with chemical weed killers, practical for individual plants and small patches but very expensive on an acreage basis.

Destruction of established bindweed plants still leaves seed in the ground as a source of reinfestation. When the plants are in the seedling stage, they are easily killed by ordinary tillage; fortunately, seedlings remain in the stage in which they can be destroyed easily for about 2 months. Once the established perennial plants have been destroyed, the seedlings can be held in check by cultivation at 2-month intervals during the growing season. This is a procedure not easily arranged but not impossible by combining cultivation of a row crop with hand hoeing. Seed production usually is not important in the far north.

Quack Grass.—Widely spread throughout the northern and eastern United States, quack grass (*Agropyron repens*) is one of the most persistent perennials in the entire grass family. It is propagated by seed and vegetatively by rhizomes, the latter often being dragged around fields by tillage implements to establish new centers of infestation. Were it not for its persistence, quack grass would not be classed as a weed, for it is a useful pasture grass and can be made into good grass hay. Even its persistence and aggressive spreading habits are not all to its discredit. It is very useful in preventing erosion, grows in the North on thousands of acres of light soil that supports most other species poorly, and is the chief source of organic matter for these soils. But because it is difficult and expensive to subdue quack grass so that other crops can be grown on the land, the plant is justifiably classed as a noxious weed.

Most tillage practices are directed toward the depletion of organic reserve foods that quack grass stores abundantly in its wide-spreading underground stems or rhizomes. Though recognizing this line of attack as contributing to effective control, Dexter and Johnson[1] have shown that starvation of quack grass by mere defoliation is exceedingly difficult. In one greenhouse experiment, quack grass defoliated completely once a week for 24 weeks was still growing steadily. Further work by Dexter[2] has shown that the sproutability

[1] DEXTER, S. T., and A. A. JOHNSON, The Response of Quack Grass to Variations in Height of Cutting and Rates of Application of Nitrogen, *Jour. Amer. Soc. Agron.* Vol. 31, No. 1, 1939.

[2] DEXTER, S. T., The Drought Resistance of Quack Grass under Various Degrees of Fertilization with Nitrogen, *Jour. Amer. Soc. Agron.*, Vol. 29, No. 7,

of quack-grass rhizomes is markedly increased by nitrogen fertilization and that rhizomes which have sprouted vigorously are far more susceptible to drought and freezing injury than low-nitrogen rhizomes which are slow to sprout but thoroughly capable of maintaining an infestation. The increased sproutability of high-nitrogen rhizomes also makes it possible to hasten depletion of food reserves.

Organic reserves in quack grass appear to be lowest, under natural conditions, in late spring or early summer just before heading time. Further depletion of the storage materials may be produced by nitrogen fertilization and close grazing during spring months or close mowing before replenishment of reserves has been advanced. Tillage can be most effective if started at this stage. Plowing may or may not be necessary, depending on the soil. It is better to use a tillage scheme that brings the rhizomes to the surface rather than one that buries them. The field cultivator accomplishes this. By working the rhizomes to the surface and subjecting them to drying out, desiccation combined with the prevention of photosynthesis effects a kill. If work is started in late May or early June and summer tillage is thorough, quack-grass-infested land can be made ready for a fall-sown crop by September.

In potato-growing areas, fall and subsequently early spring tillage of quack grass produce starvation, winterkilling, and desiccation of rhizomes to control the grass in time for normal planting of potatoes. A complete kill does not result; but the grass is so weakened, if tillage is thorough, that it offers little competition to the potatoes. It may readily reestablish itself in later crops.

It is difficult to kill quack grass in wet weather; for the rhizomes do not dry out, and they may establish roots very rapidly. Also, in extremely dry weather, effective control becomes difficult because of the dormant condition of the rhizomes. Vigorous sprouting while control measures are being practiced is desirable, but tillage must be repeated frequently enough to prevent the sprouting rhizomes from establishing roots.

The chief evil of quack grass is the demand for constant thorough work, with its added expense, if the grass is to be subdued to the point where other crops can be grown and reasonable yields secured.

Chemical Weed Killers.—Several chemicals will kill growing plants, and some have been found practicable as weed killers if the area of infestation is small.

Common salt (sodium chloride) will kill weeds, but it must be used in such large quantities that the land becomes useless for crop produc-

1937. The Winterhardiness of Weeds, *Jour. Amer. Soc. Agron.*, Vol. 29, No. 6, 1937.

tion for 10 or 15 years. Arsenical compounds (usually sodium arsenite) are effective as herbicides; but because they are extremely poisonous, their use is very hazardous.

Iron sulphate dissolved in water in the proportion of 1½ to 2 lb. per gallon and applied as a fine spray at the rate of 1 gal. to 500 sq. ft. of area is effective against broad-leaved weeds if the leaves are not too waxy. It of course kills similarly broad-leaved crop plants. If applied when the plants are young, it destroys the leaves of dandelions, hoary alyssum, plantain, wild mustard, and others, and also such crop plants as clover and alfalfa. If new leaves are sent out, another application is necessary. Eventually the stems and roots die. Grass will be blackened but not killed by this treatment. The material is corrosive and should not be used in galvanized receptacles. Nor should it be used in the hot part of the summer, but only in the cooler spring and fall.

Sodium chlorate is widely used as a weed killer. It may be applied in solution as a spray or in dry form. A common rate of application is 3 to 4 lb. per square rod. Late summer applications are considered most effective. Some top growth on the weeds to be treated is desirable, and the land should be left undisturbed until the chlorate has had its full effect. Eventually both tops and roots are killed. Any new growth requires additional treatment. Land treated with chlorate will not produce that season and may be partly sterile for three or four seasons. Sugar beets are particularly susceptible to chlorate injury, the effect on this crop having been noted in Michigan 4 years after treatment, although a preceding crop of beans showed no evidence of injury.

The use of sodium chlorate entails a fire hazard, for any organic material saturated with this chemical and then dried ignites easily and burns with great rapidity. Even the shoes and clothing of the person handling a chlorate spray become sources of danger when they have dried out; any chlorate residue should be washed out of them before they have dried out. Chlorate should never be permitted to become mixed with straw, dust, or other organic material. The drums in which the chemical is shipped are best stored out of doors away from buildings.

Chlorates in small quantities are not poisonous to livestock. If large areas are treated and salt-hungry stock have access to the field, some danger is encountered. It is therefore best to keep stock off recently treated areas until rain has washed the chlorate into the soil.

Chemical weed killers are expensive. If they are used for large areas, the cost is often greater than the value of the land. However, if used on small patches or individual plants, they should prevent the spread of the weed infestation before any large area becomes involved.

Review Questions

1. What are the objectives of plowing?
2. What is meant by the scouring of a plow?
3. Under what conditions is a disk plow preferable to a moldboard plow?
4. Under what conditions is a spring-tooth harrow preferred to the disk harrow for seedbed preparation?
5. What is the function of a Cultipacker? A weeder? A rotary hoe? A lister?
6. Field sorrel will grow on neutral as well as on acid soil. Why is it often so prevalent in acid meadows and scarcely noticeable after such meadows have been limed, fertilized, and seeded to clover or alfalfa?
7. Why is a firm seedbed important for small, hard-coated seeds?
8. Wild mustard (charlock) is an annual that reproduces by seeds. Why is it considered a particularly noxious weed, difficult to control?
9. How should you use sodium chlorate for the control of small patches of quack grass?
10. Why is bindweed so difficult to control with ordinary tillage practices?

Problems

1. You have a field of sandy loam soil with a much lighter colored subsoil. This field has never been plowed more deeply than 5 in. You prefer to plow at a 7-in. depth. How will you handle this field?
2. You have harvested your corn with a mechanical picker. The field was infested with European corn borers. Describe in detail how you will prepare this field for oats to be planted the next spring.
3. Make a list of operations you would normally follow in preparing a seedbed for alfalfa to be seeded with oats on a sandy loam soil that had previously grown corn.
4. Consult the literature, especially that of your own agricultural experiment station, dealing with the influence of cultivation on weed control and moisture conservation; and prepare a summary of this literature, giving your conclusions with respect to the functions of cultivation.
5. Outline a 6-year cropping and tillage program for a field that has become badly infested with bindweed (*Convolvulus arvensis*).

References

COLE, JOHN S., and O. R. MATHEWS: Tillage, "Soils and Men," *U.S. Dept. Agr. Yearbook of Agriculture*, 1938.

DARLINGTON, HENRY T., ERNST A. BESSEY, and CLIVE R. MEGEE: Some Important Michigan Weeds, *Mich. Agr. Expt. Sta. Spec. Bul.* 304, 1940.

GUSTAFSON, A. F.: "Soils and Soil Management," McGraw-Hill Book Company, Inc., New York, 1941.

HUGHES, H. D., and E. R. HENSON: "Crop Production," The Macmillan Company, New York, 1930.

MUENSCHER, WALTER C.: "Weeds," The Macmillan Company, New York, 1935.

WEAVER, JOHN E.: "Root Development of Field Crops," McGraw-Hill Book Company, Inc., New York, 1926.

CHAPTER VI

LEGUMES FOR FORAGE

Legume forages give stability and permanence to agriculture. Worked into effective crop rotations they make a protective cover for the land while growing and supply it with organic matter and plant nourishment when plowed under. They provide a means by which nitrogen may be drawn from the limitless supply in the air and converted into forms available to plant life. Their leaves are high in proteins and related compounds, giving them special value as livestock feed to balance the more carbonaceous materials produced by other crops. Well-balanced farming systems designed to ensure enduring productivity of the soil have an important place in the cropping program for legumes.

Legumes and Nitrogen Fixation.—A thrifty field of clover or alfalfa makes possible the fixation, in a season, of 100 to 200 lb. an acre of atmospheric nitrogen. This is equivalent in amount to the nitrogen contained in 500 to 1,000 lb. of a 20 per cent nitrogen fertilizer. Some of the nitrogen is harvested with the crop as proteins and related substances; some is left in the roots and stubble; some is used by associated plants, as when grass is grown with a legume; and some is lost. Alfalfa with its broad crown and extensive root system leaves more nitrogen in the soil than other legumes. The growing of field beans, with removal at harvest of much of the root system as well as the top growth and with leaching encouraged by intertillage, results in some nitrogen depletion. For the most part, some top as well as root growth must be turned under if a legume is actually to increase the soil's nitrogen supply; but legume forages, fed on the farm that produced them, do much to maintain nitrogen through the return of this constituent to the soil in farm manures. The protein they supply as feed and the soil nitrogen they make possible are among the most expensive nutrients when purchased as feed or fertilizer.

How Nitrogen Is Fixed.—The ability of legumes to secure nitrogen from the air is contingent upon there being associated with the plants the proper strains of nitrogen-fixing bacteria. The bacterium that works with legumes is called *Rhizobium*. The bacteria infect the root hairs of legume plants, causing the development of clusters of nodules. The relationship between the plant and the bacteria is

82

normally mutually beneficial. The bacteria secure carbohydrate nutrients that the plant manufactures by photosynthesis; the plant secures nitrogen that the bacteria are able to assimilate in gaseous form from the atmosphere.

There are groups of free-living bacteria that also have the ability of assimilating and fixing free nitrogen; but most organisms must get their nitrogen in organic compounds, like proteins, in inorganic nitrates, or in ammonium salts. Hence, the great importance both to plant and to animal life of nitrogen-fixing organisms working with leguminous plants which are subject to a considerable extent to manipulation and control.

Inoculation.—Legumes can grow without their symbiotic bacteria, and these bacteria can exist for long periods without their legume hosts. But a legume that does not receive nitrogen from nitrogen-fixing bacteria must get its nitrogen from the soil. If the supply of nitrogen in the soil is abundant and other conditions are suitable, the legume will thrive. In fact, if the supply of nitrogen in the soil is abundant, little or no atmospheric nitrogen is fixed even though the proper bacteria are present.

However, if nitrogen is lacking in the soil and the legume does not have its bacterial benefactors, the nitrogen supply is diminished, growth is stunted, and the color of the plant is usually pale and yellowish. With the proper bacteria present a deficiency of nitrogen in the soil is in itself no handicap to a legume. If other conditions are suitable, a legume inoculated with its particular strain of nitrogen-fixing bacteria will yield just as well in a soil deficient in nitrogen as in one liberally supplied with a nitrogen fertilizer.

Because soils that have never grown some particular legume may lack the organism that works with that legume, the practice of inoculation has been developed. Even in ancient times, alfalfa growers noted superior vigor and color in the crop grown on land that had received a dressing of soil from an old alfalfa field. But a less laborious means of inoculation has been devised for the modern legume grower. From a commercial laboratory, he can purchase the desired culture of the bacteria, grown on agar, in moistened peat, or in some other suitable preparation; and he applies this to the legume seed at seeding time. This inoculation ensures that the legume will get all the nitrogen it needs from the air.

Inoculants Limited to Specific Groups.—Fresh culture must be used, and the culture must consist of the particular strain of bacteria that works with the legume being sown. The following leguminous crops are arranged in groups that can use the same inoculant:

Alfalfa, sweet clover, yellow trefoil, and bur clover.
Red, white, alsike, and crimson clover.
Field peas and vetches.
Lespedeza, peanuts, cowpeas, velvet beans, and crotalaria.
Soybeans.
Field beans.
Lupines and serradella.

Once a well-nodulated legume has been grown, the bacteria will live in the soil for several years, and further inoculation is ordinarily unnecessary. Many farmers regard the small expense involved in seed inoculation as good insurance, however, and inoculate each new legume seeding even though the land may have grown this legume before.

Legumes and Lime.—The relationship of lime to soil acidity and crop production has been discussed in a previous chapter. The most important legume forages, alfalfa, red clover, and sweet clover, require an abundance of lime and a soil reaction at or near neutrality. Liming becomes increasingly important for these crops because the bacteria that make nitrogen fixation possible work best at a soil reaction that is most favorable to the host crop. Under conditions of high acidity, these bacteria may cease to function entirely and gradually die out.

In studying the effect of soil acidity on nodule production by soybeans, Albrecht[1] of the Missouri Agricultural Experiment Station found that the degree of soil acidity is responsible for nodulation failure on excessively sour soils. The acidity at which this failure occurred was at pH5.0 and lower values. On soils with a pH of 5.5 and higher, nodulation failure was brought about not so much by the degree of acidity as by the deficiency of available calcium in the soil. Thus is emphasized the need for fertilizing with calcium on the less sour soils as well as changing the reaction of those of a higher degree of acidity.

The legumes highest in lime requirement are alfalfa, sweet clover, red clover, and white clover. Alfalfa is probably more demanding in its lime needs than any. Alsike and crimson clover, peas, beans, and soybeans are moderately tolerant to soil acidity; and cowpeas, peanuts, and lespedeza are considered very tolerant.

One of the major reasons for the popularity of lespedeza in the South is its acid tolerance. The fact that this and other "poor-land" crops can be grown on depleted soils presents a problem. E. N. Fergus, Kentucky agronomist, has stated:

[1] ALBRECHT, WILLIAM A., Inoculation of Legumes as Related to Soil Acidity, *Jour. Amer. Soc. Agron.*, Vol. 25, No. 8, 1933.

The outcome of this practice of choosing poor-land crops to suit a soil as it becomes impoverished, unattended by liming, manuring, and fertilizing, is certain to have serious consequences. For example, red clover once regularly produced excellent crops on land in Kentucky on which even adapted varieties will not now grow without lime and phosphorus. Instead of applying these materials to the soil, farmers use crops adapted to poorer soil. Redtop, orchard grass, and especially lespedeza are used. They require less calcium and phosphorus than clover, and lespedeza, at least, also seems able to obtain

Fig. 20.—Spreading lime. The most important legume forages, alfalfa, red clover, and sweet clover, require an abundance of lime and a soil reaction at or near neutrality. (*Courtesy of E. E. Patton.*)

appreciable amounts unavailable to clover and other crops. Consequently, it seems that sooner or later the supplies of calcium, phosphorus, and other essential elements must become so much reduced that they are no longer sufficient even for lespedeza.[1]

Fertilizers for Legumes.—It is important that the legumes grown in a rotation be vigorous and productive. The insurance of an adequate supply of phosphorus and potash is favorable to the nitrogen-fixing bacteria. Well-fertilized legumes not only receive proper nutrition with respect to the minerals applied but get more nitrogen, are

[1] FERGUS, E. N., Shall Crops Be Adapted to Soils or Soils to Crops? *Jour. Amer. Soc. Agron.*, Vol. 28, No. 6, 1936.

improved in quality because of increased protein content, and produce higher yields of feed. The vigorous well-nourished legume likewise has a greater soil improvement effect from which other crops in the rotation may benefit.

Theoretically, farm manure is a poor fertilizer for legume forages because it is high in nitrogen, which the legume should get from the air, and low in phosphorus, which all legumes require. Actually, legumes often give an excellent response to light manurial applications. Salter and Schollenberger state:

In general farm rotations, the successful growth of sod legumes—alfalfa, clovers, etc.—is so important to economic production and soil conservation that, wherever difficulty in getting a stand is experienced, the first use of manure might well be for a light top dressing, 2 to 4 tons to the acre, in winter or immediately after spring planting. If a good stand can be obtained without this measure, it offers no advantage.[1]

In considering commercial fertilizers, recognition should be given to the fact that the vegetative portion of legumes is high in potash, that phosphorus also is essential, but that nitrogen for the legume can and should come from the air. A liberal application of nitrogen fertilizer for a leguminous crop merely depresses fixation of atmospheric nitrogen. The quantity of mineral nutrients in the soil must also be considered. Many heavy soils contain an abundance of potash although sandy soils and peats are deficient in this constituent. The following table may serve as a guide to effective use of commercial fertilizers for forage legumes, based on the widely applicable consideration that most soils are normally low in content of phosphoric acid:

Type	Soil	Fertilizer analysis
Soils high in potash...............	Heavy loams, clay loams, and silt loams	0-20-0
Soils of moderate potash content..	Medium clay and silt loams, sandy loams	0-14-6
Soils low in potash...............	Light sandy loams, sands, mucks, and peats	0-8-24

Fertilizers approximating the analyses suggested may be substituted.

[1] SALTER, R. M., and C. J. SCHOLLENBERGER, Farm Manure, "Soils and Men," *U.S. Dept. Agr. Yearbook of Agriculture,* 1938.

FORAGE LEGUMES IMPORTANT IN AMERICAN AGRICULTURE

Alfalfa. *Importance and Distribution.*—Alfalfa has come to be the most important forage legume in the United States. It was tried by the colonists on the eastern seaboard with indifferent success, probably because much of the land did not contain sufficient lime to ensure vigorous growth. It was brought into California during the gold-rush days of the early 1850's and has been grown there success-fully ever since.

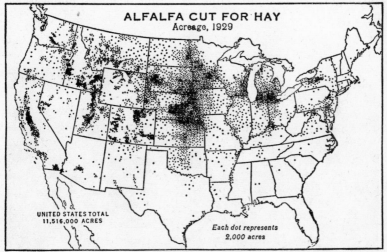

ALFALFA CUT FOR HAY
Acreage, 1929

UNITED STATES TOTAL
11,516,000 ACRES

Each dot represents
2,000 acres

Fig. 21.—Alfalfa demands soils that are not acid, and it is most easily cured in a climate that is not rainy during the summer. Consequently it thrives in the arid western states, where it is grown mostly under irrigation, and in the subhumid parts of the Great Plains. It also does well in the limestone sections of the East, where its culture has been increasing rapidly. Alfalfa is associated with the livestock industries and enters prominently into the farming system of the western cattle country and of the dairy belt from Minnesota to New York. (*U.S. Department of Agriculture.*)

At first, alfalfa was regarded largely as a western crop. Up to the beginning of the twentieth century, Colorado and California led in both acreage and production. Ten years later, that leadership had shifted to Kansas and Nebraska. With a better understanding of its cultural requirements, the development and dissemination of hardier varieties, and the importance of alfalfa to the growing dairy industry, acreage increased faster in the Middle West than in any other region. By 1940, Michigan, Minnesota, Wisconsin, and Iowa were the leaders in alfalfa acreage, although California, by virtue of superior yields produced in a long season under irrigation, led all states in alfalfa tonnage.

Acreage increase in the United States has been very marked. In the census covering production for 1899, 2,094,000 acres were reported. Crop estimates for 1940 indicated a production of 14,048,-000 acres, and the tonnage that year comprised over 35 per cent of all tame hay produced in the country.

Adaptation.—Alfalfa needs a well-drained soil approximating neutrality in reaction. It will grow on moderately alkaline soil but not on strongly alkaline soils such as are frequently found in the West. Many acid soils, otherwise not too unfavorable, have been conditioned to produce excellent alfalfa crops by means of liberal applications of lime.

Fig. 22.—Turkestan alfalfa in the Platte Valley of Nebraska. (*Courtesy of F. D. Keim, Nebr. Agr. Expt. Sta.*)

From the standpoint of climate, alfalfa is extensively grown in Montana where winters are extremely cold and in Arizona where summers are extremely hot. It is grown below sea level in the Imperial Valley of California and at altitudes of 8,000 ft. in the mountains of Colorado. Alfalfa utilizes much water but is poorly adapted to very humid areas. It is of least importance in the warm, humid southeastern part of this country and in New England. Its best yields are produced under irrigation in California, the 1928–1937 average for this state being 3.9 tons an acre. For the country as a whole the average acre yield is normally about 2 tons.

Alfalfa Varieties.—The growing of alfalfa under such markedly different environmental conditions is made possible by varieties distinctly different in adaptation. Hairy Peruvian alfalfa is very productive in the South and Southwest. It recovers quickly after cutting, and it grows rapidly. However, it has no place outside very mild regions, for it seldom survives winters in which the temperature falls below 10°F.

The common alfalfas are usually designated by the state in which the seed is produced. If alfalfa is grown in a given locality for several generations, nature tends to select and perpetuate the strains particularly suited to that locality. Thus, Arizona Common is not winter hardy, and Kansas and Montana Common are moderately winter hardy.

One group of alfalfa varieties is described as being *variegated*, so-called because many of the flowers are of a green to yellowish-green color (a few are yellow), rather than being of the typical purple color of common alfalfa. These variegated alfalfas are believed to have originated from a natural cross between purple-flowered common alfalfa (*Medicago sativa*) and the extremely hardy yellow-flowered alfalfa (*M. falcata*). Variegated alfalfas as a class are hardier than the common alfalfas. They have made alfalfa a dependable crop in the North where once the crop was not grown because ordinary strains were not hardy enough to endure severe winters.

At one time, much was made of the difference in root systems between common and variegated alfalfa. Variegated varieties are supposed to have a more branching root system, inherited from the yellow-blossomed parent. To some extent, this is true; but both variegated and common alfalfa are distinctly taprooted, the number of heavy lateral branches depending almost as much on environment as on heredity. On heavy soils, with the water table fairly near the surface, the tendency for branching is more marked. Both kinds are deep feeders, where environmental conditions permit, and readily develop roots 10 to 12 ft. in length. Occasionally they grow much longer.

Grimm Alfalfa.—The most widely grown of the variegated varieties is Grimm alfalfa. The original seed for this variety was brought into Carver County, Minnesota, by Wendelin Grimm, a German immigrant, in 1857. Aided by the severity of Minnesota winters, Grimm selected a strain of unusual winter hardiness, which bears his name. It has done much to ensure the dependability of alfalfa growing in north central and eastern states.

Other Variegated Alfalfas.—Cossack, introduced from Russia through the work of the U.S. Department of Agriculture, Baltic, named after Baltic, S.D., where it was grown for several years, and Canadian variegated, widely grown in Ontario, are variegated strains of alfalfa similar in appearance and hardiness to the Grimm variety. Hardigan is a profuse blossoming strain selected by the Michigan Agricultural Experiment Station from the Baltic. It is a superior seed producer when environmental conditions permit seed production.

Ladak alfalfa, brought to this country from northern India by the U.S. Department of Agriculture, is very winter hardy and drought resistant and moderately resistant to bacterial wilt. It recovers slowly after being cut and makes a slow growth in the fall, lessening somewhat its ability to compete with grass.

Nonvariegated Varieties.—Turkestan alfalfa was introduced into the United States in 1898. Strains grouped under this name vary considerably but have usually been less productive than domestic alfalfas and rather susceptible to leaf diseases. Some strains of Turkestan are winter hardy and offer much promise as source material in the efforts to breed strains resistant to wilt. The Hardistan variety of Nebraska, the Kaw of Kansas, and the Orestan of Oregon are of Turkestan origin.

Alfalfa and Winter Hardiness.—Fully 80 per cent of the alfalfa in the United States is grown in regions where winter hardiness is of some importance. Low temperatures as such undoubtedly cause a substantial amount of winter injury, but they are by no means the only reason for winter losses. Winterkilling may also be due to heaving, brought about by freezing and thawing in early spring. As a result, many roots are exposed, and often they are broken off 6 in. or more from the crown. Smothering occurs when the alfalfa is under dense ice sheets for prolonged periods. Physiological drought results when the soil moisture is tied up by freezing so that the plant cannot get an adequate supply. Plant physiologists have been unable to establish the exact reasons why some strains of alfalfa are much more resistant to winterkilling than others, but the property of being able to harden off so as to resist winter injury is undoubtedly hereditary and is passed from one generation to another by hardy lines. The first consideration of the farmer who would grow alfalfa in a region of severe winters is to choose seed of a variety that, by test and experience, has been proved sufficiently hardy for that region.

Management in Relation to Winterkilling.—The correct choice of variety alone is not complete insurance against winterkilling. A prolonged ice sheet may take its toll from the hardiest of lines. Management of the stand also has an important bearing on the ability of the alfalfa to survive the winter.

Alfalfa, like all green plants, carries on photosynthesis. The chlorophyll, energized by the sun, transforms carbon dioxide and water into carbohydrates. These are used in the growth of the plant structures, and eventually a surplus is stored in the roots. When alfalfa tops are cut or frozen off, new growth derives its nourishment from organic reserves stored in the roots until green leaves are formed and the plant can again carry on photosynthesis. If the new growth of alfalfa is cut or frozen off repeatedly before the plant has a chance to restore reserve food to the roots, exhaustion of the root reserves occurs and the plant dies.

These facts are particularly pertinent to the fall management of alfalfa in the North. Rather and Harrison[1] have shown the cutting of alfalfa in September to be a hazardous procedure in Michigan, early September or even late August cuttings being most hazardous in the northern, late September or early October cuttings in the southern part of the state. Farther south the critical period for fall cutting is later than in Michigan because of a later fall growing period.

When alfalfa is cut or closely pastured off during this critical fall period, it still has time to make a renewed growth. The amount of growth made is sufficient greatly to deplete root reserves, and fall freezing stops further top growth before they can be restored.

Alfalfa low in root reserves, especially starch, is weakened in its ability to harden off and become resistant to winter injury. Not

TABLE 8.—INFLUENCE OF DIFFERENT FALL CUTTING TREATMENTS ON DRY MATTER, TOTAL SUGARS, HEMICELLULOSE, AND INSOLUBLE STARCH IN ROOTS COLLECTED THE FOLLOWING FEBRUARY. AVERAGE YIELDS SECURED THE FOLLOWING SEASON. EAST LANSING, MICH.*

Fall treatment	Percentage dry matter	Root analysis, percentage dry weight consisting of			% Total sugars, hemicellulose and insoluble starch in 100 g. of fresh tissue	Yield the following season, average of 12 trials (tons of 15% moisture hay)
		Total sugars	Hemicellulose	Insoluble starch		
No cutting...	34.80	16.06	8.33	2.10	9.22	3.54
Cut Sept. 1...	36.52	16.59	6.53	2.03	9.18	3.11
Cut Sept. 15..	32.56	15.88	7.67	0.0	7.67	2.95
Cut Oct. 1....	32.86	17.51	7.63	0.0	8.26	3.18
Cut Oct. 15...	32.54	18.14	7.45	0.73	8.56	3.22
Cut Oct. 31...	33.74	19.79	7.84	1.72	9.90	3.44

* Adapted from H. C. Rather, and C. M. Harrison, Alfalfa Management with Special Reference to Fall Treatment, *Mich. Agr. Expt. Sta. Spec. Bul.* 292, 1938.

[1] RATHER, H. C., and C. M. HARRISON, Alfalfa Management with Special Reference to Fall Treatment, *Mich. Agr. Expt. Sta. Spec. Bul.* 292, 1938.

A. Cross section of an alfalfa root, dug in November, where no fall cutting was taken. The dark coloring in the rays (starch stained with iodine) indicates that the roots were well supplied with organic food reserves.

B. Alfalfa not cut the previous fall making a good growth the next May.

FIG. 23.—In northern states cutting alfalfa during September

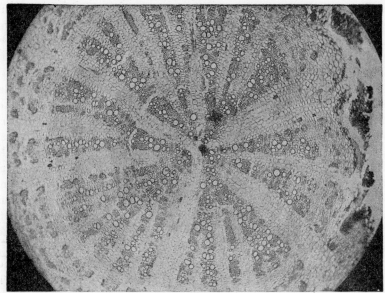

C. Cross section of an alfalfa root, dug in November, where a third cutting was taken for hay Sept. 15, thereby depleting the roots of stored food.

D. The alfalfa stand in May showing injury as the result of being cut the previous Sept. 15, a critical period in central Michigan during which top growth is necessary to synthesize organic food reserves.

is often injurious to the stand. (*Mich. Agr. Expt. Sta.*)

only is it more susceptible to the direct effects of low temperature, but heaving is far more prevalent in plants with inadequate root reserves than in plants with abundant starch storage. Perhaps in this instance heaving is a result rather than the direct cause of winterkilling.

Logically, alfalfa with a plentiful storage of root reserves is much less likely to be injured by late fall cutting or grazing than by similar treatment earlier. If the cutting is done so late that the alfalfa makes practically no subsequent fall growth, root reserves are not then utilized and the plants have an excellent chance for survival. When no fall cutting is made or only very light grazing is practiced, there is the combined favorable effect of permitting roots high in storage to go into the winter along with top growth which tends to hold snow and prevent exceedingly low soil temperatures. This type of management reduces the number of cuttings in a season from three to two, four to three, etc., depending on the length of the growing season, but makes for a longer lived stand and eventually greater total productivity.

The principles involved in root-reserve storage influence summer as well as fall management. Alfalfa cut in the bud or really early bloom stage may not have had sufficient opportunity to replenish the root reserves. The repeated following of this practice weakens the plants and reduces yields. In reporting Kansas experiments, Granfield stated:

It was found that when growth starts in the spring, and after each cutting, there is a rapid decline of total carbohydrates and of nitrogen (in the roots) until a minimum is reached, after which there is a rapid increase. During the seasons studied, the minimum carbohydrate and nitrogen content was reached about 20 days after cutting. The maximum accumulation apparently occurred when the plants were about in full bloom.[1]

Alfalfa and Water.—Alfalfa is resistant to drought, but it is not at all conservative of moisture. It gets its drought resistance because its roots go deeply into the soil in search of moisture. Kiesselbach and Anderson,[2] working at Lincoln, Neb., reported a water requirement ratio of 858 lb. of water per pound of dry matter for alfalfa during 1916, which is 3.2, 2.1, and 2.7 times that found for corn, oats, and wheat, respectively. With this high moisture requirement and the ability to get its water from the deeper soil strata, alfalfa has the capacity to dry out the soil to the point where subsequent yields are greatly reduced. The water used by alfalfa, in regions of adequate

[1] GRANFIELD, C. O., The Trend of Organic Food Reserves in Alfalfa Roots as Affected by Cutting Practices, *Jour. Agr. Res.*, Vol. 50, No. 8, pp. 697–709, 1935.

[2] KIESSELBACH, T. A., and A. ANDERSON, Alfalfa Investigations, *Nebr. Agr. Expt. Sta. Res. Bul.* 36, pp. 1–125, 1926.

precipitation, relatively high humidity, and comparatively shallow soils, is rapidly replaced by rain and snow. But where soils are deep, rainfall is moderate, and humidity is low, the growing of alfalfa involves a permanent moisture problem. Kiesselbach and his associates[1] found that the productivity of alfalfa meadows occupying the land for the first time at Lincoln, Neb., declined abruptly about 4 to 5 years after sowing, even though a good healthy stand remained. This was found to be due primarily to depletion of the available subsoil moisture. Alfalfa drew upon this supply to a depth of 33 ft. in a 6-year-old meadow and 25 ft. in a 2-year-old meadow. A 6-year-old alfalfa meadow reached its peak of production in the third year, with 7.2 tons of cured forage per acre, but during the fifth and sixth years yielded only 2 tons an acre except where irrigated, the yield then being 6.7 tons.

Under ordinary cropping conditions on upland soil in areas subject to the conditions described above, restoration of subsoil moisture is so slow that further alfalfa production is greatly handicapped. In Kansas and Nebraska, where this situation prevails over wide areas, the alfalfa acreage in 1940 was less than half that grown 20 years earlier.

Along the western border of the Great Plains, in the Southwest, throughout the Rocky Mountains, and along the Pacific coast the great volume of water that alfalfa needs is supplied by irrigation. As a result of abundant irrigation water and long growing seasons, permitting of five to eight cuttings a year, the southern parts of Arizona and California are able to produce as much as 8 to 10 tons of hay to the acre. The normal irrigation for much of the arid region where three to five cuttings are usually taken is 35 to 40 in. of water in three to eight applications throughout the season.

Alfalfa Cultivation.—Although tillage of alfalfa meadows to control grass and prolong the life of a stand has frequently been recommended and practiced, there is practically no experimental evidence to support cultivation as a paying procedure. At the Nebraska Agricultural Experiment Station[2] in a 4-year trial, plots receiving no cultivation averaged 3.39 tons an acre. Plots disked three times yielded 3.22 tons; those harrowed three times with a spring-tooth, 3.31 tons an acre. No method of tillage increased production.

---

[1] KIESSELBACH, T. A., J. C. RUSSEL, and A. ANDERSON, The Significance of Subsoil Moisture in Alfalfa Production, *Jour. Amer. Soc. Agron.*, Vol. 21, No. 3, 1929.

[2] KIESSELBACH, T. A., and A. ANDERSON, Alfalfa in Nebraska, *Nebr. Expt. Sta. Bul.* 222, 1927.

These results, typical of those secured in the vast majority of experiments, are not surprising. The need for cultivation arises from infestation by weeds or grass; and a thrifty, well-nourished field of alfalfa is seldom troubled by such infestations. As alfalfa plants die out owing to winterkilling, summer killing, disease, lack of sufficient nourishment, and perhaps old age, grass and weeds invade the stand. No amount of tillage can restore the lost alfalfa plants, nor does any amount of tillage seem able to restore the yield for in no way does it correct the conditions that have resulted in the death of the alfalfa plants. When an alfalfa stand becomes weedy or appears to be on the retreat from grass invasion, it is time to break it up and begin again.

Can Thin Stands Be Rejuvenated?—Trying to restore thinned-out alfalfa stands by applying more alfalfa seed is in the same class with cultivation: it does not correct the condition that caused a thin stand to develop in the first place. Alfalfa growers have tried to thicken weak stands time after time, and almost always the added alfalfa seed has been wasted. This has not been true when grass seed was added, for a thinning alfalfa stand can be converted into a good mixed hay stand.

An example of this is reported by Dexter[1] working in Michigan. A somewhat poorly drained field was losing its alfalfa after the second season of harvest; therefore, in 1935, the alfalfa land was scratched up lightly with the spring-tooth harrow, and both spring and fall seedings were made. Although reseedings with alfalfa, red clover, and sweet clover failed, some of the grasses did well, the best results being secured with timothy. Subsequent yields were as follows:

Alfalfa	Yield, pounds dry hay per acre	
	1936	1937
No reseeding	4,002	3,269
Reseeded with timothy	4,565	5,683

Alfalfa Diseases.—Bacterial wilt caused by *Aplanobacter insidiosum* is the most destructive of alfalfa ailments. Badly infected plants are stunted; they often develop an abnormally large number of stems; and the leaves are smaller, turn a sickly green color, and often are

[1] Dexter, S. T., Experiments on the Production of Alfalfa Hay, *Mich. Agr. Expt. Sta. Quart. Bul.*, Vol. 22, No. 4, pp. 265–271, 1940.

bleached at the margins as though frosted. When the bark of a diseased root is stripped back, a brownish-yellow, diseased woody tissue appears, in contrast to the white appearance of a healthy root. The disease can be spread with a mower, in manure from infected plants, by soil blowing, and by water running from infected to uninfected areas. The condition becomes progressively worse as stands get older; and if the infection is severe, it is hard to hold a stand in profitable condition for more than two or three seasons. Progress has been made in the development of wilt-resistant varieties, these being largely of Turkestan origin. Smooth brome in mixture with alfalfa appears to retard the spread of wilt and, at the very least, provides a luxuriant grass to grow in the place of wilted alfalfa plants that have died. Thus, brome grass in the mixture prolongs the life of a good forage stand.

Of the foliage diseases, leaf spot, caused by the fungus *Pseudopeziza medicaginis*, is most prevalent. The spots are circular in shape, of pinhead size, and dark brown to black in color. Infected leaves soon turn yellow and drop off. In a bad case of leaf spot, defoliation is so complete that there is nothing left but the bare stems. Early cutting reduces leaf losses and also the source of infection for succeeding cuttings, for a new outbreak comes from infected leaves that fall among the plants.

Insect Pests.—Leafhoppers of several species, the same greenish or brownish little hoppers that attack potato vines and clover leaves, infest alfalfa and may give it a bad case of yellowing or stunting. They suck sap from the leaves and spread disease. In the North, they do their greatest damage to second cuttings. When early- and late-cut alfalfa are side by side, the early-cut alfalfa suffers a double infestation, for the hoppers migrate from the stubble of the late cutting onto the fresh, succulent new growth where the adjacent alfalfa was cut earlier. Serious yellowing of alfalfa where this migration occurs is often limited to a strip 10 to 20 ft. wide. In itself, late cutting does not appear to be a broadly effective control measure. Nor has any other method been found very practical in alfalfa fields; for the adult hoppers are tough and hard to kill at any time, and the wingless young hide on the underside of the leaves.

The alfalfa weevil (*Phytonomus posticus*) is an Old World insect that became established in Utah in about 1904 and spread into the near-by mountain states. The adults hibernate in trash in or near the alfalfa and deposit great numbers of eggs in the spring. These hatch into larvae which may feed on the leaves enough to stop growth about 2 weeks ahead of the first cutting. Control measures involve cultural practices that reduce the overwintering population, coupled with the use of arsenical dusts.[1]

The alfalfa-seed chalcid, a minute wasplike insect, produces larvae that devour the inside of the seed, at times doing much damage. The lygus bug also interferes with seed production, working on the flower in a manner that prevents seed development. Army worms, aphids, and grasshoppers all take their toll from alfalfa fields when environmental conditions favor the building up of a damaging population.

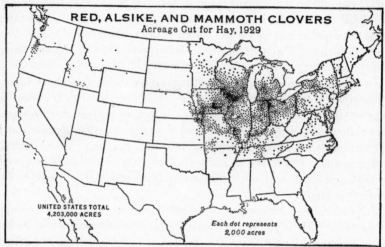

Fig. 24.—This map shows the acreage of red, including mammoth, and alsike clover grown alone. Most of the clover acreage is located in the dairy belt and the corn belt, but only as far west as the two eastern tiers of counties in Kansas and Nebraska, and in the corn and winter wheat belt to the south, particularly in the Nashville Basin of Tennessee. Much of this clover is grown for seed as well as for hay. There is a small but dense district in western Oregon. (*U.S. Department of Agriculture.*)

Red Clover. *Distribution.*—Once the most important legume in American agriculture, then surpassed only by alfalfa, red clover benefits soils and produces protein-rich fodder as a major crop in a score of states. Red clover and the leading hay grass, timothy, are so commonly grown in mixtures that census reports and crop estimates for the United States group the two. New York leads all states in clover-timothy production, with Pennsylvania, Wisconsin, and Ohio following in order. There are more acres of clover-timothy in the country than alfalfa but the acre yield is not so high. As a 10-year average (1929–1938), clover and timothy hay constituted 42 per cent of the tame-hay

[1] Reeves, G. I., T. R. Chamberlin, and K. M. Pack, Spraying for the Alfalfa Weevil, *U.S. Dept. Agr. Farmers' Bul.* 1185, 1920.

acreage of the United States, and 37 per cent of the tonnage; alfalfa made up only 23 per cent of the acreage but yielded well enough to comprise 35 per cent of the total tame-hay production.

Growth Habits.—Red clover has been described as both a biennial and a perennial. A native of Asia and Europe, many strains found there are truly perennial; but in the United States the crop behaves more like a biennial although a proportion of the plants in any stand seem to be short-lived perennials. Red clover does not have the deep root system characteristic of alfalfa but develops about 95 per cent of its root growth in the top 8 in. of soil. It is a little more tolerant to soil acidity than alfalfa but makes its best growth on soils well supplied with calcium, phosphorus, and potassium.

Cross-pollination is essential for seed production and is brought about through the activity of bees and other insects. When conditions are unfavorable to bees, seed production is low.

Red-clover Strains.—Because of the nature of pollination, the red-clover population as a whole is exceedingly variable as to its hereditary properties. As a result, in the areas that have grown red-clover seed for many years, nature has selected the strains especially well adapted to that environment. When seed is brought in from a locality presenting distinctly different growing conditions, the performance of the crop is often unsatisfactory.

The U.S. Department of Agriculture, testing red-clover seed in cooperation with a number of clover-growing states,[1] found foreign clovers, with few exceptions, unsatisfactory for use in the eastern United States. When they overwintered successfully, these foreign clovers gave a fair to good first cutting but a very inferior second crop. This did not apply to seed from Canada which was comparable in winter hardiness and yield with that grown in the northern United States. Italian seed was especially susceptible to disease (anthracnose) and winterkilling and was generally unsatisfactory throughout these tests.

The Tennessee Agricultural Experiment Station has developed a line of red clover resistant to the form of anthracnose prevalent in that general southern area. The strain is superior to northern seed where anthracnose is the chief factor limiting clover production. Seed grown in the corn belt and northern states is satisfactory throughout that area; but seed grown in western Oregon, where winters are mild, is local in adaptation and is not recommended in the states where winters are severe.

[1] PIETERS, A. J., and R. L. MORGAN, Field Tests of Imported Red Clover Seed, *U.S. Dept. Agr. Cir.* 210, 1932.

European and South American red-clover plants have smooth stems and leaves in contrast to the pubescence, or hairiness, characteristic of American varieties.

Mammoth Clover.—Most of the red clover grown in the United States produces two cuttings. The second crop may be used for hay, pasture, or seed production. Mammoth clover is larger, coarser stemmed, and later in maturing than ordinary red clover. It does not recover quickly from cutting; therefore, only one crop, whether for hay or seed, can be harvested. On moist, fertile land the stems of mammoth clover tend to become coarse and woody; but on lighter soils a good quality of hay is produced, and some insect injury caused by the clover-leaf midge is avoided because of the 2 weeks' later maturity. Cutting in early bloom rather than later reduces the tendency of the stems to become woody and undesirable as feed. When cut for seed, most of the mammoth-clover straw goes back to the land.

Clover Diseases.—Red clover when grown on a soil well supplied with the needed nutrients is not usually seriously injured by diseases. Those most commonly found are leaf spot, characterized by great numbers of small black specks on the leaves; rust, showing as small reddish-brown spots; and powdery mildew, a whitish, cobweblike mass containing small black bodies within the meshes. There are also certain rots affecting the roots and stems that occasionally prove damaging.

Anthracnose is prevalent in many areas but most serious in the southern part of the corn belt centering in Tennessee. It attacks both seedling and mature plants, starting at the base of the leaflet and along the leaf stems. Infected leaflets droop and die off. The disease is most serious when it attacks the crown and taproot, producing a dark rotting so that the plants break off at the soil line, though the roots below the lesion appear healthy. It is at its worst during periods of hot, humid weather, and this disease has made clover production exceedingly difficult where conditions favor its development. The only practicable control thus far is the use of strains inherently resistant to anthracnose infection.

Alsike. *A Lowland Legume.*—Alsike clover is the lowland legume. It thrives with "wet feet" and even appears to benefit from occasional flooding. When Linnaeus found some pinkish-blossomed clover growing in Alsike Parish near Uppsala, Sweden, he thought it was a hybrid between the red and the white kinds and so he called it *Trifolium hybridum*. But alsike clover is a distinct and incidentally a very useful species. Though it benefits from applications of lime if the soil is sour, it tolerates much more acidity than red clover, sweet clover, or alfalfa and thrives on land far too wet for these legumes. Seldom does it winterkill even in northern Wisconsin, Michigan, and New York. Its rather hard seeds often lie buried for years to sprout in a meadow during some wet season and produce a volunteer crop of fine forage.

It is grown extensively north of the Ohio River, west to the edge of the Great Plains, and again in the far northwest. But almost no alsike is grown in the South or in dry areas, for it thrives best where summers are cool and moisture is abundant. Sandy soils of a droughty nature produce only a stunted growth.

Fig. 25.—Alsike clover is adapted to low-lying, moist soils. (*Courtesy of C. M. Harrison.*)

Plant Characteristics.—Alsike is a perennial though it is usually managed as a biennial crop. Its pink to white flower heads develop at each leaf axil. In red clover, all the flowers tend to be at the same height from the ground. In alsike, flower heads are borne along the entire stem, which increases potential seed production. The stems are fine, and both stems and leaves are free from the hairiness that helps cause dusty hay. The seeds are small, and thus only very light seeding rates provide plenty of plants for a thick stand. Only one hay crop or one seed crop is produced in a single season, and clipping at any immature stage greatly reduces seed yields.

Alsike Uses.—Timothy, red clover, and alsike constitute one of the most widely used hay mixtures throughout the clover country.

According to Cornell experiments,[1] a mixture of red and alsike clover yields more forage, makes possible the fixation of more nitrogen, and produces greater benefit to crops that follow than does either clover grown alone. Timothy in the mixture reduces lodging and makes possible more rapid curing of the hay by keeping the cut forage in a loose, airy condition in swath or windrow.

Alsike is commonly included in lowland-pasture mixtures. The plants last only 2 or 3 years but may produce considerable seed which perpetuates the clover in a fairly open sward but not in a closely formed turf. It is most productive of either hay or pasture when used as such in relatively short rotations, with the forage stand left for 2 years. On moist soils the aftermath of hayfields makes good pasture; but if moisture is lacking, there will be very little growth of alsike after hay harvest.

The volunteering habit of alsike is due to the fact that the lower flowers on the stem are dead-ripe and shatter much seed before the seed in the latest top flowers is fully mature. It may be spread from field to field in manure and in flood- and irrigation water.

Though occasionally attacked by aphids, alsike is seldom seriously affected by either disease or insect enemies.

White Clover. *Description and Use.*—White clover (*Trifolium repens*) is primarily a pasture plant. It is a moderately short lived perennial that reseeds abundantly under favorable conditions and that also spreads by stolons. The plant is fine-stemmed, with pure-white flowers. Like other clovers, it is high in calcium, phosphorus, and protein and is very nutritious. In the cool, damp climate of Great Britain it persists indefinitely in properly managed pastures (see Chap. XI); but, in much of the United States, where it grows it is a sporadic constituent of pastures, most likely to appear in quantity under moist conditions if phosphorus is supplied liberally and competing grass is checked by close grazing. Common on the heavier soils throughout the United States clover regions, white clover is at its best in the New England states and parts of New York, northern Michigan, and Wisconsin, where the weather is cool, humidity high, and moisture doubly effective because of a comparatively slow rate of evaporation.

Nearly all the white-clover seed sown in the United States is used in lawn-grass mixtures. For the most part, that found in pastures volunteers there from seed originally an impurity in regular seedings and later disseminated by livestock and otherwise.

[1] LYON, T. L., The Residual Effects of Some Leguminous Crops, *Cornell Univ. Agr. Expt. Sta. Bul.* **645**, 1936.

The so-called *wild strains* of white clover have been adapted to various local conditions by natural selection. Where environmental conditions favor white clover, it should seldom be necessary to seed it for pasture production. Phosphatic fertilization and close grazing should be all that is necessary to develop the locally adapted volunteer seeding. Where the plant is not well adapted, sowing seed is useless.

Ladino is a large type of white clover brought to this country from Italy in 1912. It is more productive than the dwarf types of white clover and has given excellent results as an irrigated pasture crop in Oregon and California. It is promising, too, in New England when grown with grasses that do not form too dense a sward. Unlike the low-growing white clovers, Ladino does not thrive under close grazing, and the life of the stand is sure to be shortened if the plants are pastured off closely in the fall. Though requiring rather moist conditions, much water can be injurious to Ladino. After a wet summer and fall, it proved much less winter hardy in Michigan than Hardigan, a variegated alfalfa.

Sweet Clover.—Beekeepers were the first to appreciate sweet clover; they scattered seed far and wide as a source of nectar, much to the disgust of crop growers who regarded it as a dangerous interloper. Eventually the latter discovered that this rough and tough pest left their land more pliable and made their impervious soils more drainable and their light-colored soils darker and richer. Cows could even be induced to eat it, if hungry enough; and often good production followed. Today sweet clover is an accepted crop.

Where Sweet Clover Grows.—Soils that contain enough lime to grow alfalfa are needed for sweet clover. Beyond this requirement, sweet clover is less restricted. It does well on soils too low in mineral foods for alfalfa because it has the capacity to use less available forms of these foods. It grows in the West on soils far too alkaline for alfalfa. It does well in the Alabama-Mississippi region, regarded as too hot and humid for alfalfa. It is as winter hardy as the variegated alfalfas and nearly as drought resistant. It is a useful legume in the eastern Great Plains, throughout the corn belt and middle western dairy states, and in the South.

Kinds of Sweet Clover.—Common biennial white sweet clover (*Melilotus alba*) represents 80 to 85 per cent of the crop grown in this country. It is a mixture of many types but, in general, is a tall (5- to 7-ft.), coarse-stemmed plant as it approaches maturity. A fleshy taproot extends deeply into the soil. Grundy County, Arctic, and Essex Dwarf are smaller, finer, earlier maturing strains of the biennial white type.

Hubam is an annual white sweet clover about which there was much ado in the early 1920's, largely because of exploitative seed prices. It has not been accorded an important place in agriculture because of the greater vigor of the biennial types.

M. officinalis is the name for yellow-blossomed biennial sweet clover. It too is smaller and earlier than common white. Madrid and Albotrea are yellow varieties. There also is an annual yellow sweet clover, but it never has attained importance.

Fig. 26.—Where moisture conditions are favorable sweet clover may be seeded in corn successfully. Seedings have a better chance to get started if made before the corn is 2 ft. high. (*Courtesy of E. E. Patton.*)

Sweet-clover Uses.—Sweet clover can be cured as hay, it is a high-yielding silage crop, it produces great quantities of spring and early-summer pasture, and it is one of the most convenient off-season green manures.

As a hay crop, it is somewhat difficult to handle. The stems are coarse and dry out slowly. Should sweet clover spoil as either hay or silage (and spoilage is not always apparent), it may develop a poison that causes blood to lose its ability to clot. Cattle, especially young cattle, are often susceptible to this ailment when their roughage for an extended period is almost exclusively sweet clover. The remedy is to hold sweet clover down to less than half the roughage ration or to discontinue it entirely for alternate 2-week intervals.

As a pasture, sweet clover has the advantage of prodigious productivity and the disadvantage that its growth ceases and the stems become coarse and woody as hazel brush in midsummer when most other pasturage is also scarce.

A second growth of sweet clover for seed or forage is dependent on cutting the first crop high—high enough to miss the lower leaves, for new growth during its second year comes from lower leaf axils, not from a crown.

As a soil builder, sweet clover is well-nigh preeminent, surpassing even farm manure. It contributes an abundance of nitrogen, most of which comes from the air and which is more available than that in manure. It picks up subsoil minerals and, on decay, releases them to other plants, and it is exceedingly effective in making tight soils more porous. Decaying rapidly at maturity or when plowed under, it improves aeration, drainage, and the general physical condition of the soil.

The corn-belt farmer, for the price of 15 lb. of cheap seed, can sow sweet clover with oats and plow it under the next spring for corn with no loss of crop time. Corn-yield increases of 18 to 20 bu. an acre have been secured following this practice in Illinois.[1]

Lespedeza.—Lespedeza, also called *Japan clover*, has, since 1925, come to be the most widely grown legume in the South. It is an annual, but much of its usefulness is based on its ability to self-seed and grow year after year; hence, it is included here with the perennial forages. Ripened seeds shatter in the fall and start growth with warm weather the next spring. Markedly tolerant to soil acidity, lespedeza provides a crop that can be used effectively under conditions unsuited to red clover and alfalfa. Where the latter legumes can be grown, they are more productive and more useful.

Distribution.—Lespedeza was introduced from Asia sometime during the early part of the nineteenth century, but its popularity in the South is a much more modern development. It is grown all through the southeastern part of the United States, as far west as eastern Texas and Kansas, and as far north as southern Illinois and Indiana. Early strains will mature in Michigan and Wisconsin, but they are so small as to have little or no practical value.

In the U.S. Department of Agriculture 1940 crop report, Tennessee leads in lespedeza-hay production with 928,000 acres. Missouri, Kentucky, North Carolina, Arkansas, and Virginia also have large acreages. The normal hay yield is about a ton to the acre. The crop

[1] CROSBY, M. A., and L. W. KEPART, Sweet Clover in Corn Belt Farming, *U.S. Dept. Agr. Farmers' Bul.* 1653 (revised), 1939.

is grown for both hay and pasture on all the principal soil types of the South but makes its best growth on the rich alluvial soils of the Mississippi River delta.

Culture.—Lespedeza is most commonly sown on winter oats or winter barley in the spring. If sown alone, weed encroachment is serious, but it becomes established readily with the grain and makes its greatest growth after grain harvest. Once lespedeza has been established, the land on which it has been grown can be prepared for winter grain by disking, with a good chance for a volunteer crop of lespedeza

Fig. 27.—A lespedeza seeding made in barley in Tennessee. The large even stand, as compared with the 8-in. grain stubble, is the result of the use of lime and phosphate in a soil-building program. (*Courtesy of U.S. Dept. of Agr. Soil Conservation Service.*)

the next spring. Lespedeza is sown in late February near the Gulf and correspondingly later farther north. On land used regularly for pasture, volunteer seedings are depended on to keep the crop growing.

Although tolerant of soil acidity, lespedeza responds to lime and makes its best growth where organic matter, phosphorus, and potash are present in liberal quantities. By supplementing its growth with phosphorus and potassium, it can be used effectively in soil improvement. When not grown with small grain or grass, lespedeza is not very effective in preventing winter erosion, for it maintains no live vegetation during the winter and early spring.

Varieties.—Common lespedeza is the old type grown in the South for many years. Tennessee No. 76 is a selection from the common. It is characterized by a more erect and more vigorous growth. Korean lespedeza is earlier than common, and it has been responsible for the northward movement of the lespedeza-growing area. Harbin is a very early dwarf type of Korean lespedeza, too small to be very useful. The Kobe variety is of the same species as common and is similar in adaptation, but it is taller and has broader leaves.

Common lespedeza (*Lespedeza striata*) and Korean lespedeza (*L. stipulacea*) represent distinct species of the annual type.

Uses.—As a hay crop, lespedeza is of good quality, almost as good as clover and alfalfa. The plants do not grow very tall, but the density of growth makes for fairly good yields, the better crops ranging from 2 to 3 tons an acre. Cutting in the South begins the last of June, and thus there is time for a second growth to produce and shatter seed.

As a pasture, lespedeza has the great advantage of producing much of its feed in midsummer when other plants so often are dormant owing to heat and drought. The plants stay green and nutritious until frost. Mixtures of lespedeza with several southern grasses are often used both for hay and pasture.

L. sericea is a perennial species of the lespedeza group. It is a coarse, hard-stemmed plant when mature, and because of its high tannin content it becomes extremely unpalatable. Possibilities of developing low-tannin varieties are good, for plants range from 5 to over 10 per cent in tannin content.

Some strains of *L. sericea* are winter hardy to a certain extent. A Michigan seeding established in 1932 on acid sandy soil gradually increased in thickness and was still doing well in 1941. When pastured early with sheep, the leaves were eaten; but when animals were turned in late in the season, the *L. sericea* was untouched. Originally, grass was almost nonexistent in this field, most of the vegetation being sorrel. Gradually, a good sward of Canada bluegrass has developed along with the *L. sericea*, and the grass undoubtedly benefited from its association with this legume on land that otherwise rated close to zero in productivity.

In the South, good stands of *L. sericea* are much more easily obtained, and this species of lespedeza is of value for erosion control on very poor soil. To be at all useful as forage, it must be pastured or cut when in a relatively immature condition.

Minor Legumes. *Kudzu.*—This legume, introduced from Japan more than fifty years ago, is proving effective as an erosion-control plant in the southeastern United States. It does not withstand poor drainage but otherwise grows on a wide range of soil types, some of which are acid in reaction. Kudzu is a deep-rooted perennial vine that grows from crown buds and from buds at the nodes of the vines. It is propagated by setting out the crowns. A thick stand develops as the vine buds take root. Dormant vine cuttings are also used. Planting is done from December to April, while the kudzu is dormant. Ordinarily, 1,000 plants an acre are set out; but, with proper soil preparation and liberal fertilization, fewer plants are required to start a stand. Where adapted, kudzu makes a good quality of legume hay. Cutting management must be such as to leave the fleshy roots high in storage material by frost time, or the plants will winterkill. Moderate grazing may also be practiced.

Crotalaria.—Three species of crotalaria are grown commercially in the United States, *C. spectabilis*, *C. striata*, and *C. intermedia*. In general, this is a semitropical legume; and, because of late maturity, it has been difficult to get a good seed crop. Earlier strains have been developed by selection. Crotalaria is highly regarded as a green manure in the southeastern United States but has no place as a stock feed because of unpalatability.

Bird's-foot trefoil (*Lotus corniculatus*) is a yellow-flowered perennial legume that occasionally attracts attention because it is found doing quite well in some sandy pasture field. If soil conditions are favorable, alfalfa, red clover, sweet clover, alsike, and white clover all are far superior as crop or pasture plants. When seeded, bird's-foot trefoil starts slowly, and the establishment of a thrifty stand is difficult.

Yellow trefoil (*Medicago lupulina*), also called *black medic*, is a small yellow-flowered legume, usually annual or winter annual but with some perennial forms. It is a prolific seed producer, and the seed often adulterates alfalfa seed. Because of its small growth, yellow trefoil is not very productive; but its quality and nutritive value are good, and where it volunteers in pastures it undoubtedly contributes to the value of the herbage. There seems to be no good reason for seeding it deliberately, for the more common legumes greatly exceed yellow trefoil in economic value.

Strawberry Clover (*Trifolium fragiferum*).—This legume seems to have a place on alkaline soils of the West and on low soils subject to prolonged flooding. It is a perennial that spreads by creeping stems as does white clover. The flower heads are round or strawberry-shaped and mostly pink to white in color. The plants are too short for hay harvest but are palatable and nutritious as pasture and withstand close grazing except in late fall.

SEEDING PRACTICES FOR FORAGE LEGUMES

The means and methods of seeding legumes for forage, the time of seeding, and the seeding rates are as diverse as are the localities in which these legumes are grown. There are a dozen ways to get alfalfa seed nicely covered in moist soil to a depth of ¾ in. If the various methods accomplish the desired result, they are all good.

Seeding Depth.—Because nearly all the forage legumes are propagated with small and frequently very hard seeds, the desired seedbed is one that is clean, fine, and granular so that the seeds have complete contact with the soil, and firm so that moisture can be kept at or very near the surface. The tiny seed of white clover contains very little reserve food and must be covered much less deeply than the large field pea with its abundance of stored food. Coarse sands cannot be packed too firmly; but clay, with its extremely minute particles, if refined and firmed too much may crust over after a hard rain and prevent seedlings from emerging. Shallower planting is advisable on moist heavy soils than on the drier sands.

Often clover seed is sown on frozen ground, and nature's action of freezing and thawing covers the seed sufficiently. Again, soil type is a consideration. Heavy soils honeycomb with this freezing and thawing and cover seeds adequately. On sands the practice is not so effective.

Grass-seed drills distribute seed evenly at a uniform depth. So do weeders with seeder attachments. But hand-operated equipment for broadcast seedings is less expensive and may be entirely satisfactory, especially if followed by light harrowing.

Suggested seeding depths are as follows: for very small seeds such as white-clover seed, as shallow as possible; for medium-sized seeds like red-clover, sweet-clover, and alfalfa seed, ¾ to 1 in. on heavy soils, 1½ in. on light soils; for larger seeds like vetch, 2 in.

Rate of Seeding.—Almost all rates of seeding in common use distribute far more seed than would be needed for a perfect stand if all the seed grew and survived. When seedbeds are in good condition, light seeding rates are ample; when they are in poor condition, heavy seedings cannot make up for the deficiency.

Table 9 presents a range of seeding rates compiled from the recommendations of numerous experiment stations.

Time of Seeding.—No one time of seeding for a given legume is best for all circumstances even in the same locality. Because localities vary greatly in climatic conditions, obviously no one time of seeding is applicable to different regions. In the North, spring seedings of forage legumes made with grain companion crops are almost the rule. Yet alfalfa may be seeded with safety from early April to mid-August in Michigan, Wisconsin, or Minnesota; fall seedings have given best results in southern states; spring and late-summer or early-fall seedings are recommended in Nebraska. The summer and fall seedings should have the advantage of cleaner seedbeds but the spring seedings develop a stronger plant in the seeding season. Red clover, alsike, and sweet clover are nearly always seeded with grain companion crops in the spring.

Because climatic conditions for the various crops do vary so widely, it is essential that the literature of the various experiment stations be consulted to secure information applicable to local conditions.

TABLE 9.—SUGGESTED SEEDING RATES FOR SEVERAL OF THE MORE IMPORTANT FORAGE LEGUMES

Crop	Seeding rate, pounds an acre	Remarks
Alfalfa....................	10–15	
Sweet clover...............	12–15	If unhulled, 20 lb.
Red clover.................	6–8	
Alsike clover..............	3–5	
White clover..............	2–5	1–2 lb. in mixtures
Crimson clover............	12–15	18–22 lb. on poor soil or if sown late
Lespedeza.................	20–25	
Strawberry clover..........	2–5	
Common vetch.............	60	30 lb. if sown with grain
Hairy vetch...............	40	15–20 lb. if sown with rye
Bur clover.................	12–15	20 lb. if unhulled
Bird's-foot trefoil..........	2–5	
Crotalaria.................	10–20	3–5 lb. if sown in rows

Companion Crops.—If alfalfa, red clover, or any of the similar forages is seeded with small grain, the grain is called a *nurse crop*. The name is misleading; for it implies benefits to the forage seeding whereas, in most cases, the grain furnishes far more competition than advantage. The name *companion crop* is more appropriate. The justification for seeding alfalfa or clover with a grain crop lies in the reduced cost of making the seeding in this manner. The grain brings an income whereas the forage, if seeded alone, usually brings in nothing or at most a little pasture or occasionally a light hay crop the year it is seeded. Often it gets just as much competition from weeds as the grain might otherwise provide.

Where experience on a given soil type in a given locality indicates that seedings are almost always successful if made with a companion crop whether that crop be grain, flax, soybeans, corn, or any other, the use of the companion crop is justified as a measure of economy. If seedings with a companion crop are uncertain, other methods become necessary.

Legumes are often seeded in the spring on wheat put in the previous fall. For this practice the land should be fertile and the locality one in which extreme summer droughts are unlikely. A better seedbed is available if these legumes are sown with a spring grain; under these conditions the legume and the grain start together, whereas a fall-sown grain has an early start over a seeding and hence is a more severe competitor.

The ideal grain companion crop is early in maturing and has a very stiff straw to avoid lodging and consequent smothering of the seeding. If the grain is cut early for hay or silage, the associated legume seeding has a much better chance for survival.

Canning peas and field peas make excellent companion crops where their culture is warranted. They do not compete seriously for moisture and are harvested before the extreme heat of summer.

Seedings in corn are sometimes successful; but if made early enough to ensure success of the seeding in a dry season, they reduce the yield of corn because of inadequate weed control. In seasons of abundant moisture, they can be made late enough to have little influence on the corn yield. Michigan trials indicate that seedings in corn must be made by the time the corn is knee-high if they are to be successful year after year. Alfalfa has succeeded in corn much better than sweet clover or red clover.

Ordinarily, summer seedings are made with no companion crop for the legume, but on sloping soils or soils that blow easily a light seeding of oats reduces erosion. At this season of the year the oats do not grow large enough to compete seriously for moisture; later, cooler weather reduces evaporation, and moisture is likely to be more plentiful.

On soils subject to crust formation under the impact of heavy rains a grain companion crop, because of its quicker germination and stronger sprouts, may have a definite advantage in preventing crust development.

Review Questions

1. How do legumes increase the supply of available nitrogen in the soil?

2. Why does the growth of a legume like alfalfa or red clover add to the quantity of nitrogen in the soil whereas, ordinarily, the growing of a crop of field beans or soybeans (also legumes) results in some nitrogen loss?

3. How may land devoid of a certain strain of legume bacteria be inoculated?

4. Why does an application of potash on a sandy soil frequently result in increasing the protein content of alfalfa?

5. Compare alfalfa, red clover, alsike, and lespedeza with respect to adaptation to soil reaction.

6. Why has alfalfa production increased faster in the middle-western dairy region than in any other?

7. What is meant by a variegated alfalfa?

8. What kind of alfalfa is recommended for your locality?

9. What evidently is one of the major reasons for the decrease in alfalfa acreage in Kansas and Nebraska?

10. What causes alfalfa to winterkill?

11. How does cutting management affect the winter hardiness of alfalfa?

12. What is photosynthesis?

13. Why has cultivation of alfalfa stands ordinarily failed to produce increased yields?

14. How may the value of a thinned-out alfalfa stand be improved?

15. What appears to be the most promising control for alfalfa wilt?

16. Why is home-grown red-clover seed often the most satisfactory?

17. What is the chief disease affecting red clover?

18. Differentiate between mammoth and ordinary red clover.

19. To what conditions is alsike best adapted?

20. Why does alsike so frequently volunteer in meadows?

21. What are the major uses for sweet clover?

22. What is sweet-clover sickness in animals?

23. Why is sweet clover so economical as a green manure?

24. Where is lespedeza most widely grown? Why?

25. What are the advantages of lespedeza as a pasture crop?

26. Describe *Lespedeza sericea.*

27. How is kudzu propagated?

28. What factors determine the depth of seeding for legumes?

29. Why is considerably less seed required for white clover than for alsike?

30. Compare spring and summer seedings for alfalfa.

31. What are the functions of a companion crop?

Problems

1. You wish to seed 20 acres of light sandy loam soil to alfalfa. The soil reaction is pH5.5. What will your requirements be for lime, fertilizer, and seed? When will you make your seeding? Will you use a companion crop?

2. You have a field of sweet clover seeded the previous season in oats. You wish to plant this field to beans June 5. When will you plow the sweet clover under? Why?

3. You have a choice of seeding alfalfa on winter wheat or with spring oats or barley. With which crop will you seed? Why?

4. You have a field containing some moderately wet areas in which alfalfa and red clover have repeatedly winterkilled. What seeding mixture can you make up to reduce this hazard?

5. You are short of forage this year and have a good fall growth on a field of alfalfa that you want to cut for hay again next year. What will be your procedure?

6. A farmer has a run-down sandy loam field that he would like to improve as economically as possible. What should you suggest?

7. A Missouri farmer wishes to establish a lespedeza pasture on land that has never grown this crop. How should he proceed?

References

BAILEY, R. Y.: Kudzu for Erosion Control in the Southeast, *U.S. Dept. Agr. Farmers' Bul.* 1840, 1939.

CROSBY, M. A., and L. W. KEPHART: Sweet Clover in Corn Belt Farming, *U.S. Dept. Agr. Farmers' Bul.* 1653 (revised), 1939.

GUSTAFSON, A. F.: "Soil and Soil Management," McGraw-Hill Book Company, Inc., New York, 1941.

McKEE, ROLAND: Lespedeza Culture and Utilization, *U.S. Dept. Agr. Farmers' Bul.* 1852, 1940.

PIETERS, A. J.: Alsike Clover, *U.S. Dept. Agr. Farmers' Bul.* 1151, 1920.

——: "The Little Book of Lespedeza," published by the author, Washington, D.C., 1934.

—— and E. A. HOLLOWELL: Red Clover Failure in Relation to Anthracnose in the Southern Part of the Clover Belt, *U.S. Dept. Agr. Leaflet* 98, 1933.

PIPER, C. V.: "Forage Plants and Their Culture," The Macmillan Company, New York, 1924.

STEWART, GEORGE: "Alfalfa Growing in the United States and Canada," The Macmillan Company, New York, 1926.

U.S. Dept. Agr. Agricultural Statistics, Superintendent of Documents, Government Printing Office, Washington, D.C., published annually.

WAKSMAN, S. A., and R. L. STARKEY: "The Soil and the Microbe," John Wiley & Sons, Inc., New York, 1931.

CHAPTER VII

PERENNIAL FORAGE GRASSES

Grass is the universal crop. On the steppes of Asia and southeastern Europe, the veldts of South Africa, the pampas of South America, and the plains of the United States of America, grass has held sway for centuries. These are naturally vast treeless plains, but grass culture is also important in what once were wooded areas. Fully 80 per cent of the agriculture of the British Isles is grass farming, and grassland management has been developed there to a high degree. Continental Europe, too, has fostered intensive grass culture. The practices involved in forage production and conservation have been carried by Europeans throughout the many lands they have colonized.

Extent of Grasslands in the United States.—In the United States, more acres grow grass than all other crops put together. According to the agricultural census of 1935,[1] there were 514 million acres of land available for crops in this country at that time. However, 99 million acres of this cropland was classed as plowable pasture, and another 56 million acres was tame hay, both representing a grass-predominant culture. The total acreage of tame and wild hay, plowable pasture, woodland, marshland, and other pasture amounted to 586 million as compared with about 360 million acres of plowland available for other crops exclusive of tame-hay and plowland pasture. Forage grasses of one kind or another predominate on most of this land. There are legume forages, to be sure, and legumes are important to the soil and as livestock feed. But legumes in pure culture occupy a relatively small acreage as compared with the vast areas growing grass. A large proportion of the legume forages are grown in association with grass.

Numbers and Kinds of Grasses.—The grass family is a large one. Hitchcock[2] in his manual of the grasses of the United States has

[1] U.S. Census of Agriculture, 1935; Vol. I, U.S. Department of Commerce, Bureau of Census.

[2] HITCHCOCK, A. S., Manual of the Grasses of the United States, *U.S. Dept. Agr. Misc. Pub.* 200, 1935.

included 159 numbered genera and 1,100 numbered species. Of these, 44 genera and 151 species are introduced, mostly from the Eastern Hemisphere. The manual includes all grass species growing in this country and is not limited to those of agricultural importance. Many are almost solely of botanic interest. Some, like Johnson grass and quack grass, are classed as weeds because of their persistence in cultivated fields. Others are objectionable for various reasons. Chess (*Bromus secalinus*), common in wheat fields, darkens and lowers the quality of flour when its seeds are present in milled grain. Downy chess (*B. tectorum*) has barbed awns which cause sore mouths and eyes to livestock that feed where its matured heads are present. Sandbur (*Cenchrus pauciflorus*) is even more irritating.

A very few of the grass species are sometimes poisonous. The occasional development of prussic acid in dangerous quantities in grasses of the sorghum group is well known. Darnel (*Lolium temulentum*), also called "*tares*" and *poison rye grass*, is found in grainfields and waste places and has long been regarded as dangerous. Stink grass (*Eragrostis cilianensis*), either green or cured, is reported as poisonous to horses. Sleepy grass (*Stipa robusta*) of the western dry lands may affect either horses or sheep, but not cattle, by inducing sleep. It is not fatal.[1] The hazards of grass or other plant poisoning in pastures are greatly reduced if desirable forage is abundantly available. Instances of animals eating poisonous plants are most likely to occur where pastures are severely overgrazed or where for other reasons safe and more palatable herbage is scarce.

The occasional poisonous species and the much more common grass weeds are secondary in economic interest to the forage grasses of marsh, range, pasture, and meadow. Nearly 70 million cattle, 50 million sheep, and 15 million horses and mules in the United States live largely on grass. The hog, chief corn consumer, lives partly on green herbage; and the grass range for poultry is an accepted part of good poultry nutrition.

Grasses are so common and production, at least of a sort, is so easy that they have been the neglected plants of agriculture. Yet grasses do respond to selection, good culture, and well-advised management. Because of the vast grass acreage and the importance of this kind of land use, these essential plants deserve the utmost consideration.

Nature's Influences.—Every plant has its natural habitat. Because for ages so many of the grass species have grown under natural

---

[1] SAMPSON, A. W., and H. E. MALMSTEN, Stock Poisoning Plants of California, *Calif. Agr. Expt. Sta. Bul.* 593, 1935.

circumstances without man's care, they have afforded us the opportunity to study their natural associations and their reactions to environment. The question of environment is a complex one. For example, moisture influences on plant growth are not accurately indicated by the amount of annual precipitation. The effectiveness of moisture is modified by the time when the rains come, by whether they are mists or violent downpours, by temperature and humidity as they influence evaporation, by the permeability of the soil, by its water-holding capacity, and by other considerations. Moisture is but one complex factor of environment, but the type of natural vegetation is the result of the interaction of all of the various factors.

The Tall-grass Prairies.—Before white men developed farming in the United States to something approaching its present state, the great grass regions began with the prairies of what is now the corn belt and extended over the expansive Great Plains to the western mountains. In the eastern portions of this area there was sufficient water available, from both annual precipitation and subsoil moisture, to grow trees. Trees have grown there readily since man has taken over. Under natural conditions in the prairie region the tall grass, bluestem (*Andropogon furcatus*), bunch grass (*A. scoparius*), Indian grass (*Sorghastrum nutans*), and others, made such a luxuriant growth that they rapidly expended the soil moisture to the depth to which the roots grow, a condition resulting in frequent late-summer and fall droughts. Conditions were thus ideal for fall grass fires which are believed to be responsible for the lack of trees on these verdant prairies.

Today the tall-grass country is a productive farming region. The native grasses have given way to the plow and tillage. The forage crops are introduced species of legumes and grasses that are easily seeded and that fit well into the crop rotations and farm-management plans of the region.

Where the corn belt and the major winter-wheat areas join, from Nebraska through central Kansas and Oklahoma to Texas, is an intermediate area the grass cover of which was largely bunch grass with admixtures of grasses of the bluestem sod type and of the short grasses of the plains. In this region the moisture supply becomes more deficient, the surface layer of moist soil is from 2 to 4 ft. in depth, and the subsoil is dry. The northern intermediate area from Nebraska into the Dakotas and Minnesota, a region of similar mixed prairie grasses, became the spring-wheat country. Also, more wild hay is still harvested in these states than in any other region.

The Short-grass Plains.—Only enough water is available in the more westerly plains to support the short grasses. No subsoil moisture is available for deep-rooted species, and the grasses that do grow depend on surface moisture which seldom penetrates more than 2 ft. Grama, buffalo grass, and western wheat grass are among the short-grass species.

The line between the tall- and short-grass country was never sharply defined. A succession of wet seasons tended to push the tall-grass region westward whereas dry seasons reversed the trend. Eventually, cattle were brought in and became an ecological factor. Where grazing was too intense, tall grass gave way to short grass and short grass gave way to weeds, barrenness, and erosion.

The plow played its part. Tillage of the prairie country was justified. It made available rich arable land for corn and livestock enterprises. Much of the intermediate and the more favored of the short-grass region proved desirable for wheat and other small grains. The sorghums have made possible effective use of some of the drier regions; and where irrigation is possible, the soil is productive of good yields of small grains, beans, potatoes, sugar beets, and alfalfa. But some of the short-grass region, in great need of conservative grazing management, got the plow instead. It has been found too arid for dry farming and too lacking in water for irrigation.

Restoration of grass is difficult. Drought-resistant, palatable, strong-rooted, long-lived range and pasture grasses are needed, especially for certain overgrazed and eroding areas of the Great Plains, the Southwest, and the Rocky Mountain states.

Other Natural Grass Areas.—The Pacific grassland area occurs in Washington, Oregon, and California and extends into Idaho, Montana, and Nevada. Moisture supply during the growing season is inadequate for a dense stand of grasses, and thus much of the vegetation is of the bunch-grass type including wheat grass (*Agropyron spicatum*), California poa (*Poa scabrella*), and needle grass (*Stipa pulchra*). Weedy annuals tend to appear where overgrazing is practiced.

The desert grassland of western Texas, New Mexico, and Arizona has a more open stand of the short grasses of the plains. Because of high temperature and low rainfall, 12 to 18 in., desert shrubs such as mesquite, creosote bush, yuccas, and blackbrush are common. Crop production is practiced only under irrigation.

Marsh grassland areas are scattered throughout many parts of the United States. They grow water-tolerant plants and when drained have been used effectively for intensive agriculture. Some of the California marshlands have been diked, drained, and used for vegetable production, as have muck lands in the Florida Everglades. In southern Louisiana, rice production has been developed.

Alpine vegetation of sedges, hardy grasses, and a variety of showy flowering plants grows in mountainous areas above the timber line. The land is nonagricultural.

Most of the eastern part of the country was originally covered with forest. Here the kinds of trees that grew tell much of the agricultural possibilities of the land. The oak-hickory forest land just east of the tall-grass country ranks as one of the most important agriculturally. Red and white pine areas are usually of mediocre agricultural value whereas spruce, fir, and jack pine lands are largely nonagricultural.[1]

GROWTH BEHAVIOR OF PERENNIAL GRASSES

The various perennial grasses have many behavior characteristics in common. Most of them are propagated by means of seed, though some of the stoloniferous bent grasses used on golf courses are propagated commercially by means of stolons. Grasses, like all green plants, synthesize carbohydrates from carbon dioxide and water, liberating oxygen in the process. All perennial grasses have storage organs in which organic foods are conserved through periods of dormancy to provide material for the initiation of plant development when growth is renewed. However, grasses vary with respect to their storage organs, their type of growth, and other characteristics, all of which must be taken into consideration when it comes to management practices.

Storage Organs.—Adequate storage of organic-food reserves elaborated by perennial grasses is essential to their continued growth. The root system provides one place for storage of such material. But food is also stored in other plant tissue. The rhizomes, or underground stems, of quack grass provide a very effective place for reserve-food storage. Many perennial grasses have rhizomes, some wide-spreading in character like quack grass, others closely clumped in a bunchlike growth like orchard grass and the bunch grasses of the western plains.

The creeping bent grasses, Bahia grass, and others store a portion of their reserve food in stolons, aboveground stem tissue decumbent in character, which may develop both erect stems and roots at the nodes. Even bulbs and tubers are found in certain grass species.

Because the carbohydrates and other organic foods are built up by the plant itself, cultural practices have much to do with their formation, storage, and utilization.

---

[1] SHANTZ, H. L., and RAPHAEL ZON, The Physical Basis of Agriculture—Natural Vegetation, "Atlas of American Agriculture," U.S. Department of Agriculture, 1924.

Effect of Defoliation on Storage.—Graber,[1] working with bluegrass, redtop, fescue, and timothy, found that the amount of underground growth and total weight of top growth ultimately tend to vary inversely with the frequency of defoliation and that reduced growth sometimes occurs for several months subsequent to excessive defoliations. The frequent interference with photosynthesis by clipping reduces the plant's opportunity to make and store organic food, and the reduced food reserves are eventually reflected in reduced growth of the plant.

Harrison and Hodgson[2] showed that there are marked differences between species in actual response to clipping. Grasses with leaves close to the ground, like Kentucky bluegrass, are less injured by being cut an inch from the ground than are intermediate species like smooth brome. Of the grasses tested, the most subject to depletion of reserve foods are timothy and orchard grass, with an erect growth habit so that they are most completely defoliated by frequent low cutting.

Utilization of food reserves by the plant is most rapid when growth is vigorous. Storage takes place as plants approach maturity or winter dormancy provided that there is adequate leaf area present. This was shown by the work of McCarty[3] with mountain brome grass (*B. carinatus*) in California. He found a minimum amount of storage in the roots and stem bases of this species during the active growth stages of the plant, with carbohydrates then being utilized in excess of their manufacture. Maximum storage occurs during the autumn period after current seasonal and secondary herbage growth have been completed.

The application of these principles to practice is that continuous close clipping or severe overgrazing is injurious to the vigor and productivity of perennial grasses and may so weaken the plants that they are destroyed, as they have been on some of the ranges. Species that have leaves very close to the ground cannot be closely grazed or clipped so readily and are less subject to such injury. The stoloniferous bent grasses endure extremely close mowing on the putting green, whereas timothy, orchard grass, reed canary grass, and similar species are almost completely defoliated by close clipping or grazing and are easily subject to injury.

[1] GRABER, L. F., Food Reserves in Relation to Other Factors Limiting the Growth of Grasses, *Plant Physiol.*, Vol. 6, pp. 43–72, 1931.

[2] HARRISON, C. M., and C. W. HODGSON, Response of Certain Perennial Grasses to Cutting Treatments. *Jour. Amer. Soc. Agron.*, Vol. 31, No. 5, 1939.

[3] McCARTY, E. C., The Relation of Growth to the Varying Carbohydrate Content in Mountain Brome, *U.S. Dept. Agr. Tech. Bul.* 598, 1938.

Stage of Maturity and Feeding Value.—Immature grass is more palatable and nutritious than that which is mature. Orchard grass and reed canary grass are illustrative of grasses which when small are readily eaten by livestock but which as they approach advanced stages of maturity are not at all relished. In general, young grasses are higher in vitamins and higher in protein. As they approach maturity, the percentage of protein decreases and the percentage of crude indigestible fiber increases. In making hay, these considerations must be balanced against total production, the objective being to harvest the crop at a time when it will be most profitable as forage, with due consideration both to nutritive value and yield.

Fertilizers for Grasses.—Grasses need all the usual plant nutrients. Nitrogen is very stimulating to leaf and stem growth and is particularly important as a grass nutrient because grasses are grown for their leaves and stems. The nitrogen necessary for vigorous grass growth may be provided in commercial fertilizers such as sulphate of ammonia, nitrate of soda, cyanamide, and others. High-nitrogen complete fertilizers, for example, 10-6-4, also are used.

Where legumes can be grown, they can provide the nitrogen needed by the grass. This is one of the great advantages of legume-grass mixtures. The phosphorus and potassium that may have to be supplied to ensure good legume growth are usually less expensive as fertilizers than nitrogen. A grass-legume mixture may be fertilized strictly in accordance with the needs of the legume. The required nitrogen for both the grass and the legume can then come from the unlimited supply in the air.

Seeding Practices.—Specific practices for the seeding of grasses vary with the different kinds of grass and the environmental conditions under which the seedings are made. Most grass seeds are small and carry but little food to support the young seedlings until they are rooted and leaves are developed to start photosynthesis. A fine, firm seedbed with moisture near the surface is highly desirable.

Times of seeding are designed to permit the grass to become well established before critical periods. Late-summer and early-fall seedings are effective for many grasses in the North, for they give the plants a chance to start in what is usually a cool, moist period. Most of the species used are hardy enough to withstand the winter even when the plants are very small.

In most localities, late-spring and early-summer seedings are at a disadvantage because the small, shallow-rooted seedlings must enter the heat and often the drought of summer when they are poorly equipped to survive such conditions. Early-spring seedings have a better chance to develop a substantial root before drought comes.

Frequently grass seedings are made with small grains as a companion crop. If conditions are not too critical, the use of the small grain is justified as a means of getting returns from the land while the seeding is being established. The grain should also tend to check annual weed competition and help to prevent the surface soil from eroding while the young grass plants are becoming established. The grain must be considered a competitor of the grass seeding, however; and under very dry conditions it is definitely advantageous to pasture it off or cut it early for green feed to give the grass a better chance when it is hard pressed for moisture.

Grass seeds are broadcast by hand, spread with various kinds of hand-operated broadcast seeders, or sown with different kinds of seeders and drills. Any method that plants the seed at the proper depth and distributes it evenly is satisfactory. In general, the drills and seeders effect a more uniform distribution and are more economical of seed. Some of the light, chaffy, or wing-tipped seed does not readily pass through a drill. Such seed is often sown effectively by mixing it with grain and sowing it with a grain drill. Instances of this kind are the mixing of orchard-grass seed with wheat in Missouri and the mixing of smooth-brome seed with oats, widely practiced in Michigan.

Grasses are sown in mixtures more commonly than in pure culture. The function of legumes in providing nitrogen in such mixtures has already been discussed. There are other advantages to mixing grasses with legumes. The European practice of using complex mixtures of short, or bottom, grasses with taller growing species may add to the total quantity of feed produced. A more definite advantage is provided by the mixing of quick-starting species with slower starting, more permanent grasses. Thus, in the region to which Kentucky bluegrass is adapted, a mixture of timothy, alsike, and red clover with a light amount of Kentucky bluegrass is more economical and will produce far more forage the first crop year than a straight heavy seeding of Kentucky bluegrass. Eventually the meadow will present a solid stand of Kentucky bluegrass or possibly a bluegrass–white-clover mixture if conditions are favorable for white clover. Mixtures also offer livestock a more variable ration, and the variation enhances palatability and increases their consumption. Early-maturing and late-maturing species together in a pasture may have some value in prolonging the most desirable grazing period.

IMPORTANT CULTIVATED GRASSES

Although the United States has great areas of natural grassland, not many of the species from these areas have been domesticated. Most of the species of cultivated grasses are of Old World origin though some of them have become far more important in this country than in regions to which they were native.

Timothy (Phleum pratense).—Timothy is one of these introduced species, but its common name is after that of Timothy Hansen, a

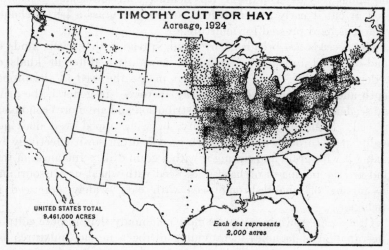

TIMOTHY CUT FOR HAY
Acreage, 1924

UNITED STATES TOTAL
9,461,000 ACRES

Each dot represents
2,000 acres

Fig. 28.—Timothy is often grown alone on the less fertile heavy soils and mixed with red or alsike clover on the more fertile soils. Timothy and red clover are usually seeded together. Clover is more important the first season, after which it declines and timothy becomes the main crop until the meadow is plowed. About 9,461,000 acres of timothy grown alone were reported in the 1925 census, and 21,112,000 acres of timothy and clover mixed. In the 1929 census these two classes of hay were combined, and 25,547,000 acres reported. (*U.S. Department of Agriculture.*)

New England farmer of colonial days, who is believed to have taken the grass into Maryland. Timothy is the most widely used hay grass in the United States. It is grown in mixtures with clover so commonly that statistical reports list clover and timothy hay together. The leading states are New York, Pennsylvania, Wisconsin, and Ohio. Timothy is widely grown throughout the northeastern quarter of the country. As it is resistant neither to heat nor drought, its production is not important in the cotton belt or in the natural short-grass region of the West. Timothy is hardy enough to survive winters almost up to the Arctic Circle. It yields best on the heavier loams and clay loam soils liberally supplied with moisture.

Uses.—Before the advent of the truck and tractor, timothy was America's great horse hay. Mixed clover and timothy still constitute an important market hay comparing favorably with alfalfa in market price. As a feed, this mixed hay is lower in crude protein than alfalfa, and straight timothy contains less than mixed hay. If harvested before its maturity is too far advanced, its protein content is improved. Properly supplemented with protein concentrates, it is a valuable roughage.

Advantages.—Timothy is important agriculturally because the seed is cheap and plentiful, because good stands are easily secured under a wide range of conditions, because the plants stand up well and are easily cut and cured, and because it grows well with either clover or alfalfa. In many places where maintaining an alfalfa stand is uncertain, especially because of wet areas in the field, the addition of timothy to the mixture ensures the growth of good grass rather than weeds. Hay yields are thereby improved. The timothy plants are more vigorous when grown in association with good stands of legumes than when growth in pure culture unless the soil itself has an abundant nitrogen supply.

Varieties.—Timothy is open-pollinated and exceedingly variable. M. W. Evans of the U.S. Department of Agriculture has carried on much selection work and has brought out varieties that show considerable differences with respect to leafiness, rust resistance, maturity, and other considerations. The plant-breeding station at Aberystwyth in Wales likewise has developed leafier, later maturing varieties considered preferable to common timothy for pasture. For the most part, however, the timothy seed on the market is a mixture of types, with the tall-growing hay-type plants predominating. Because timothy cross-pollinates readily, the maintenance of separate varieties is difficult except in the cases of lines that differ materially from the common in time of blossoming.

Seeding Practices.—Timothy may be seeded in the fall with winter wheat or rye or in the spring with any of the spring-sown grains. If a mixture is intended with fall-sown timothy, the legume seed is normally applied in the spring. The customary rate of seeding in pure culture is 9 to 12 lb. an acre, 4 to 6 lb. being used in the case of timothy-legume mixtures. In the work at the Michigan Agricultural Experiment Station at Chatham in the Upper Peninsula, Churchill[1] decided that, where satisfactory stands of legumes were obtained, the addition of more than 10 per cent of timothy to the seed mixture was a waste of

[1] CHURCHILL, B. R., Hays and Haying Methods for the Upper Peninsula, *Mich. Agr. Expt. Sta. Quart. Bul.*, Vol. 18, No. 4, 1936.

seed. The proportion of timothy in the resultant crop proved entirely adequate in these trials when only 1 lb. of timothy seed was included in the mixture. This proportion of timothy was conditioned more by the success of the legume seeding than by the amount of timothy seed used.

Kentucky and Canada Bluegrass.—Kentucky bluegrass (*Poa pratensis*) occurs naturally over much of Europe and Asia. Although it is an introduced species in America, it has become so widespread and so famed in the verdant bluegrass region of Kentucky that it is often thought of as a native species. Canada bluegrass (*P. compressa*) likewise is not a native of Canada but was introduced from Europe. It is shorter and darker in color than Kentucky bluegrass. It is differentiated from Kentucky bluegrass by its compressed stems which tend to hold their dark-green color, the single shoot at the end of each rhizome, and its close, narrow panicles. Canada bluegrass is considered by stockmen to be more nutritious than Kentucky bluegrass, and it tends to replace the latter at lower levels of fertility on stiff clays, thin gravels, and sandy soils. If the productive capacity of such soils is improved, Kentucky bluegrass is likely to crowd out the Canadian species.

Both are primarily pasture grasses which, with underground stems, tend to form a dense sward. Kentucky bluegrass is the favorite lawn grass where it is adapted; it is also widely used for recreation fields, golf fairways, roadsides, and airports. It is often called *June grass*.

Bluegrass pastures have attained their greatest fame in Kentucky and Virginia on soils of limestone origin high in mineral nutrients. They make up the major portion of the permanent pastures in the corn belt, the middle-western dairy states, and the northeastern section of the country. They are most productive in spring and early summer but become dormant and nonproductive during hot, dry periods, thereby leaving a marked gap in the summer pasture season when supplementary feeds or pastures become necessary.

When included in seed mixtures, 5 to 15 lb. of seed per acre is used. However, bluegrass has become so widespread in the areas to which it is adapted that it volunteers readily and tends to take over old meadows regardless of the original seeding. White clover is the legume most frequently grown in association with Kentucky bluegrass.

Rough meadow grass (*P. trivialis*) is a very shade-tolerant bluegrass that spreads by stolons rather than by the underground stems characteristic of Kentucky bluegrass. Though spreading naturally in permanent pastures under cool, moist conditions, the seed is used mostly in shady-lawn-grass mixtures.

Redtop (Agrostis alba).—Redtop is a perennial of the bent-grass group which grows particularly well on wet soils. Its principal uses are as a wet-land or acid-land hay crop; as a component in mixtures for pastures, lawns, and golf courses; and as a soil binder. It is grown largely in the northeastern quarter of the country. It is relatively unpalatable both as hay and pasture. Nevertheless, because it will grow under so wide a range of unfavorable conditions, it has attained a distribution next in importance to that of Kentucky bluegrass.

Nearly all the commercial redtop seed is grown in southern Illinois. Two or three pounds an acre provides an adequate proportion in hay and pasture mixtures; for the seed is small, and the plants spread out readily. When seeded alone, 8 to 10 lb. of seed an acre is used.

Bent Grasses.—Colonial bent (*Agrostis tenuis*) is closely related to redtop but is much smaller in size and has narrow leaves and a more open panicle. It is most commonly found on acid, well-drained soils of New York and New England but is also grown farther south in the seaboard states and in the Pacific Northwest. The plants are too small to be handled for hay but can be grazed. Colonial bent makes a fine turf for lawns and golf courses. South German mixed bent seed contains a large proportion of Colonial bent.

The Washington and Metropolitan bents are varieties of creeping bent (*A. palustris*) propagated by stolons and used extensively for putting greens. Bent lawns are fine-textured and very beautiful if properly cared for but are subject to several diseases that make proper care difficult and expensive.

Orchard Grass (Dactylis glomerata).—Orchard grass is a rather coarse perennial with a bunchy habit of growth. Its hay is often woody unless cut early; and unless it is kept very closely grazed, it is unpalatable as a pasture. However, it is very aggressive and yields well under many conditions. Its name, *orchard grass*, comes from its ability to grow well in the shade. In England, it is called *cocksfoot*. Leafy varieties have been developed especially for pasture.

In this country, orchard grass is most important in the Kentucky-Tennessee-Virginia-Carolina region. In the North, it is often yellowed by spring frosts; and if it is closely grazed so as to keep it in a palatable condition, it winterkills.

The seed weighs 14 lb. to the bushel, and heavy rates of seeding (2 bu. an acre) are used to reduce the bunchy growth characteristics and keep the stems as fine as possible.

Smooth Brome (Bromus inermis).—Smooth brome is a drought-resistant, very palatable perennial grass with a moderately spreading growth habit. It is native to relatively dry regions from central

Europe to China and has been called *Hungarian brome, Austrian brome,* and *Russian brome.*   It was introduced into the United States in about 1884.

Because of its drought resistance it first attained importance in this country from Minnesota and western Iowa westward to Washington and Oregon.   More recently, it has been found very well adapted in the middle-western dairy states, especially when grown in a mixture with alfalfa.   In Michigan, it has been seeded successfully in every

month from April through October. The seedlings start slowly, and plants attain their best growth the second and third years after seeding. The slow start is not objectionable where brome grass is seeded with alfalfa; for it permits the legume to become well established, whereas in cases where alfalfa has been seeded with a quick-starting grass such as tall fescue (*Festuca elatior*) the legume frequently does not become well established and its advantages to the mixture are lost. When grown in pure culture, the older stands of brome grass attain a *sod-bound* condition due to an inadequate supply of nitrogen. This condition does not develop in the presence of a good growth of alfalfa.

The vigorous roots of smooth brome penetrate 5 or 6 ft. into the soil, a condition giving it drought resistance.   None of the perennial

Fig. 29.—Smooth brome grass is a tall, leafy, drought-resistant perennial.

grasses is more palatable, and this palatability is retained at advanced stages of growth.   The leaves remain green when the seed is mature, and the seed itself is readily eaten by sheep and cattle.

The seed weighs 14 lb. to the bushel.   It is difficult to run it through a seeder because of its light weight.   One of the most convenient methods of seeding is to mix it with oats or such other small grain as may be used as a companion crop.   Five to ten pounds of seed in mixtures with alfalfa or 15 lb. an acre when seeded alone is sufficient.

The Fescues.—Three fescues have attained some importance in the United States, tall fescue (*Festuca elatior*), sheep fescue (*F. ovina*), and red fescue (*F. rubra*). Tall fescue is by far the most vigorous of the three species. It is also called *meadow fescue* and sometimes *English bluegrass*. Tall fescue and meadow fescue are really tall and medium varieties of the same species, the tall fescue being the more valuable, according to Piper.[1] This species is adapted to wet soils. It is used as pasture more commonly than hay and characteristically starts early in the spring and grows late in the fall. It has attained its greatest importance in eastern Kansas and Nebraska and in near-by parts of Missouri. The seed weighs 22 to 24 lb. to the bushel and is usually sown at 25 to 30 lb. an acre.

Sheep fescue has been found in the Northern Hemisphere of both the Old and the New World. It is a small densely tufted grass that heads out very early in the season. The leaves are stiff, slender, and almost blue gray in color. The chief advantage of this grass is its ability to grow on poor, sandy soil where few other grasses do well.

Red fescue is larger than sheep fescue and of a much brighter green color. It is also much later in maturity. It has some tendency to creep by means of short underground stems. It is an excellent lawn grass, particularly for light soils and shady areas, and has some value as a pasture on the poorer soils. It has also shown some promise as an orchard cover crop on sandy soils, binding the soil effectively without competing seriously with the trees for moisture. Chewings fescue is a New Zealand variety of red fescue. The seed imported from New Zealand is often of low germination owing to storage conditions on shipboard. A seeding rate of 25 to 30 lb. an acre is liberal for both sheep and red fescue if germination is satisfactory.

Rye Grasses.—Perennial rye grass (*Lolium perenne*) is famous as a pasture grass in the British Isles where it is grown in combination with wild white clover. It has not attained prominence in the United States. Its general adaptation should be in the bluegrass regions but it is excelled here by Kentucky bluegrass for pasture and by timothy as a hay crop. Most strains are thinned severely by winterkilling in the northern states, the life of a perennial-rye-grass stand in this country being only 2 or 3 years. Although the plants seem highly palatable and nutritious in Europe, in the United States they become very tough. They are hard to cut with a lawn mower; and in grazing trials at East Lansing, Mich., in 1937 and 1938, sheep in perennial-rye-grass paddocks had their teeth ground down very severely. This did not occur with any of the other grasses tried. The use of perennial

[1] PIPER, C. V., Important Cultivated Grasses of the United States, *U.S. Dept. Agr. Farmers' Bul.* 1254 (revised), 1934.

rye grass in lawns is desirable because of the very rapid start the plants make from seed.

Italian rye grass (*L. multiflorum*) is normally grown as an annual or winter annual, though some plants in an Italian-rye-grass stand may endure longer; it is possible that these are hybrids with perennial strains. Awns occur on the seed of Italian rye grass, whereas this is usually not the case with perennial rye grass. The stems of Italian rye grass are cylindrical; those of the perennial species are slightly flattened. Italian rye grass is used as an annual hay or pasture crop, more especially on the Pacific coast. Under favorable conditions, it

Fig. 30.—Reed canary grass, a long-lived perennial, is widely used for pasture on low-lying areas subject to flooding. (*Courtesy of E. B. Swingle.*)

may produce two cuttings. It is also used to some extent in lawns because of its quick early growth.

The domestic rye grass of commerce consists of a mixture of the annual and perennial species.

Reed Canary Grass.—Reed canary grass (*Phlaris arundinacea*) is a wet-land perennial native to the northern part of both hemispheres. It grows from 4 to 7 ft. tall and has coarse stems and broad leaves. It tends to grow in bunches but spreads by creeping, underground stems to form a dense turf. The hay is eaten readily; but, as pasture, reed canary grass must be grazed heavily enough to keep up with new growth, or the plants get too large and tough. Extremely close grazing is injurious to the plants. It is more palatable and nutritious than most of the native vegetation found growing on the wet, marshy soils to which reed canary grass is best adapted. It is best for hay if cut when the first heads appear.

The seeds are oblong, blackish, brown, or gray in color, smooth, and free from chaff. They mature at the top of the plant first and then successively downward. Ripe seed shatters readily in hot, dry weather. Seed can be sown in fall or early spring, preferably on a clean, firm seedbed to a depth of ¼ to ¾ in. A seeding rate of 4 to 6 lb. an acre is adequate. Better distribution is secured if the seed is mixed with timothy. The slowly starting reed canary grass will eventually take over the stand.

Tall Meadow Oat Grass.—The species *Arrhenatherum elatius* is known as *tall oat grass, evergreen grass,* and *tall meadow oat grass.* It is most widely grown in parts of Europe where it is native. Though occasionally grown over most of the United States, it has never attained much importance because its seed shatters readily. It is also difficult to get the large chaffy seed through a seeder. The grass is a tall (2- to 5-ft.) perennial that tends to grow in bunches. Its seed is produced in an open panicle somewhat similar to that of ordinary oats. The grass holds its green color and succulent condition well and makes a good recovery growth after being cut. It is not very palatable; but when stock have been accustomed to it, the grass is consumed and is nutritious. It requires a well-drained soil and does better than many species on land that is sandy or gravelly in character. It has yielded well in mixtures with red and alsike clover and with alfalfa. It is often mixed with orchard grass, another relatively unpalatable species.

The Wheat Grasses.—*Slender wheat grass* (*Agropyron tenerum*) is a native American grass and occurs from New Mexico to Alaska. It is grown under culture most extensively in the Dakotas and neighboring Canadian provinces. It is typically a bunch grass growing 2 to 4 ft. in height and forming dense heads not unlike wheat but much more slender. It will grow well on alkali lands where most other grasses cannot survive. Most of the seed is produced in western Canada. It weighs about 20 lb. to the bushel and is seeded at 15 to 20 lb. an acre in the fall. Larger amounts of seed are used where conditions are not too favorable.

Crested wheat grass (*A. cristatum*) is a close relative of slender wheat grass. It was brought to this country by the U.S. Department of Agriculture and is native to the cold, dry plains of Russia and Siberia. It has been found especially well adapted to the northern Great Plains of this country where temperatures are severe and moisture is limited. It remains dormant during periods of drought but is not killed, and it renews its growth when rains occur. According to Westover,[1] it does not appear promising for the southern half of the United States except possibly at high altitudes and is not equal to timothy and other adapted grasses under the more favorable moisture conditions of the eastern states.

A clean, firm seedbed such as may be secured following corn or a summer fallow is required for the establishment of this grass. Early-spring seedings are preferred, but many fall seedings have been successful. The seed is usually sown in close drills at 10 to 12 lb. an acre and covered at a depth of ½ in. If soil moisture is very limited or if seed production is intended, row seedings are often used and interrow cultivation is practiced.

Experiments and experiences in the northwestern states where crested wheat grass is adapted indicate that this species ranks unusually high among the grasses in nutritive value and palatability and holds great promise for the reseeding of depleted ranges and abandoned farm lands. The seed is far easier to grow, harvest, clean, and sow than that of native wild grasses. It can be handled with the same equipment as that used for small grains.

SOME SOUTHERN GRASSES

Increasing interest in soil conservation and the diversification of southern agriculture has served to direct attention to several grasses that are particularly adapted to warm regions. A brief description of some of the species being used follows:

Bermuda grass (Cynodon dactylon) is adapted to the better clay and silt loam soils of the South where it has become the most important pasture grass. It is also an important southern lawn grass. It is grown as far north as Maryland and to some extent in the warmer valleys of the Pacific Northwest. Common Bermuda grass has large, white rhizomes and leafy creeping stolons. It is propagated both by seed and vegetatively by rhizomes or stolons.

Carpet grass (Axonopus compressus) is a perennial creeping grass adapted to lighter soils than Bermuda grass. It has compressed two-edged creeping stems, rooting at each joint, and blunt leaf tips. Its short (1- to 2-ft.) stems produce seed abundantly even under grazing, for stock tend to eat only the lower leaves. Heavy grazing is considered necessary to keep the grass in nutritive condition. Admixtures of lespedeza or bur clover make a desirable adjunct to carpet-grass pastures. In establishing new seedings, 5 to 10 lb. of seed an acre is used.

[1] WESTOVER, H. L., Crested Wheat Grass, *U.S. Dept. Agr. Leaflet* 104, 1934.

Rhodes grass (Chloris gayana) is a South African perennial propagated by seed, but it also spreads by long decumbent branches that root at each node. It does not withstand temperatures below 18°F. and so is limited in this country to Florida, a narrow strip along the Gulf coast, and other areas of very mild winters. Where it grows as a perennial, as many as six or seven cuttings may be made in a season. Early-spring seeding at the rate of 10 lb. an acre is practiced.

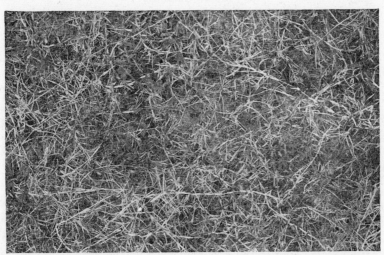

Fig. 31.—Bermuda grass in Tennessee established by seeding 5 lb. of hulled seed per acre with white clover, hop clover, and lespedeza. (*Courtesy of U.S. Dept. of Agr., Soil Conservation Service.*)

Dallis grass (Paspalum dilatatum) is a deep-rooted perennial bunch grass introduced from South America. It is essentially a pasture grass, the stems lodging too readily to make harvest for hay feasible. It stands persistent grazing; tends to remain green in mild winters; and makes its best growth on moist, dark-colored, heavy soils. The seed is light and generally of low germination. Seed harvest is difficult because of shattering.

Johnson grass (Sorghum halepense) is a perennial of the sorghum group, more of a weed than a cultivated crop because of its persistence. However, it is widely used on the more productive soils of Alabama, Mississippi, and Texas. It grows as a perennial throughout the Gulf states and westward to southern California. Its long, underground stems penetrate to a depth of 2 and 3 ft. and are very difficult to kill by tillage.

Other southern grasses of value are Napier grass (*Pennisetum purpureum*), an 8- to 12-ft. bunch grass used as a silage and soiling crop; Para grass (*Panicum barbinode*), a wet-land, tropical, creeping perennial hay and pasture grass; rescue grass (*Bromus catharticus*), a short-lived perennial grown as a winter annual on the better soils of the Gulf states and Carolinas; and Bahia grass (*Paspalum notatum*), another creeping perennial that is an excellent turf former in Florida and other areas adjacent to the Gulf.

Review Questions

1. What kind of agriculture predominates in what once were the tall-grass prairies of the United States?

2. Why are these tall-grass areas treeless?

3. In general, what sort of grass cover predominated over most of the Great Plains region? Why?

4. What effect does repeated defoliation have on the reserve organic foods stored by grasses?

5. Why do species differ in their response to a given height of cutting?

6. How does young grass differ from that which is more mature with respect to protein content? Vitamins? Fiber?

7. What are some of the advantages of mixing legumes with grasses? Of using more than one kind of grass in a mixture?

8. What are the characteristics of the leading perennial grasses grown in your state?

Problems

1. Explain why dandelions and other weeds are much more prevalent in a closely grazed bluegrass pasture than in one moderately grazed.

2. A southern farmer wishes to establish a permanent pasture on rather sandy soil. Which grass would be preferable, Bermuda or carpet grass? Why? How should the seeding be made?

3. A corn-belt farmer wishes to return a sloping field, which has been under cultivation, to bluegrass pasture. How should he proceed?

4. Under what conditions does it appear advisable to mix timothy with alfalfa? How much timothy seed should be used in the mixture?

5. A farmer in western North Dakota has acquired an abandoned farm on which he wishes to establish permanent grass cover. What grass should be used, and how should it be seeded?

References

ARNY, A. C., R. E. HODGSON, and G. H. NESOM: Reed Canary Grass for Meadows and Pastures, *Minn. Agr. Expt. Sta. Bul.* 263, 1930.

HELM, C. A.: Growing Orchard Grass in South Missouri, *Mo. Agr. Expt. Sta. Bul.* 294, 1930.

HITCHCOCK, A. S.: Manual of the Grasses of the United States, *U.S. Dept. Agr. Misc. Pub.* 200, 1935.

HOOVER, M. M.: Native and Adapted Grasses for Conservation of Soil and Moisture in the Great Plains and Western States, *U.S. Dept. Agr. Farmers' Bul.* 1812, 1939.

KIRK, L. E.: Crested Wheat Grass, *Saskatchewan Dept. Agr. Ext. Bul.* 54, 1932.

NORTH, H. F. A., T. E. ODLAND, and J. A. DEFRANCE: Lawn Grasses and Their Management, *R.I. Agr. Expt. Sta. Bul.* 264, 1938.

PIPER, C. V.: "Forage Plants and Their Culture," The Macmillan Company, New York, 1924.

————: Cultivated Grasses of Secondary Importance, *U.S. Dept. Agr. Farmers' Bul.* 1433, 1925.

————: Important Cultivated Grasses, *U.S. Dept. Agr. Farmers' Bul.* 1254, (revised) 1934.

SAVAGE, D. A.: Grass Culture and Range Improvement in the Central and Southern Great Plains, *U.S. Dept. Agr. Cir. Bul.* 491, 1939.

TALBOT, M. W.: Johnson Grass as a Weed, *U.S. Dept. Agr. Farmers' Bul.* 1537, 1928.

CHAPTER VIII

ANNUAL FORAGE CROPS

On most of the hay and pasture acreage of the United States, perennial forage-plant species predominate. However, according to the U.S. Census of Agriculture for 1935, there were over 24 million acres of annual forage crops cut for hay in 1934, the year covered by that census. This acreage included forage sorghums, small grains cut green, and annual legumes other than lespedeza, but not millet and Sudan grass. It far exceeded the reported acreage of either alfalfa or clover and timothy.

The Place of Annual Forages.—Some annual forage crops have special advantages, and their growth and use have become an established part of farming under the conditions to which they are adapted. For example, the forage sorghums are better suited to certain hot, dry areas than any of the cultivated perennial species. Thus, year after year they are depended on to supply a substantial portion of the livestock feed in these hot, dry areas.

The millets, on the other hand, are typical emergency crops. They may be seeded late in the season after failure of the regular forage crop has become evident. They make a rapid growth and yield well but are mediocre as feed; hence, they are used as substitutes in the forage-production program. Other crops like Sudan grass, oats and peas mixed, and soybean hay are regularly grown on some farms but are regarded as emergency crops on others.

Good farm practice is designed greatly to reduce the need for emergency crops. Annuals have one very obvious disadvantage as compared with well-adapted perennials—the expenditure that must be made each year for seed, seedbed preparation, and seeding. These items cost two or three times as much a year for Sudan grass or soybeans as they do for alfalfa if the alfalfa is harvested for only 3 years. For long-enduring pastures the annual charges for seed, seedbed preparation, and seeding are negligible.

Besides reducing the cost of tillage and seeding, perennial forages provide winter cover and more effective control of erosion during the growing season. Nevertheless, because some annuals are the best forage crops under special conditions and because emergencies may

134

develop even in highly favored areas, annual forage crops have become exceedingly important and are worthy of careful study.

Small Grains for Hay.—In 1934, over half a million farmers cut small grains in immature condition for hay.[1] Nearly 7,000,000 acres were so handled. The situation that year was unusual because of severe drought. This made necessary the wide use of small grains for forage in the emergency. Ordinarily, about 4,500,000 acres of small grains are cut green for hay in this country.

Oats make one of the better small-grain hays and often are regularly grown for this purpose. In the South, fall-sown oats either grown alone or in mixtures with a winter legume such as hairy vetch make very good hay, and the growing of fall-sown oats for pasture is widely practiced, especially in Texas. In northern states, spring-sown oats are used, and here both yield and feeding quality are improved by growing field peas with oats in a mixture. Where a valuable perennial-forage seeding has been made with oats, cutting the oats green for hay or silage or pasturing it off makes establishment of the seeding more certain.

In Missouri, winter barley is highly regarded as a dual-purpose crop for pasture and grain. Here it exceeds the other grains in earliness and size of fall growth and vigorously renews itself under grazing.[2] When grown with a natural reseeding of lespedeza, the early harvest of winter barley makes possible 3 or 4 months' pasturage on lespedeza. The winter cover provided by the barley reduces erosion.

Both wheat and rye as fall-sown crops are used for hay and pasture. The pasture usage is of greater importance. They may provide light fall grazing and the earliest of spring forage. Rye, unless cut very early, is less desirable than the other small grains for hay because of its lower palatability and its coarse, tough, hairy stems. Barley and wheat are the chief grains grown for forage in the Pacific coast states, largest users of cereal hays.

When cut in the late-milk to early-dough stage, small grains make hay comparable with timothy in feeding value. Cut at this same stage, the cereal grasses can also be preserved effectively as silage (see Chap. X). Loose cereal hay is often fluffy and hard to handle with a fork; hence, cutting with a binder and curing the green sheaves in small shocks are considered the most convenient method of handling. Cereal hay requires a protein supplement to balance the ration properly for dairy cows in milk, for fattening beef cattle, and for sheep.

[1] U.S. Census of Agriculture, 1935.
[2] ETHERIDGE, W. E., C. A. HELM, and E. M. BROWN, Winter Barley, a New Factor in Missouri Agriculture, *Mo. Agr. Expt. Sta. Bul.* 353, 1935.

A relatively new practice is the harvest of cereal grasses when they are very young just before jointing occurs. The young grass leaves are artifically dried and, on a dry basis, often contain 20 per cent or more crude protein. They are unusually high in vitamins, and their nutrients are highly digestible.

Sorghums for Forage.—Approximately 8 million acres of sorghum were grown for forage in the United States in 1934.[1] For the most part, sorghum forage is produced by the sweet-sorghum varieties originally brought to this country in about 1853 for sorghum-sirup production. However, the sorghum varieties developed especially for grain production are used for forage on occasion though their forage yields are generally materially less than those produced by the sweet sorghums, commonly called *sorgos*.

The forage sorgos, like their grain-producing relatives, are especially suitable for hot, dry regions, not because their productivity is greatest under such conditions but because it is under these conditions that few, if any, other crops can yield so well. The chief area of production lies in Texas, Oklahoma, and Kansas, extending westward into eastern New Mexico and Colorado. The forage sorgos have a wider range of adaptation than the grain sorghums and are recommended to some extent as far north as South Dakota. They are occasionally grown for silage in humid areas but under such conditions cannot ordinarily compete with corn.

The culture of forage sorghums in Texas[2] may be regarded as typical. There sorghums are regarded as the most important source of cultivated roughage, for they provide the bulk of hay, bundle forage, and silage and are also used extensively for pasture. The average yield of cured forage for the state is 1½ tons an acre, but this may be materially increased by use of better varieties and better culture.

The sorghums cannot be successfully planted until the soil is thoroughly warm in the spring. A close spacing of 1 to 4 in. apart in the row is recommended for forage production; such a spacing is secured with 5 lb. of seed an acre. Where the seed is broadcast for fine-stemmed hay, 1 bu. per acre of seed is used on average soil and 2 bu. on rich soil if moisture is more adequate.

Silage yields from row plantings of sorgo in Texas have averaged 9 to 13 tons an acre, the larger yields being secured in the regions of greater rainfall. The sorgos yield 2 to 4 tons an acre more silage than the best forage-producing varieties of the grain sorghums.

[1] U.S. Census of Agriculture, 1935.

[2] QUINBY, J. R., J. C. STEPHENS, R. E. KARPER, and D. L. JONES, Forage Sorghums in Texas, *Tex. Agr. Expt. Sta. Bul.* 496, 1934.

Among the more important forage varieties are Gooseneck and Honey of a late group; Sumac, Sourless, Orange, and Atlas, medium in maturity; Red Amber, Black Amber, and Folger, which are classed as early.

Sweet Sorghum for Sirup.—Sorghum-sirup production is about a half-million-acre industry and utilizes the same varieties as are used

FIG. 32.—Sudan grass in full head.   The row at the left is a disease-resistant strain being tested in Texas.   (*Courtesy of R. E. Karper, Texas Agricultural Experiment Station.*)

for forage production. The crop is harvested when the seed is in the hard-dough stage. The leaves are first stripped off. Then the plants may be cut with a corn binder, the heads cut off by hand, and the stalks run through rollers which press out the juice. Sweet-sorghum stalks contain over 80 per cent water, and about half of this is extracted as a juice containing 10 to 18 per cent sugar. This juice is concentrated into a thick sirup by boiling it down in shallow vats. The stalks from which the juice has been pressed make only fair feed and are usually discarded.

Sudan Grass.—Sudan grass (*Sorghum vulgare var. sudanense*), a close relative of the sorghums, was introduced from Africa by the U.S. Department of Agriculture in 1909. It is finer stemmed than the sorghums but coarser than timothy, brome grass, and the other common perennial forage grasses. Under good conditions it may grow to a height of 5 to 7 ft.

Sudan grass is a very quick-growing annual with a range of adaptation similar to that of corn. It does not grow well in cool, wet weather and under such conditions appears yellow and stunted.

Its greatest use has been as a one-season pasture. Planted a few days later than the normal corn-planting date, it should be 2 or 3 ft. high in about 6 weeks. Greatest grazing returns are secured if the animals are not turned on Sudan-grass pasture until the plants have attained this height. It should then provide very palatable and nutritious pasturage until killed by frost. Sudan grass is exceedingly effective in providing pasturage during the dry, hot part of the summer when many pastures are nonproductive.

A seeding rate of about 25 lb. an acre may be secured by setting a grain drill to sow 2 pk. of wheat. Some prefer to sow 30 to 35 lb. of seed an acre. The seed is usually inexpensive. Best growth is secured in the corn-belt region on soils high in organic matter and available nitrogen.

Sorghum Poisoning.—Occasionally members of the sorghum group develop prussic acid in dangerous amounts and become poisonous to sheep and cattle. Sudan grass is much less likely to do so than the other sorghums. The greatest hazard occurs in the case of very hungry animals grazing on small plants stunted by severe heat or making renewed growth after frost, according to work done by the Wisconsin Agricultural Experiment Station.[1] The danger in the case of Sudan grass appears to be eliminated almost entirely if the plants are allowed to attain a height of 2 ft. before grazing is started. This investigation also indicated that freezing does not increase the prussic acid content of these large Sudan-grass plants but that a high level of available nitrogen and a low level of available phosphorus in the soil do tend to increase the poison content, whereas a low level of available nitrogen and a high level of available phosphorus have the opposite effect. There is essentially no danger of prussic acid poisoning in Sudan-grass hay or silage because the plants are usually 3 ft. or more in height and consequently very low in prussic acid before

---

[1] Boyd, F. T., O. S. Aamodt, G. Bohstedt, and E. Truog, Sudan Grass Management for Control of Cyanide Poisoning, *Jour. Amer. Soc. Agron.*, Vol. 30, No. 7, 1938.

being cut. However, according to this study, if short Sudan grass, high in prussic acid, is made into hay it is dangerous as a feed. Sudan grass is difficult to cure as hay because the thick, juicy stems lose moisture slowly.

Effect of Sorghums on the Soil.—Growers of the sorghums, including Sudan grass, have frequently observed that the crops immediately following their culture are depressed in yield. The reason suggested for this effect is the strong competition for available plant nutrients, particularly nitrogen, between the soil microorganisms and the growing

Fig. 33.—The liklihood of the development of prussic acid in dangerous quantities in Sudan grass appears to be eliminated if the plants are allowed to attain a height of 2 ft. or more, as in this picture, before grazing is started, according to work done at the Wisconsin Agricultural Experiment Station.

crop. The work of Conrad[1] at the California Agricultural Experiment Station tended to confirm this. His analyses of sorghum roots at maturity showed total sugars to be 15 to 55 per cent of the dry organic matter whereas, in the case of corn (a crop causing little or no injury), the percentage of total sugars ranged from less than 1 to about 4.5. When a succeeding crop of wheat was grown, the rows of wheat parallel to the previous crop rows showed marked decreases adjacent to and over the row centers of sorgo and milo, but no significant yield

[1] Conrad, John P., Distribution of Sugars, Root Enclosed, in the Soil Following Corn and Sorghums and Their Effects on the Succeeding Wheat Crop, *Jour. Amer. Soc. Agron.*, Vol. 30, No. 6, 1938.

depression adjacent to the previous rows of corn. Considering the high yields of sorghums, it is also to be expected that these crops make heavy drafts on available soil nutrients thereby leaving less for succeeding crops, a yield deterrent in addition to the depressing effect of the microorganisms that decompose the roots and root-contained sugars.

The Millets.—The various millets are quick-growing, hot-weather annuals that can be used effectively as emergency crops for hay but that otherwise have no important place in agriculture. They may be sown in late June or early July in northern states and in fact do not

Fig. 34.—Left, common millet. Center, Japanese millet or barnyard grass. Right, Proso or hog millet. (*Courtesy of C. R. Megee.*)

make a good growth anywhere until the soil is warm. From 15 to 40 lb. of seed an acre is recommended in various localities, the lighter rate being used where seed production is intended. They are productive, frequently yielding over 2 tons of air-dry hay an acre, but the hay is inferior to timothy and the other good perennial grasses in feeding value and may be definitely injurious to horses if fed continuously.

Proso, otherwise called *broomcorn millet* or *hog millet*, is inferior to the other millets as hay but is grown to some extent for its seed which has about the same feeding value as oats. Generally it is less productive than oats but it occasionally outyields oats on sandy soil. It has been grown in Asiatic countries for centuries, both for human food and for livestock.

The varieties primarily grown for forage are Japanese, or barnyard, millet, German, Hungarian, and Common, which are foxtail millets; and pearl, or cattail, millet, a very tall, pithy-stemmed type that must be cut very early to have any feeding value whatsoever. The other millets should be cut just as they are heading out, for they all rapidly become unpalatable as they approach maturity.

Rape.—The rape plant (*Brassica napus*) is used as an annual pasture and is eaten readily by cattle, sheep, hogs, and poultry. The plant really is a biennial, but forage interest lies strictly in the first year's growth. It survives as a biennial to produce seed only in regions of very mild winters. The Dwarf Essex variety is the important one for agricultural purposes.

Rape grows best on fertile soils in a cool, moist growing season. Under less favored conditions, its growth is not large, and infestation with plant lice may be very heavy.

Wisconsin agronomists[1] state that a seeding of 2 bu. per acre of oats and 4 to 6 lb. of Dwarf Essex rape will usually make an excellent pasture for hogs or, in an emergency, for sheep or dry stock. This combination should be sown early in the spring and only on fertile land. The grazing of the oats can begin about the middle of June. At first the hogs prefer the oats to the rape; but after the straw has ripened, it loses its palatability, and hogs may graze for the remainder of the year (often until late autumn) on the frost-resistant rape.

In regions where field peas do well, this crop is sometimes added to the rape-oat mixture.

Rape is almost as high in protein on a dry-matter basis as alfalfa, but the latter is considered the more valuable pasture because of a slightly superior feeding value and because of its beneficial effect on the soil. Hogs, especially white ones or those with thin hair, sometimes sunscald on rape pasture when they get wet from the dew or rain on the rape leaves and then are exposed to bright sunlight. Generally the difficulty is not serious. If dairy cows are pastured on rape just before milking time, the milk is likely to be off-flavored, hence, if rape is to be used for milking cows, they should be turned into the pasture just after milking and removed 3 or 4 hours before it is time for the next milking.

If rape is pastured so that all leaves are removed, the yield is greatly reduced. Good management of rape pasture calls for sufficiently light stocking so that there will be an abundance of leaf growth at all times. Late seedings ordinarily are not so productive as seedings made in early

[1] AHLGREN, H. L., G. M. BRIGGS, and L. F. GRABER, Supplementary Pastures and Hays, *Wis. Ext. Cir.* 315, 1941.

spring, but a reasonably good growth should be available for pasturage in 6 weeks with seedings made on productive, moist soil up to the last week in July.

ANNUAL LEGUMES

Soybeans for Forage.—In 1940, there were 6,500,000 acres of soybeans grown for hay, grazed, or plowed under in the United States.[1] This acreage made up nearly 57 per cent of the total of the rapidly expanding soybean acreage of the country. The soybean is the most important annual legume forage. As a forage it is primarily a hay crop although more than 1,500,000 acres were grazed or used for soil building in 1940. The hay yield, on the average, is about 1¼ tons an acre. If the crop is cut and successfully cured when the beans are well formed, the protein content is as high as that in average alfalfa, and the two hays are comparable in feeding value.

In leading soybean states of the corn belt a little over 40 per cent of the soybean acreage is cut for hay. Thus, more acres of soybeans are cut for hay in this than in any other region, but the proportion of the crop used for hay is greatest in the southeastern states including North Carolina, Kentucky, Tennessee, Alabama, Mississippi, and Arkansas.

Culture of Soybeans for Hay.—Soybeans are usually planted about corn-planting time for maximum seed yields. If the same varieties are to be used for hay, planting may be delayed 3 or 4 weeks without significant loss of yield. In southern states, summer plantings as late as Aug. 1 are sometimes made for late hay, green manure, or soiling purposes.

If the seedbed is very clean and troubles from weeds are unlikely to be serious, a finer stemmed hay will result if the soybeans are drilled in solid with a grain drill so that seed of good germination will be spaced 1 in. apart in the drill rows. The seeds of such varieties as Manchu, Dunfield, and Illini are relatively large, and at this spacing about 2 bu. an acre is required. Smaller seeded varieties are spaced the same but seeded at a lower bushel rate in accordance with the increased number of seeds per pound.

If weeds are likely to give trouble, a better quality of hay will be secured if the soybeans are drilled in rows and cultivated. In this case, too, the drill should be calibrated to space the seeds 1 in. apart.

Forage Varieties.—With respect to varieties, E. S. Dyas of Iowa makes the following statement:[2] "In repeated trials at the Iowa

---

[1] *U.S. Dept. Agr. Crops and Markets*, Vol. 17, No. 12, 1940.

[2] DYAS, E. S., Soybean Production in Iowa, *Iowa Agr. Expt. Sta. Bul.* P30 (new series), 1941.

Agricultural Experiment Station and elsewhere, yields and quality of hay from the varieties used for seed production and from so-called hay varieties have been so nearly alike that the seed varieties have come into general and satisfactory use as hay."

Manchu, Mukden, Dunfield, and Illini are typical corn-belt varieties used for both hay and seed production. The Wilson, a black-seeded variety, and the Virginia, with brown seed, are representative of later varieties; in the North, they are suitable only for forage.

Cultivation.—Even where soybeans are drilled solid, some cultivation is advisable. This work can be done with a spike-tooth harrow, a weeder, or a rotary hoe prior to emergence of the beans and also after they are up and until they are 6 in. high. Such interrow cultivation as is necessary to control weeds follows, if the planting is in the wider rows.

Time of Soybean-hay Harvest.—If varieties that will mature seed are used for hay production, the greatest returns are secured by cutting the crop when the pods are one-half to three-fourths filled but just before the lower leaves turn yellow and start falling off. If cut earlier, the protein content should be somewhat higher but the yield will be materially lower. Varieties too late to mature seed have to be cut at a much earlier stage of development, preferably when favorable weather for curing may still be expected.

Curing Soybean Hay.—Soybean hay is difficult to cure. At the normal time for hay harvest, weather conditions in many sections are none too favorable. At any time the thick stems dry out slowly, and the leaves are easily lost. One of the most satisfactory methods is to cut the crop with a binder and cure the sheaves in shocks. By this method, only the outer leaves turn brown, and few are lost. If the soybeans contain weeds and grass, however, the development of molds and spoilage is likely.

Megee[1] reports the successful curing of weedy soybean hay by cutting it with a mower, allowing a partial cure in windrows raked with a side-delivery rake, and completing the curing in field stacks built around steel fence posts. These stacks are 4 ft. in diameter, with straight sides, and are built well over the top of the posts. The method is suggested where adverse curing weather is the rule. If weather conditions are favorable, mower-cut soybeans may be cured in the windrow and handled with the usual hay-loading equipment, or the hay may be piled in cocks and loaded by hand.

Cowpeas for Forage.—Cowpea hay is another of the South's legume forages. It is a large-seeded legume. Around 1⅓ million

[1] MEGEE, C. R., Soybean Production in Michigan, *Mich. Agr. Expt. Sta. Cir. Bul.* 161, 1939.

acres are annually grown for seed, but the hay acreage is more important and generally exceeds 2 million. The Carolinas, Georgia, and Arkansas are the leading cowpea-hay states. The crop is also important as a pasture and green manure. In these uses, Texas leads, but the acreage is also extensive in the states named above.

As a southern summer annual the cowpea competes to some extent with soybeans and velvet beans; but it has a wider range of adaptation, succeeds fairly well on nearly all kinds of soil, and withstands considerable drought. Its disadvantage compared with soybeans is its vine rather than erect type of growth.

Fully half the crop is not grown in pure culture but is interplanted with corn or grown in mixtures with sorghum, Johnson grass, Sudan grass, or soybeans.

Seeding Cowpeas for Forage.—When cowpeas are grown for hay, pasture, or green manure, the seed is usually drilled solid or broadcast at the rate of about 90 lb. an acre. This can be done with a grain drill set to sow 1½ bu. of wheat. If cowpeas are drilled in the row with corn, the peas and corn are planted with a corn planter in one operation. When cowpeas are grown in rows, 30 to 40 lb. of seed to the acre is used. More frequently, when cowpeas are grown with corn, the cowpea seed is either broadcast in the corn and covered by the last cultivation or drilled between the corn rows with a one-horse wheat drill. Mixed seedings consist of 1 bu. of cowpeas with ½ bu. of sorghum; 1 bu. of cowpeas and 10 lb. of Sudan grass; ½ bu. of cowpeas and 1 bu. of soybeans. Where Johnson grass persists, the seeding of 1½ bu. of cowpea seed on a prepared seedbed in which the Johnson grass has not been subdued will result in a mixture of Johnson grass and cowpeas, the mixture making very good hay.

Because the cowpea is a warm-weather crop, when grown alone the seed is sown at corn-planting time to 2 weeks or so later.

Cowpea Harvest.—The seeds of cowpeas do not ripen simultaneously, blossoms, green pods, and ripe seed occurring on the vines at the same time. For a hay crop, it is considered best to let the first pods ripen. At this stage, most of the balance of the pods will be well developed, curing will be less difficult than at an earlier stage, and the hay will be of better quality than if cut later when ripe seed and leaves have begun to shatter and the stems have become more woody.

Velvet Beans.—The velvet bean (*Stizolobium* Spp.) is also a warm-weather legume more restricted in adaptation than the cowpea but excelling it as a fall and winter pasture for cattle and hogs. It, too, is a vine plant, the vines growing to a length of 12 to 15 ft. and occasionally 30 to 40 ft. The favored area for velvet-bean culture is on well-drained soils of the Atlantic coast and Gulf Plain area. Georgia grows over a million acres annually, and this constitutes about half the total United States crop.

Because of the extreme viny nature of the velvet bean, this crop is not satisfactory for hay but is usually interplanted with corn, preferably very stiff-stalked varieties which can best support the bean vines. Otherwise, very few pods are produced, and the real feeding value of the plant is largely in the pods, although the leaves are also eaten by cattle. The preferred method of planting is either in alternate rows with corn or one row of velvet beans to two or three of corn.

Peanut Hay.—Peanuts are grown primarily for their seed, but this legume can be made into very good hay. When grown for nuts, the crop is restricted to sandy soils to prevent discoloring the hulls, but peanut hay can be grown on many kinds of soil so long as the drainage is good. Often the tops are cut for forage, and hogs are then turned into the field to feed on the pods. The entire crop can be used for hog pasture. The crop is of greatest importance for both seed and hay in the southeastern states, Georgia and Alabama leading in production. The acreage for hay and the acreage for seed are about equal. If the crop is harvested for the nuts, the straw is still used as fodder. Well-cured peanut hay is not so good a forage as good cowpea hay, but the combined use of the tops for hay and the pods for hog feed makes peanuts of considerable importance to the livestock industry of peanut-growing areas. The general culture of this crop is discussed in Chap. XVIII.

Field Peas for Forage.—The field pea is adapted to colder growing conditions than any of the other important annual legumes. In Canada and such northern states as Washington, Idaho, Montana, Wisconsin, and Michigan, field peas are grown both for forage and for seed. The crop can also be grown in regions of high altitude farther south in the Rocky Mountains and is useful as a winter legume in the southern states.

The crop requires a reasonably fertile soil and does not grow well on sands or soils high in acidity. It is much more sensitive to heat than to cold, does not do well in Kansas and Nebraska, but produces good yields in western Canada under even more limited rainfall. Frosts are unlikely to prove seriously injurious unless unusually severe at the time the pods are setting.

In the northern pea-growing states the crop is planted as soon as the land can be worked in the spring. Where the crop is grown as a winter legume in southern states and the warmer areas of the Pacific coast, planting may be done in the fall or early winter.

It is highly desirable to mix oats and peas, bushel for bushel, when the crop is to be grown for forage. The mixture is sown at 2½ to 3 bu. an acre. In Michigan trials,[1] oats and peas materially outyielded Sudan grass, millet, and soybeans at Chatham, in the Upper Peninsula of Michigan, but the reverse was true at East Lansing, in southern Michigan. Hay yields of 2 or 3 tons an acre are not uncommon. This mixture is cut for hay when the oats are in the late-milk stage and the peas are forming in the pod. In western states where the peas are sometimes used for hog pasture alone or in mixture with grain, the crop is allowed to develop to maturity before the animals are turned in so that the entire plant may be utilized.

Field peas may have a place in northern areas as a summer-sown green manure following small-grain harvest especially if a seeding in the grain has failed. In Michigan trials,[2] peas seeded Aug. 12 had produced over 1¼ tons of dry matter an acre 6 weeks later. Left standing, most of the pea plants were still green Dec. 15, though they were blanketed with snow. The chief drawback to this practice is the relatively high cost of seed and the difficulty of getting an adequate supply.

Seedings of alfalfa, red clover, sweet clover, and other northern forages do exceptionally well when made with a companion crop of field or canning peas. This is true even where peas are not harvested early and therefore seems due less to the early maturity of the peas than to the fact that the peas do not compete too severely for moisture. The intense shading by pea vines does not appear to be objectionable.

OTHER LEGUMES

Crimson Clover.—Most beautiful of all clovers when in full flower is *Trifolium incarnatum*, commonly known as *crimson* clover, less commonly as *scarlet clover*, *French clover*, *incarnate clover*, and *annual clover*. Crimson clover is an annual or a winter annual with long brilliantly colored flower heads of rich scarlet.

As a winter annual, crimson clover is strictly southern in adaptation. It is grown in the southeastern states and northward along the seaboard through Virginia, Maryland, Delaware, and New Jersey. As a summer annual, it can be grown where summers are moist and cool as in northern Minnesota, northern Michigan, and Maine. It is a favorite green-manure crop for potatoes in Aroostook County, Maine.

---

[1] MEGEE, C. R., Emergency Hay and Pasture Crops, *Mich. Agr. Expt. Sta. Spec. Bul.* 150 (revised), 1934.

[2] PETTIGROVE, H. R., Field Peas Offer Possibilities as a Summer-seeded Green Manure, *Mich. Agr. Expt. Sta. Quart. Bul.*, Vol. 18, No. 4, 1936.

As tolerant of soil acidity as alsike, crimson clover may be grown on both light and heavy soils but not on soils of low fertility. There, stands are obtained with great difficulty, and growth of this legume is stunted. Its most effective use in soil management is to maintain the productivity of fairly good soils rather than to build up that of poor ones.

The seed is large, about twice the size of that of red clover, can be easily cleaned to high purity, and in good condition germinates rapidly. Seed over 2 years old, however, becomes dull in color and often is low in germination.

Fig. 35.—Crimson clover that was grown between cotton rows for soil improvement in Tennessee. (*Courtesy of U.S. Dept. Agr., Soil Conservation Service.*)

As a winter annual in the South, this clover is seeded in August and September. Earlier seedings encounter too much dry and hot weather; later seedings winter kill. Rye, wheat, vetch, or Italian rye grass, if sown with crimson clover at half their normal rate, ensure a crop stand should the clover fail.

The hairs on the stems and heads of mature crimson-clover hay become hard and may form into indigestible hair balls in the stomachs of horses and mules. When the clover is cut in early bloom or pastured in immature condition, no such difficulty is encountered. Because it can be grown between normal crop seasons, it is unusually effective and economical as a green manure.

Bur Clover.—Another southern legume used for winter cover and soil improvement is bur clover. The bur clovers are more closely related to the alfalfa group than they are to the true clovers.   They are annual legumes that branch at the crown, with 10 to 20 or more spreading or decumbent branches.   The seeds are borne in pods that usually have short spines; hence the name *bur clover*.   Bur clover grows well during the winter months in the warm South.   The seed is difficult to harvest; but once land is thoroughly seeded, the clover volunteers after the last cultivation of corn or cotton, to produce winter cover and pasture.   The reseeding of the land is provided for by leaving alternate strips unplowed which ripen seed to be scattered by subsequent tillage.

VETCHES

Though vetches number well over 100, two are most significant in agricultural practice.   These are common vetch (*Vicia sativa*) and hairy vetch (*V. villosa*).

Common vetch is an annual or, in mild climates, a winter annual. In the North, it must be sown in the spring and is not so productive there as hairy vetch, a more hardy winter annual.   Because common vetch does not withstand hot weather either, it is most useful on the Pacific coast where it can be sown in the fall and harvested before the heat of the following summer.

Hairy vetch, also called *winter vetch* and *sand vetch*, can grow on soils of very low fertility.   It is grown for seed and forage as well as for green manure in the North and as a winter legume for soil-improvement purposes in the South.   American seed is grown in Michigan and Oregon, often as part of a combination of rye and vetch.   Seed imported from Europe is largely the by-product of grain harvest, the vetch being something of a weed in grainfields there.

Uses.—Both common and hairy vetch are used for pasture, hay, and green manure, the latter use being of greatest importance.   The hay crop is easy to cure but hard to handle because the vetch vines form a tangled mass difficult to pull apart.

In northern Michigan, farmers with poor, sandy pastures have been seeding vetch in the thin, thriftless grass sods.   Once a stand gets started, enough seed shatters to keep the crop going, and eventually the grass itself improves because of its association with the nitrogen-gathering vetch.

Culture.—Early-fall seedings of hairy vetch with rye are most likely to be successful, late ones often failing to survive the winter.   Thick stands of vetch do not set seed so well as relatively thin stands, secured with 10 to 15 lb. of vetch and 1 bu. of rye an acre.

Review Questions

1. What are the advantages of winter barley as a pasture in areas to which the crop is adapted?

2. Why is rye less desirable than other small grains for hay?

3. How are cereal grasses of unusually high protein and vitamin content grown and harvested?

4. Under what conditions is the growing of sorghums for forage most advantageous?

5. Why are sweet-sorghum varieties preferred to grain sorghums for forage production?

6. In what different ways are sorghums harvested and utilized for forage?

7. If sorghum is to be grown in rows and cultivated, what rate of seeding is customary?

8. Why is Sudan grass more commonly used as a pasture crop than as hay?

9. To what conditions is Sudan grass adapted?

10. What is meant by sorghum poisoning, and how may it be avoided?

11. Explain the depressing effect that sorghums often have on the yield of crops that follow.

12. Why are the millets regarded almost solely as emergency crops?

13. Compare soybeans and cowpeas as forage crops with respect to adaptation, culture, and use.

14. At what stage should soybeans and cowpeas be cut for hay?

15. Why are the seed varieties of soybeans also preferred for hay?

16. Where are velvet beans most widely grown?

17. What are the major forage uses of this plant?

18. How is the peanut crop used for forage?

19. Describe the culture of field peas for forage.

20. What are the advantages and disadvantages of rape as a pasture?

21. Crimson clover is largely a southern crop. How do you account for its extensive use in Maine?

22. What are the chief uses of common and hairy vetch.

Problems

1. You have a farm in Missouri on which you wish to grow a field of winter barley and lespedeza. How will you handle this field?

2. The clover seeding on which a corn-belt farmer was depending for hay winterkilled. How can he best proceed to make up for this hay shortage?

3. A southern Minnesota dairyman has only bluegrass pasture for his herd of 20 cows. This pasture is nonproductive in midsummer. What should you suggest as a one-season supplementary pasture? How many acres should be provided? How should this crop be handled?

4. A southern farmer has a field of Johnson grass. How should he proceed to grow a mixture of Johnson grass and cowpea hay?

5. A farmer who has never grown rape wants to use this crop for hog pasture. Write a letter in answer to his inquiry for detailed information on rape culture.

References

HUTCHESON, T. B., T. K. WOLFE, and M. S. KIPPS: "The Production of Field Crops," McGraw-Hill Book Company, Inc., New York, 1936.

KEPHART, L. W.: Growing Crimscn Clover, *U.S. Dept. Agr. Farmers' Bul.* 1151, 1920.

MARTIN, J. H., and J. C. STEPHENS: The Culture and Use of Sorghums for Forage, *U.S. Dept. Agr. Farmers' Bul.* 1844, 1940.

MORRISON, F. B.: "Feeds and Feeding," 20th ed., The Morrison Publishing Co., Ithaca, N.Y., 1936.

MORSE, W. J.: Cowpeas: Culture and Varieties, *U.S. Dept. Agr. Farmers' Bul.* 1148, 1920.

PIPER, C. V.: "Forage Plants and Their Culture," The Macmillan Company, New York, 1924.

—— and W. J. MORSE: The Velvet Bean, *U.S. Dept. Agr. Farmers' Bul.* 1276, 1922.

QUINBY, J. R., J. C. STEPHENS, R. E. KARPER, and D. L. JONES: Forage Sorghums in Texas, *Texas Agr. Exp. Sta. Bul.* 496, 1934.

VINALL, H. H.: The Field Pea as a Forage Crop, *U.S. Dept. Agr. Farmer's Bul.* 690 (revised), 1926.

CHAPTER IX

HAYMAKING

The advice to "make hay while the sun shines" is an ancient and worthy adage. But to make hay whether the sun shines or not is one of the farmer's most troublesome problems. Before he first ventures into haymaking the farmer must have selected suitable plants adapted to the environment that he is able to provide. The seed must be well chosen and planted in a soil rich in the nutrients that support a vigorous forage growth lest the plants be stunted and thriftless. There must be adequate moisture. These facts are self-evident.

Haymaking also entails harvest of the crop at a stage of development chosen with reference to well-balanced considerations of yield, feeding value, and the future vigor of the forage stand. The crop must be cured and stored, and during this process there may be rains which leave the forage darkened and unpalatable, with vitamins and nutrients dissipated. The forage may be stored when too moist, a condition associated with the development of molds, objectionable fermentation, and destructive oxidation sometimes so intense as to result in spontaneous combustion.

By no means of least concern are economic considerations such as are involved in the high labor requirements of the "clothesline" or rack hay-drying methods of Scandinavian countries on the one hand and the highly mechanized field baling operations or artificial drying on the other.

HAY QUALITY

The one real measure of the quality of hay is its feeding value. Hay may be palatable without being highly nutritious. It is occasionally leafy and of good color yet unpalatable to the point of being refused by livestock. Chemical analysis and theoretically digestible nutrients sometimes indicate quality very inaccurately. Research still has many problems to answer with respect to hay quality. Still, color, leafiness, purity, fineness, and the usual feeding analyses do give some indications of the probable value of the hay as livestock roughage. Stage of maturity when cut, leafiness, color, foreign material, soundness, size and pliability of stems, and aroma all are

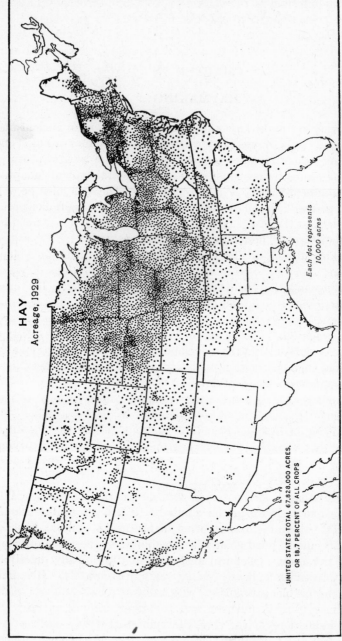

HAY
Acreage, 1929

Each dot represents
10,000 acres

UNITED STATES TOTAL 67,828,000 ACRES,
OR 18.7 PERCENT OF ALL CROPS

FIG. 36.—No crop in the United States is so widespread as hay, largely because so many plants with varying climatic requirements are made into hay. Most of the hay is produced in the hay and dairy belt, in and around the corn belt, and in the winter
wheat belt. Timothy, clover, and alfalfa are the dominant hay crops in these regions. Alfalfa is very important locally in the irrigated districts of the West and a considerable quantity is grown in the spring wheat belt. (U.S. Department of Agriculture.)

considered in determining the market value of hay, and these considerations have been responsible for wide differentials in hay prices.

Color.—Good hay is green hay—not green in the sense of being immature, not green because of being only partly cured, but bright green in color as a result of having been thoroughly dried in such a manner as to avoid bleaching, browning, molding, and mustiness.

Green grass is rich in carotene, the basic substance from which vitamin A develops. Vitamin A promotes health and vigor. An adequate supply of carotene in the ration of a dairy cow not only helps to ensure that animal's well-being but makes for the production of milk high in vitamin A and consequent benefits to human nutrition. In green-colored hay, considerable carotene is saved. In bleached or otherwise discolored hay, most of the carotene is lost; such hay is less palatable and lower in feeding value and, if marketed, sells at an appreciable discount.

A certain amount of sun bleaching is unavoidable. Any hay exposed to the sun as it is being dried develops a brownish-yellow color instead of its natural green. Swath-cured hay is more exposed to the sun's rays and is most subject to bleaching. Exposure of a high proportion of the hay crop can be avoided by raking wilted but still green forage into windrows within a few hours after it is cut and completing the curing in windrows, cocks, small field stacks, or similar arrangements. The bleaching is thereby limited to the surface of these structures, and the small percentage thus left exposed does not seriously affect the color and quality of the crop as a whole.

Effect of Rain on Quality.—Rain intensifies color damage to hay and affects it adversely in other respects. It prolongs the curing period, often necessitates turning, or tedding, to expose a greater proportion of the forage to bleaching, induces decay, and, if prolonged, results in a blackened stemmy mass of material not at all tempting in the manger or feeding rack.

But rain damage does not stop with destruction of the desirable bright-green color. Some of the nutrients in hay are readily soluble in water. This is true of energy-giving sugars and soluble starches, of proteins and closely related nitrogen compounds. Heavy, prolonged rains may leach out considerable amounts of these highly nutritive constituents, especially the proteins, the fibrous, stained, and indigestible material thus being left. Weathered hay is harsh and brittle. It is unpalatable to the discriminating animal and is probably discounted even more severely by the discriminating hay buyer.

Hay Curing and Fermentation.—Fermentation is a form of respiration or oxidation. A very little fermentation is desirable in hay curing.

Hay cocked, stacked, baled, or put into a mow with just the right moisture undergoes a light sweat, a fermentive action, that softens the stems, gives it a pleasing aroma, and enhances its palatability. But excessive moisture in stored, stacked, or baled hay induces too much fermentation, mold organisms develop, and the hay becomes musty and dark.

Sometimes the fermentation, or oxidation, accompanied by the development of considerable heat, produces a brown hay that smells like cured tobacco. Feeders call this *tobacco-brown hay* and almost universally report that livestock eat it greedily. But palatability does not tell the whole story of tobacco-brown hay. In the oxidation process, a considerable portion of the original dry matter may be lost. Wet hay containing 100 lb. of dry matter may be put into storage, and there may be but 65 to 75 lb. of dry matter left to feed out. That which remains may be palatable; but, according to nutritional research, it is less digestible and less valuable pound for pound than well-dried hay, only slightly fermented, which is green in color and of mildly pleasing aroma.

The farmer who puts wet hay into storage is fortunate if he gets no worse than mowburnt or tobacco-brown hay. Sometimes oxidation gets out of hand, temperatures rise to extremes, and finally, at 300 to 400°F., spontaneous combustion may take place. The stories of burned barns during an unfavorable hay-harvest period provide ample testimony to the hazards of putting wet or insufficiently cured hay into storage.

Importance of Leaves.—Every time a leaf drops off a hay plant the yield is reduced by the weight of that leaf. If all the leaves should be lost from alfalfa, the yield would be reduced by about 50 per cent because about 50 per cent of the weight of cut alfalfa consists of leaves. But leaf loss involves more than weight loss; for leaves are far higher in proteins, minerals, and vitamins than stems. In the case of alfalfa, essentially two-thirds of the feeding value is in the leaves. The stems are fibrous and much less digestible.

The tendency is for leaves to dry out much more rapidly than the stems. If this occurs, by the time the stems are dry enough for storage the leaves are too dry and shatter readily; or should the hay be stored when the leaves are just right, the stems often contain too much moisture and excessive heating results. In good curing procedure the leaves and stems are dried at as nearly the same rate as possible, to reduce leaf losses to a minimum. Even under the best of field-curing conditions, leaf loss cannot be entirely eliminated.

Purity.—The cleanliness of hay is important. Dock, sorrel, white-top, thistles, and a host of other weeds do not make good hay. Nor do corn and grain stubble, nor the partly decayed rakings of a previous cutting. Market hay cannot grade U.S. No. 1 if it contains in excess of 5 per cent foreign material; the limit for U.S. No. 2 grade is 10 per cent; and if foreign material is present in excess of 15 per cent, the hay is sample grade. The lower market grades are also substantially lower in price and feeding value.

Influence of Maturity on Quality.—The stage of maturity at which any forage plant is cut is closely associated with the analysis of the plant and its potential quality. It also has a direct bearing on

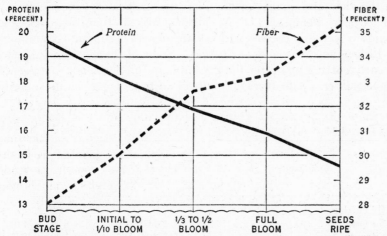

FIG. 37.—Protein and fiber content of alfalfa cut at different stages of growth. Alfalfa hay cut early has the highest protein and the highest feeding value, and there is a uniform decrease in protein and increase in fiber as the plant becomes more mature. (*U.S. Dept. Agr. Farmers' Bul.* 1839.)

immediate yield and likewise on the future vigor of the stand because of its influence on the storage of food reserves. No one stage of cutting is best under all circumstances, nor is it possible to cut all of a crop at one stage of development, especially when large acreages are involved. However, an understanding of the behavior of the different hay plants as influenced by stage of cutting helps the farmer to determine wisely the best time to start his harvest.

In general, all hay plants are higher in percentage of protein and lower in percentage of fiber when in immature condition than when they have reached a relatively advanced stage of maturity. Alfalfa cut in the bud or very early bloom stage often contains 18 to 20 per cent protein on an air-dry basis. At half bloom a normal protein content would be 15 to 16 per cent; at full bloom, 12 to 14 per cent. The average protein content of alfalfa hay in general is about 14 to 15 per cent.

The leaves of young timothy 6 or 8 in. tall may contain as high a percentage of protein as young alfalfa. When nitrogen is abundantly available, the protein content of any of such young grasses may be 20 per cent or even more. As these grasses mature, the percentage drops rapidly so that hay from timothy, redtop, the rye grasses, orchard grass, and others generally contains 6 to 8 per cent of protein; the percentage in smooth brome is usually a little higher.

The effects of both nitrogen fertilization and time of cutting on the yield and quality of grass hay are illustrated by work done in the Upper Peninsula of Michigan. Mixed timothy-quack-grass meadows were top-dressed with 200 lb. an acre of sulphate of ammonia at 12 locations over a 3-year period. Some of the hay was subjected to early cutting just after the grass was in full head; late cutting was 3 weeks later. The average results of all trials are given in Table 10.

TABLE 10.—INFLUENCE OF TIME OF CUTTING AND NITROGEN FERTILIZATION ON THE YIELD AND PROTEIN CONTENT OF GRASS HAY IN NORTHERN MICHIGAN*

Treatment	Hay yield, pounds per acre at 15 per cent moisture	Protein content, per cent	Pounds of protein to the acre
Early cutting:			
No fertilizer	1,660	8.8	146
Nitrogen fertilizer	3,144	9.1	287
Late cutting:			
No fertilizer	2,249	6.0	135
Nitrogen fertilizer	3,310	6.5	214

* DEXTER, S. T., and D. L. CLANAHAN, Early Cutting and Fertilization of Quack Grass Meadows, *Mich. Agr. Expt. Sta. Quart. Bul.*, Vol. 21, No. 3, 1939.

In these trials the stage of cutting had far more influence on quality than had nitrogen fertilization. The two factors together made possible substantial improvement in both yield and quality.

Factors Affecting the Time of Cutting.—The following factors have a direct bearing on the determination of the most practicable time to cut hay:

1. Hay cut at the earlier stages of development is higher in percentage of protein, minerals, and vitamins and lower in fiber. Its feeding constituents are more digestible. On the other hand, plants have not attained full growth so that the dry-matter yield is less and

the forage is higher in water content, is spongy, and is more difficult to cure.

2. Hay cut at more advanced stages of maturity should yield more dry matter, and the later cutting permits more adequate storage of food reserves (see pages 94 and 119). Abundant reserve-food storage is beneficial to the future vigor and productivity of the crop.

3. Late-cut forage contains less moisture and is more easily dried. On the other hand, it is more brittle and is subject to greater loss of leaves.

4. If, in the handling of large acreages, cutting is delayed until the crop has reached the accepted proper stage of maturity, much of it is likely to be too advanced before harvest is completed.

Time of Cutting Alfalfa.—There have been more experiments dealing with the time of cutting alfalfa than with that of any other forage crop. The stage of bloom is most commonly used as the indicator of maturity despite considerable variation due to environmental factors. Bloom is likely to be light and delayed in cool, wet weather, profuse and early in hot, dry weather. The development of new shoots from the crown is also considered. It was once believed that cutting off these new shoots was injurious to the next crop, but no experimental evidence supports this.

As might be expected with so many factors involved, there is considerable difference of opinion as to which stage of cutting is best. The Wisconsin Agricultural Experiment Station[1] places greatest emphasis on the importance of permitting abundant storage of root reserves. Wisconsin recommendations call for the cutting of two crops a season in that state, at as near the full-bloom stage as possible.

On the other hand, Michigan experiments[2] have shown no serious damage to the stand from an occasional prebloom cutting; but fall cuttings are hazardous, and two cuttings a season are safest in that state. These experiments show, further, that to secure the greatest yield in two cuttings the first cutting should be taken when the plants are blooming but that there is no advantage in delaying cutting until full bloom. The second cutting should be taken, in most of Michigan, about the middle of August. If the third growth of hay is badly needed, there will be less injury to the alfalfa if this crop is not cut until the weather is too cold for subsequent growth and the resultant depletion of root reserves.

---

[1] MOORE, R. A., and L. F. GRABER, Wisconsin's Opportunity with Alfalfa, *Wis. Agr. Expt. Sta. Bul.* 374, 1925.

[2] DEXTER, S. T., Experiments on the Production of Alfalfa Hay, *Mich. Agr. Expt. Sta. Quart. Bul.*, Vol. 22, No. 4, 1940.

Except where a much-needed fall growth is cut really late, agronomists are in agreement that the last cutting of a given season should be early enough to permit 1 ft. or more of top growth to replenish root reserves before winter sets in. In sections of very mild winters such as in the southwestern United States, management to avoid winter injury is not a problem.

Experiments conducted by the U.S. Department of Agriculture[1] involving comprehensive harvesting and feeding trials strongly support the desirability of cutting alfalfa in the early- to half-bloom rather than in the full-bloom stage. In these experiments, conducted with irrigated alfalfa at Huntly, Mont., no injury resulted from cutting alfalfa for 3 years in initial bloom and half bloom as compared with cutting in full bloom, and lowest yields were secured from that cut in full bloom. The differences between alfalfa cut in initial bloom and half bloom were not material from either the yield or the feeding standpoint. However, the alfalfa cut in full bloom was distinctly inferior in percentage of protein, calcium, and phosphorus, had a higher fiber content, and was less leafy and of poorer color. The full-bloom alfalfa was also lower in digestion coefficient. When these hays were fed to dairy cows without supplementary feeds, consumption was about the same for each kind of hay but more milk and more butterfat per cow were produced with the earlier cut hay.

In summarizing the experiment, these investigators stated:

Considering all phases of this experiment, it is evident that alfalfa hay cut at the initial- or half-bloom stage is markedly superior in all respects to alfalfa cut at the full-bloom stage. While cutting at the initial-bloom stage has some advantages over cutting at the half-bloom stage, especially in yield of total digestible nutrients, the advantages are too slight to have any great significance, especially when considered from the practical standpoint. The line of demarcation, or the change that takes place in the plant between the initial-bloom and the half-bloom stage, is rather indistinct; and cutting at either stage, or between the two stages, would be good practice.

Where alfalfa is grown in mixtures with grasses, the crop is generally cut at the proper stage for the alfalfa. This tends to be somewhat early for most grasses and results in a mixed hay comparable with straight alfalfa in feeding value, especially if alfalfa predominates in the mixture.

Mixtures of alfalfa and such grasses as timothy or smooth brome are easier to cure than straight alfalfa. This is largely due to the

[1] DAWSON, J. R., D. V. KOPLAND, and R. R. GRAVES, Yield, Chemical Composition, and Feeding Value for Milk Production of Alfalfa Hay Cut at Three Stages of Maturity, *U.S. Dept. Agr. Tech. Bul.* 739, 1940.

fact that the grasses contain less moisture than alfalfa when they are cut rather than to a more rapid rate of moisture loss. In northern and corn-belt states, when first-cutting alfalfa contains 72 to 75 per cent moisture, timothy, smooth brome, orchard grass, and others of a similar nature can be expected to contain 65 to 68 per cent. It is also possible that windrows of mixed grass-legume hay are better aerated than straight alfalfa or clover.

Time of Cutting Other Hay Crops.—In cutting red clover the quality of the hay and the influence of time of cutting on the potential seed crop from the second cutting are considerations. Both hay quality of the first crop and seed yield from the second growth are favored if red clover is cut after blossoming is well under way but considerably before the full-bloom stage has been reached. The yield of protein per acre is greatest when approximately 50 per cent of the plants are in bloom.

Sweet clover is difficult to cure as hay regardless of the stage of cutting. If cut early, the stems are very succulent and often the weather is unfavorable for curing. If cut late, the stems are very woody. If this crop is to be used for hay, as practicable a procedure as any is to cut it with the grain binder just as the first blossoms appear and allow for a prolonged curing period for the sheaves set up in shocks. The outside of the sheaves will discolor rapidly; but discoloration will usually not penetrate deeply, and fairly good hay should result.

Lespedeza contains less moisture than any of the other hay crops and is therefore more easily cured. Lespedeza harvest is usually carried on at a season when weather conditions are likely to be favorable for curing. It is preferably cut for hay considerably before the full-bloom stage. This permits development of seed on the second growth for a volunteer seeding.

The general tendency with grass hays is to cut them much too late to make very nutritious feed. With respect to timothy, Pollock and Hosterman[1] of the U.S. Department of Agriculture state:

Timothy should be cut for hay after it is fully headed out but before it has reached the full-bloom stage. Experiments conducted at North Ridgeville, Ohio, . . . showed that timothy cut when fully headed produced 1,781 lb. of dry hay per acre, which contained 128 lb. of protein. Timothy cut in the early-bloom stage produced 2,113 lb. of dry hay per acre, which contained 136 lb. of protein. Timothy cut after it had just passed the full-bloom stage produced 2,228 lb. of dry hay per acre, of which 119 lb. were protein. . . .

[1] POLLOCK, E. O., and W. H. HOSTERMAN, High-grade Timothy and Clover Hay, *U.S. Dept. Agr. Farmers' Bul.* 1770, 1937.

Examinations of the meadows from which the hay was cut disclosed no weakening or thinning effects for any stage of harvest.

HAY CURING

The curing of hay is the process of getting it dry enough so that it may be stored in stack, mow, or bale without danger of future spoilage due to excessive fermentation and heating and the development of molds. The methods employed vary greatly in different areas and with different crops. The choice of a method is influenced by climatic conditions, the kind and amount of hay to be handled, and the cost and availability of labor and equipment.

Fig. 38.—Harvesting alfalfa with a sweep rake. (*Courtesy of John Deere, Moline, Ill.*)

Curing Methods for Extremely Humid Areas.—In Norway, Sweden, and Finland where summer temperatures are generally cool, humidity is high, and rains are frequent, most of the hay is draped on pole or wire frames shortly after it is cut. Most of the spoilage during the prolonged curing period necessary in such regions is thus limited to the hay on the immediate surface. The method is very effective in making possible the curing of good hay despite unfavorable weather but is extravagant with respect to hand labor. It is occasionally used in the northern United States by farmers of Scandinavian descent in handling small acreages.

Curing hay on tripods is another laborious method sometimes used where curing is unusually difficult. A quantity of partly cured hay, amounting to 500 to 600 lb. when dry, is piled into a large cock built over a tripod to keep the center hollow as an aid to ventilation.

VanderMeulen[1] has reported on a third method suitable where weather conditions are adverse. It consists in building high straight-sided cocks, about 4 ft. in diameter, around poles set firmly in the ground. The poles are made from young trees about 3 in. in diameter at the base. When the branches are trimmed off, prongs 2 or 3 in. long are left, which tend to hold up the hay and keep the center loose. The hay is piled well over the top of each pole to form a rain-shedding cap as the hay settles. Hay thus stacked, with 50 per cent moisture but free from external rain or dew, cured into much better condition than that cured in cocks or windrows. The labor was not materially greater than that involved in ordinary cock curing. The hay is kept off the ground by 6-in. boards nailed at right angles to the pole.

Curing in Cocks.—When most of the hay crop was handled by hand, curing was usually completed in cocks. These are small field piles which, if well built, are not greatly injured by light rains but are subject to weather damage during prolonged adverse periods. If conditions are reasonably favorable, hay cured in cocks is likely to be of good color and condition. The chief disadvantages are that cocked hay dries more slowly, longer, though not necessarily greater, weather hazards being thus entailed, and that there are much greater man-labor requirements than are involved in windrow and swath curing.

Windrow Curing.—In windrow curing the hay is raked into long windrows, usually with a side-delivery rake. When curing is completed, the hay may be gathered from the windrows by hand, with a hay loader, a field baler, or a field chopper. Two or more swaths are raked together to make one windrow.

Swath Curing.—The swath is the layer of hay left as it has fallen over the mower bar. In heavy hay the stems tend to be covered and the leaves more exposed. Hay left in the swath for long periods is subject to a greater percentage of bleaching and leaf shattering than is involved in any other method of curing.

Field-curing Methods Compared.—Several methods of curing alfalfa have been studied in Michigan experiments,[2] swath curing proving the most unsatisfactory. In every instance the swath-cured alfalfa was the lowest of all in protein. The ground from which the swath-cured hay was raked was coated with leaves that had shattered off the alfalfa, and the hay was stemmy and brittle and faded or

[1] VANDERMEULEN, E., Pole-stacks for Curing Hay in the Upper Peninsula, *Mich. Agr. Expt. Sta. Quart. Bul.*, Vol. 23, No. 4, 1941.

[2] RATHER, H. C., and R. H. MORRISH, Experiments with Curing Alfalfa Hay, *Mich. Agr. Expt. Sta. Quart. Bul.*, Vol. 17, No. 4, 1935.

bleached in appearance. The best hay was that cured in cocks, its protein content being 16.7 per cent as compared with 15.7 per cent for that cured in windrows and 13.7 per cent for that cured in the swath. However, the windrow-cured hay dried much faster than that cured in cocks and only slightly more slowly than that cured in the swath, so that the window-curing method proved by far the most practical for the handling of any substantial acreage.

As a result of comprehensive experiments conducted in Nebraska, Kiesselbach and Anderson[1] likewise advise windrow curing. They suggest that raking be done after the hay has been in the swath 4 to 8 hours to facilitate rapid drying, emphasizing that, in any case, the raking should be done before the leaves dry sufficiently to cause much shattering. Cocking was found objectionable because of its retarding influence on moisture loss and the consequent exposure of the hay in the field to greater chances of damage from rain.

Curing Practice and Vitamins.—The vitamin content of hay is influenced by the crop grown, its general vigor, the stage at which it is cut, curing practice, and storage conditions. With respect to curing practice, vitamin D is formed under the influence of the sun's rays when hay is dried in full sunshine and in thin layers. The conservation of the other vitamins in hay is favored by artificial drying or drying in diffuse light, as in cocks or windrows. Krizenecky,[2] a European investigator, found that vitamin A (carotene) is conserved best by artificial drying, next by drying on stands in thick layers, and finally by ensilage where the sap is retained. Greatest vitamin A losses occur when hay is dried in full sunlight. His work indicated that vitamins B and E are similarly least affected by artificial drying, more so by drying on stands, and most by drying on the ground and that any drying practically destroys vitamin C.

Operations in Windrow Curing.—In curing hay by the windrow system mowing may be started early in the morning regardless of dew on the standing hay. If the day is clear and hot, all hay cut in any one day should be raked by that evening. If the weather is cool and cloudy, there is no objection to delaying the raking until the next day; but prolonged swath curing, especially with crops that easily lose their leaves, such as alfalfa and the clovers, is damaging to color and quality.

In some instances, tractor-drawn mowers with long cutting bars have the rake hooked behind the tractor so that one swath is mowed

[1] KIESSELBACH, T. A., and A. ANDERSON, Quality of Alfalfa Hay in Relation to Curing Practice, *U.S. Dept. Agr. Tech. Bul.* 235, 1931.

[2] KRIZENECKY, J., Vitamin Content of Conserved Forage, *Casové Otásky Zemedal.*, No. 56, 1936, *Sect. Biol. Inst. Zootechn*, Brno, Czechoslovakia.

and the previously mowed swath is raked in one trip around the field. Hay raked so soon after being cut usually dries out a little more slowly than that allowed to wilt in the swath for a few hours.

Raking can be done most conveniently with a left-hand side-delivery rake. This will rake two 5- or 6-ft. swaths into one windrow. By running the rake in the same direction as that in which the mower was operated the leaves are worked toward the center and the stems toward the outside of the windrow, with a consequent desirable tendency toward the two drying out at about the same time. Raking in the opposite direction or with a dump rake will give essentially the same curing results if windrows are of the same size; but the mechanical operation is less convenient, and there is more tendency to leave occa-

Fig. 39.—Curing alfalfa in Michigan. In well-raked windrows the leaves and stems dry out in about the same time to make leafy hay of good quality.

sional heavy bunches which dry out more slowly and may provide small centers for heating and spoilage in storage.

The tedding of alfalfa or clover hay tends to increase leaf losses. Windrows can be turned without undue disturbance with the side-delivery rake run so that the windrow is just tipped over with the rear end of the rake. Turning the windrow probably is only very slightly advantageous except in the case of hay that has been rained on. Repeated turning makes possible greater discoloration.

When Is Hay Dry Enough for Storage?—There is no very satisfactory specific answer to the question of when hay is ready for storage. Certainly, no particular length of curing time can be established as a guide; for curing time varies tremendously with the weather components, temperature, humidity, wind velocity, rain, and dew.

Such a rule-of-thumb method as twisting small handfuls of representative stems in two and noting whether any moisture is brought to the surface has little practical value except for long-experienced haymakers, and then other factors more or less intangible and not readily described aid these experienced operators in making their decision. The best indication that the determination of the fitness of hay for storage is exceedingly difficult is the vast amount of hay that is put up with too much moisture every season and that as a result heats excessively and is partly damaged in storage.

If quick field moisture tests could be made accurately,[1] the problem would be simplified but not completely solved. Unfortunately, there is still considerable uncertainty as to just how much moisture hay may contain and still be safe for storage. Hay containing 30 per cent moisture might be safe on the edge of a well-ventilated mow or stack, but severe heating and discoloration of hay containing only 25 per cent moisture have occurred in the center of large mows. In 1940, H. H. Musselman of the Agricultural Engineering Section, Michigan Agricultural Experiment Station, made 100 hay bales only 1½ ft. square, with hay of various moisture contents and under different degrees of pressure. Some of these small bales were ventilated with holes through the center. In the case of every bale made with hay containing 25 per cent moisture or more, the hay discolored or molded or did both, regardless of pressure or ventilation. Some of the hay containing between 20 and 25 per cent moisture and under high pressure, which reduced further drying out, showed discoloration.

It seems justified to conclude, in the light of present information, that hay will very probably heat, discolor, and develop molds if put into storage containing over 25 per cent moisture and that hay to be baled, chopped, or stored in the center of poorly ventilated mows must be even drier than this if it is to be stored without undergoing excessive fermentation and marked discoloration.

HAY STORAGE

Hay storage involves problems of economics and mechanics to a far greater extent than problems of agronomy. If losses incurred in stacking amount to about 10 per cent, barn space secured at a reasonable cost is probably a sound investment from the standpoint both of saving the hay and of the economy of feeding it out to livestock. A

---

[1] One such method has been reported: see R. I. Parks, A Rapid and Simple Method for Determining Moisture in Forages and Grains, *Jour. Amer. Soc. Agron.*, Vol. 33, No. 4, 1941.

10 per cent saving on 100 tons of $10 hay would amount to $100, or 5 per cent interest on a $2,000 storage. Fancy, elaborate structures have to pay dividends on their aesthetic value; they do not pay dividends because of their intrinsic value as places in which to store hay. The cheapest structure that will last, that is conveniently located with respect to feeding out the hay, and that will protect it from rain and snow is the most practical for hay storage.

Stacking.—Stacking provides a cheap and easily accessible place to store hay. The hay can be got into the stack quickly and cheaply with sweep rakes and any of the various stackers. Spoilage is much greater in humid areas than in the semiarid sections of the West. It can be reduced by making long but relatively narrow stacks, well tramped in the center, bulging 4 to 6 ft. above the ground level, and narrowing into a peak at the top. Because grass hay sheds rain better than legume hay, it is desirable to cap the stacks with only partly dried grass hay. Heavy waterproof paper, canvas, or corrugated sheet iron is even more effective.

Barn Storage.—When loose hay is stored in the barn, it is brought in by wagon or truck and unloaded with rope slings or large hayforks of diverse types. As the slings or fork are tripped in the mow, there is a tendency for too much packing where the hay falls. Overpacked hay is subject to heating of greater intensity and possible spoilage. Frequently farmers suspend poles horizontally in such a position as to break the fall of the hay and roll it to either side of the mow. Heating is much less likely if the hay is stored in narrow bents 12 to 16 ft. wide rather than in wide mows which greatly limit air circulation. Ventilator shafts placed across the mow at 8-ft. intervals also reduce the possibilities of overheating but are inconvenient.

Chopping Hay.—In recent years the practice of chopping hay and blowing it into the barn or other storage has become common. Chopping the hay does not increase its feeding value, but it does reduce space requirements very materially. Two to two and one-half times as much chopped hay as unchopped long hay can be stored in a given space. This necessitates first of all greater strength in the storage structure to hold the greatly increased weight. Of even greater importance is the necessity for more adequate ventilation. Chopped hay is more subject to heating than long hay of the same moisture content. It must be drier than long hay before storage is attempted in order to reduce the risk of spoilage in storage due to excessive heating. In experiments at the Michigan Agricultural Experiment Station,[1]

[1] RATHER, H. C., *et al.*, Alfalfa in Michigan, *Mich. Agr. Expt. Sta. Cir. Bul.* 154, 1936.

one stack of chopped hay in which the moisture content did not exceed 30 per cent, except for occasional bunches, was ignited by spontaneous combustion. Numerous barn fires have been reported where chopped hay containing too much moisture had been placed in storage. Because chopped hay must be drier, the longer field curing required entails longer weather hazards each season.

Some farmers have stacked hay rapidly in the field at harvesttime and later, when work was less pressing, hauled it to the barn where this thoroughly cured material was chopped into the mow. This obviously entails extra labor but reduces both weather and storage hazards.

Field Baling.—The field baler, operated with its own power unit or by a power take-off from a tractor, bales hay directly from the windrow.

Fig. 40.—The field pick-up baler reduces labor and transportation costs in hay harvest Hay must be thoroughly cured if it is to be baled from the windrow.

The equipment is economical only for the handling of large acreages but has been made available to smaller operators through custom work. The usual custom charge of $2 to $2.50 a ton gives a good indication of the cost of this operation. Baled hay saves greatly on storage space and is conveniently handled at feeding time.

The general experience seems to be that hay may be safely baled at a 20 per cent moisture content but that hay containing 25 per cent moisture is almost certain to mold and discolor. If the bales are left in the field and are not too tightly packed, the additional drying helps ensure quality but the time involved entails the risk of sudden rains. Ventilation in storage is aided if the bales are piled on edge with the chaff edge of one bale next to the fold edge of the other. A few narrow spaces between tiers of piled bales will likewise aid in ventilation.

Baling for the Market.—The advisability of selling hay from the farm depends on the circumstances. A ton of alfafa hay contains approximately 48 lb. of nitrogen, 11 lb. of phosphoric acid, and 45 lb. of potash. Alfalfa and other legume hays can get nitrogen from the air, but the phosphoric acid and potash are direct removals from the soil and must be replaced if soil productivity is to be maintained. The livestock farmer who feeds his hay is in a position to return much of its fertilizing constituents to the land. However, when hay is high-priced and a surplus is available on a given farm, the sale of some of it is warranted.

Top grades of hay command a premium. High-grade hay is dependent not only on the production and curing of a good crop by methods already described but also on good baling procedure. Baling undercured hay results in molding, heating, and discoloration. On the other hand, baling hay, especially legume hay, in very hot, dry, windy weather is accompanied by shattering of the leaves and a resultant stemmy material of decreased sales and feeding value. Hay that has already gone through a sweat in the stack or mow may be baled to best advantage after the harvest season in cooler, more humid weather. In baling stacked hay, the discolored outside portions of spoiled hay from any part of the stack should not be included lest it spoil the price of the good hay.

Artificial Drying.—There are numerous types of artificial driers that by means of high temperatures quickly reduce the moisture content of freshly cut or partly cured hay to a low point where it is safe for storage and shipment. None of these are suitable for handling small quantities of hay because of the high investment in essential equipment and the high cost of fuel and operation. These forage driers are used commercially, however, in the preparation of alfalfa meal and the high-protein high-vitamin products made from very young grasses. Artificially dried forage is originally high in carotene, basis of vitamin A; but this constituent is unstable and is usually partly lost in storage. Sun curing is essential for the development of vitamin D, and thus artificially dried forage is low in this constituent.

The artificial drying of forage involves various economic and agronomic implications. If either the cereal grasses or the perennial grasses are to be used, the crop must be cut at a very early stage of development to ensure high protein and vitamin content of the dried product. Yields are relatively low at this early stage, and therefore the price and value of the material must be high to make the enterprise economically sound.

Driers must be operated for as long a season as possible to reduce overhead expenses and maintain continuous labor. Thus a succession of suitable forage material is needed for drying, beginning with the first growth of cereals and perennial grasses and carrying on through the summer and fall harvest of alfalfa. In the case of alfalfa, trade interests demand harvest of the crop when very high in protein; therefore, a portion of it is cut at early stages of development for each growth, some of it at critical fall periods, resulting in lowered yields and a shortened life of the stand. Again these yield deterrents must be compensated for by adequate prices, or the selling of forage for artificial drying and the processing of the special feeds that this process makes possible may become an enterprise that is unsound financially and destructive to the continued productivity of the soil. Very little artificially dried forage is fed on the farm of the producer. Its development thus far has been as a cash-crop enterprise. All cash-crop enterprises demand special attention to considerations of soil management.

Measuring Hay.—It is sometimes desirable to estimate the quantity of hay in a stack or mow. This involves first of all determination of the volume of hay, an easy procedure in the regularly shaped mow but a little more complicated in the stack. Hosterman[1] of the U.S. Department of Agriculture has developed several formulas for determining the number of cubic feet in haystacks of various shapes. For rectangular stacks the formulas suggested are

Square flat-topped stacks $(0.56 \times O - 0.55 \times W) \times WL$
High round-topped stacks $(0.52 \times O - 0.46 \times W) \times WL$
Low round-topped stacks $(0.52 \times O - 0.44 \times W) \times WL$

In these formulas, O equals the over from the ground on one side to the ground on the other, W equals the width, and L the length, all in feet. The result gives the approximate number of cubic feet in the stack.

For round stacks, Hosterman suggests the formula

$$\text{Volume} = (0.04 \times O - 0.012 \times C)C^2$$

In this formula, C equals the circumference at the ground and O the over.

These estimates are completed on the basis of the approximate number of cubic feet in a ton of hay. This varies with different kinds of hay, the moisture content of the hay, and the degree of settling.

[1] Hosterman, W. H., Measuring Hay in Stacks, *U.S. Dept. Agr. Leaflet 72,* 1931.

The following figures are given by Hosterman as averages obtained from a large number of stacks:

Kind of hay	Length of time in stack	
	30–90 days	Over 90 days
Alfalfa	485 cu. ft. per ton	470 cu. ft. per ton
Timothy and timothy mixed	640 cu. ft. per ton	625 cu. ft. per ton
Wild	600 cu. ft. per ton	450 cu. ft. per ton

Review Questions

1. Why is a bright-green color desirable in hay?
2. What are the effects of rain during the curing process on the quality of hay?
3. What takes place as a result of excessive fermentation of hay?
4. Discuss the importance of leaves with respect to hay quality.
5. How does stage of maturity of the crop when it is cut affect the quality of hay and the vigor of the plants?
6. What factors are involved in determining the proper time to cut hay?
7. Why are mixtures of alfalfa and timothy ready for storage in less time after cutting than straight alfalfa?
8. What are the advantages and disadvantages of curing hay in the swath? Should this method be used?
9. Compare the procedures of curing hay in cocks and in windrows, and indicate the circumstances under which each method might be used advantageously.
10. Why has there been a marked increase in the field baling of hay?
11. What are the advantages and disadvantages of chopping hay?

Problems

1. A farm has 100 acres of alfalfa to be cut for hay. Is it economically sound to start harvest of this crop when the first cutting is in the bud stage? What difficulties might be expected, and how can they be minimized?
2. Describe a hay-curing method for a cool humid climate, and indicate a situation where the extra labor involved might be justified.
3. Make a list of the equipment needed for curing hay in windrows and putting it into the barn, giving the approximate cost of each piece of equipment.
4. Outline the steps in hay harvest where the hay is to be stacked in the field by using a sweep rake and a field stacker.
5. A farmer has twice as much hay as can be stored in his barn in the usual manner. How can he handle this hay most advantageously? Explain fully.
6. A farmer is offered $12 an acre for his alfalfa by a hay-drying company. The farmer is to cut and rake the hay; the company will haul it from the windrow to the drier. Should he sell? Explain your answer in detail.
7. A well-settled, high, round-topped stack of alfalfa is 20 ft. wide, 50 ft. over, and 60 ft. long. One hay buyer offers the owner of this stack $6 a ton for the hay; another bids $300 for the stack. To which buyer should he sell?

References

HENSON, E. R.: Curing and Storage of Alfalfa Hay, *Iowa Agr. Expt. Sta. Res. Bul.* 251, 1939.

MORRISON, F. B.: "Feeds and Feeding," The Morrison Publishing Co., 20th ed., Ithaca, N.Y., 1936.

POLLOCK, E. O., and W. H. HOSTERMAN: High Grade Timothy and Clover Hay, *U.S. Dept. Agr. Farmers' Bul.* 1770, 1937.

WESTOVER, H. L., and W. H. HOSTERMAN: The Uses of Alfalfa, *U.S. Dept. Agr. Farmers' Bul.* 1839, 1940.

CHAPTER X

SILAGE

Silage is green fodder preserved by a natural fermentation process. It may be made from any edible green crop containing 65 to 70 per cent moisture. The process of making silage is of extremely ancient origin, but the first experimental silos of modern design used in the United States were built in 1881. About 5 per cent of the United States corn acreage is annually harvested for silage. The sorghums, small grains cut when green, and in more recent years grass and legume forages are widely preserved in this manner.

PRINCIPLES OF SILAGE MAKING

Respiration.—Preservation of silage is accomplished by taking advantage of natural processes. Every living cell carries on respira-

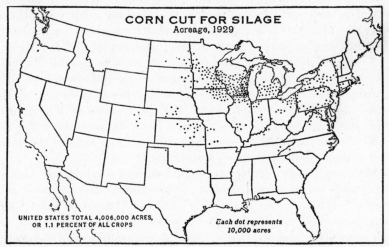

Fig. 41.—Corn is used for silage principally in providing dairy cows with a succulent winter feed high in vitamins. The acreage of corn for silage is located mostly in the dairy belt, notably in Wisconsin, Minnesota, Michigan, and New York, and along the northern margin of the corn belt. Some use is also made of corn silage to feed beef cattle and sheep, notably in Kansas, Nebraska, and Colorado. Corn cut for silage in 1929 constituted a little more than 4 per cent of the total corn acreage. (*U.S. Department of Agriculture.*)

tion, and the cells of a green forage plant remain alive for some time after the plant is cut. When a green crop is properly packed into a

171

silo, the amount of air trapped with it is restricted. However, this air provides oxygen for normal aerobic respiration and the release of its by-products carbon dioxide and water. This respiration, or oxidation, process is associated with a rise in temperature and the destruction of some organic matter. If too much air is trapped with the fodder, heating, and the destruction of feeding constituents is excessive, and the silage becomes darkened in color. It may be palatable, but its digestibility is reduced. In the more extreme cases the fodder becomes musty, and molds develop.

The necessity for restricting respiration of plant cells and aerobic bacteria suggests the first essential to good silage preservation. The material must be so packed as to avoid trapping any quantity of air. Aerobic respiration must be held within bounds.

Fermentation.—When the air in the packed fodder is exhausted, fermentive bacteria become active. In good silage, the chief end product of this fermentation is lactic acid, the same as that developing in sour milk. This should make up 1 to 2 per cent of the silage. Acetic acid (vinegar) and alcohol also result from the fermentive action.

These organic acids act as the silage preservative. If they are present in sufficient amount to give the silage an acidity of pH4 or under, the activities of undesirable putrefactive bacteria are inhibited. The lactic acid organisms can continue to develop at high acidities.

A lack of fermentable carbohydrates, such as soluble starches and sugars, fermentation in the absence of air (anaerobic), as with excessive pressure, or very wet material may result in slowing up the formation of lactic acid and permit the development of butyric acid which has the smell of rancid butter. Thus, the more favorable the conditions for the rapid development of lactic acid, the less the likelihood of unfavorable types of fermentation.

Molasses Silage.—Such plants as corn and sorghum are high in fermentable carbohydrates and, on fermentation, develop lactic acid rapidly. They are easy to preserve as silage. Immature grasses and legumes, such as alfalfa, red clover, sweet clover, and soybeans, are high in protein and relatively lower in fermentable carbohydrates. If these crops are cut and packed in exactly the right manner, containing neither too much nor too little water, they will make good silage. But it is more difficult to make good silage from them than from corn or sorghum.

The addition of readily fermentable material is naturally suggested. For example, if corn and soybeans or corn and alfalfa are mixed in the silo, the corn, with its liberal quantities of fermentable carbohydrates, ensures satisfactory preservation of all the material. Because corn is not always available when alfalfa or some other protein-rich forage is to be ensiled, a more concentrated form of carbohydrate material is desirable. Any form of sugar could be used; but ordinarily in this country the most economical concentrated material is molasses, by-product in the refining of both cane and beet sugar. Molasses is essentially 50 per cent sugar; it can readily be applied in solution to the fodder being ensiled; and it has definite feeding value, molasses at $15 a ton being comparable with corn at $0.56 a bushel.

The quantity of molasses is varied with different crops. In general, the higher the protein content of the forage, the greater the quantity of molasses that is added. In the case of corn or sorghum, none is necessary.

The Missouri Agricultural Experiment Station[1] recommends the following approximate amounts to be added to each ton of ensiled material:

Cereal grasses 40 to 50 lb. (3½ to 4 gal.).
Mixed grasses and legumes 60 to 70 lb. (5 to 6 gal.).
Legumes 70 to 80 lb. (6 to 7 gal.).

How Molasses Is Added.—Silo fillers are now designed to handle forage crops to which preservatives are added. This type of filler has an attached valve that automatically regulates the proper flow of molasses into the blower and shuts it off entirely when no material is going through the cutter.

If the automatic valve is not available, molasses can be added through the blower housing by running it from an elevated drum, usually a sticky job, or by running it from a drum on the ground in which air pressure is maintained with a tire pump and the flow of molasses is regulated through valves. Two valves are preferable, one set in a fixed position to regulate the rate of flow, the other a shut-off. To obtain ease of flow the molasses may be diluted with water. Whatever system is used, the molasses should be turned off just before finishing each load to avoid clogging the blower pipes.

Acidified Silage.—The usual ensiling process depends on the development of organic acids to preserve the material. The system of adding inorganic acids, while the fodder is being packed, to secure immediate acidification has been widely used in Europe and to a lesser extent in this country. A. I. Virtanen of Finland showed that in order to reduce silage losses to a low level it was necessary to bring

[1] RAGSDALE, A. C., and H. A. HERMAN, Legumes, Grasses and Cereal Crops for Silage, *Mo. Agr. Expt. Sta. Cir. Bul.* 209, 1940.

the whole mass to an acidity of between pH3 and pH4 as rapidly as possible, the formation of butyric acid being thus inhibited. This he accomplished by adding a solution of twice normal sulphuric and hydrochloric acids in equal proportions, although ¼ sulphuric and ¾ hydrochloric is sometimes used.

This method, known as the *A.I.V. process*, after Virtanen, is patented. It is effective in preserving good silage and especially in conserving the carotene of the green fodder. However, it has several disadvantages. The acids used have no value other than as preservatives; hence, their cost is a full charge against the ensiling process. The amount of acid used must be adjusted to the moisture content, the protein content, and the original acidity of the crop. If the acidity is in excess of pH3, the silage is too acid, and the excess inorganic acids are objectionable in the feed and must be neutralized by feeding lime. If an acidity of at least pH4 is not attained, preservation of the silage is incomplete.

The acid is very corrosive to machinery and hard on the skin and clothing of persons handling it. It should not be introduced into the cutter but must be sprayed directly over the surface of the silage. It must be handled in acid-resistant containers and is not suitable for paper-lined temporary silos.

Commercial phosphoric acid may also be used to preserve silage. The phosphoric acid (68 to 75 per cent) is diluted by adding one part of acid, by volume, to five parts of water. (Water should never be added to acid. A better mixture is secured if the heavier acid is poured into the water, and the risk of acid spattering out of the container is eliminated.) The diluted acid may be applied directly over the feeding table as close to the knives as is feasible or in the lower part of the blower housing. Approximately 16 lb. (1½ gal.) is used to a ton of legumes. Lesser quantities are used with grasses, and none is required with corn or sorghum.

Not only does the proper use of phosphoric acid aid in silage preservation, but this material is of value in the livestock ration, and much of it eventually goes back to the soil with the manure. Like molasses, phosphoric acid serves more than one purpose.

SILAGE CROPS

Advantages of Ensiling Corn.—Corn is by far the most important silage crop in the United States. From four to six million acres of corn are made into silage each year. In the major dairy areas of such states as New York, Wisconsin, Minnesota, and Michigan, more than one-half the corn crop is grown for the silo. Silage is made from over two-thirds the entire corn crop in New York. Wisconsin, however, leads in number of silos and normally puts up well over a million acres of silage corn.

Some of the reasons why corn has assumed such importance as a silage crop are as follows:

1. Corn is high in fermentable carbohydrates and can be made into good silage with little difficulty.

2. The forage portions of a corn plant are far more readily eaten by livestock and have greater feeding value when made into silage than if fed as dry fodder or stover.

3. Corn silage provides a succulent feed for winter use at much less expense than is entailed in the production and storage of root crops.

4. Corn may be put up as silage under wet weather conditions that make it exceedingly difficult to preserve the grain and stover or to harvest hay of good quality.

5. Silage has extended corn growing into areas too cool for really effective grain production.

Very early varieties, which make small stalk growth in the corn belt, mature more slowly but get much larger when taken into the cooler North. Thus, though growing corn for grain is hazardous for the northern farmer, he. can produce silage comparable in yield, though perhaps not in quality, with that secured in better corn country.

6. Corn, as silage, is harvested early enough to permit the sowing of fall grain or a winter cover crop to aid in soil conservation.

7. The silo provides a most effective way to handle immature corn.

8. In areas where the European corn borer is troublesome, the crop can be harvested for silage before serious breakage and rotting of the stalks occur. Furthermore, if the corn is cut low, nearly all the borers will be removed from the cornfield and all those so removed will be destroyed in the ensiling process.

The Place for Grass and Legume Silage.—Where corn is well adapted, it will produce more effective digestible nutrients to the acre than almost any other crop. However, it has some close rivals, especially when costs are considered. The digestible nutrients in 100 lb. of alfalfa can be produced on good alfalfa land at but little more than one-half the cost of the digestible nutrients in 100 lb. of corn. There are many areas in which high yields of alfalfa can be secured but in which corn is not well adapted. In other areas, yields from corn and suitable forage crops are very similar.

At East Lansing, Mich., a yield of 10.9 tons green weight an acre was secured from two cuttings of an alfalfa-brome-grass mixture in 1939 and of 11.4 tons in 1940. Corn-silage yields secured under comparable conditions at the same place were 8.5 tons an acre in 1939 and 11.7 tons an acre in 1940. Dry-matter percentages were almost identical. Sweet clover not uncommonly yields over 15 tons of green material to the acre.

The above yields are, of course, much better than average. Grass or legume silage weighs approximately three times as much as the same

Fig. 42.—Making alfalfa silage in Michigan. (*Courtesy of E. E. Patton.*)

material would if cured as dry hay. Thus, a 3-ton crop of alfalfa hay is equivalent to about a 9-ton yield of alfalfa silage.

Silos cost money, but so do haymows. There are about 470 cu. ft. in a ton of well-settled alfalfa hay.[1] A cubic foot of alfalfa hay therefore contains about 3.8 lb. of dry matter. Because it is packed more closely, 1 cu. ft. of alfalfa silage should contain 12 to 14 lb. of dry matter. Thus, 1 ton of dry matter put up as alfalfa silage requires only about one-third as much space as 1 ton of dry matter put up as alfalfa hay.

[1] Hosterman, W. H., Measuring Hay in Stacks, *U.S. Dept. Agr Leaflet* 72, 1931.

Forage Silage Aids Soil Conservation.—It has come to be generally appreciated that intertilled crops such as corn permit the land to be subjected to the destructive effects of erosion whereas sod-forming crops reduce erosion to a negligible quantity. On land subject to such erosion the production of silage from a suitable grass-legume mixture, rather than from corn or any row crop, should be sound economy both from the standpoint of reduced tillage costs and also with respect to the long-time conservation of the productivity of the soil.

Grass Silage vs. Hay.—The argument for grass-legume silage advanced in the preceding paragraph is fully as valid for hay. At the outset, it should be stated that livestock farms can use both hay and silage to advantage. It is generally agreed among livestock feeders that animals will consume more dry matter if fed some hay along with silage than if fed either alone.

Strong reasons for definitely planning for and making silage from a portion of the hay crop may be advanced for most livestock-producing areas. For example, the harvest of the first cutting of alfalfa or an alfalfa-grass mixture normally comes when weather conditions are none too favorable. Rains are almost sure to damage part of the crop as it is being field-cured for hay. These weather hazards are also a deterrent to good haymaking in the humid East and South where but little alfalfa is grown.

Good silage can be made despite bad weather. However, it is not an emergency procedure to be worked out as a guessing game with the "weatherman"; rather, it is a process of forage conservation which, if used at all, needs to be a definite year-to-year part of the farm plan.

Associated with weather hazards is the loss of leaves and nutrients in hay that is too dry or the loss of nutrients and color by rain leaching and sun bleaching of field-cured hay. These losses likewise may be eliminated by putting the green hay crop into the silo.

In areas where hay can be cured without difficulty and in the handling of second- and third-cutting alfalfa when weather is usually favorable, the making of hay is the cheaper process. In general, a pound of dry matter in silage has the same feeding value as that which a pound of dry matter of the same crop, cut at the same stage of maturity, would have if cured into good hay.

Silage and Vitamin A.—One nutritional advantage is possessed by good silage over good hay. Carotene, the source material for vitamin A found in the green parts of growing plants, is preserved far more effectively in silage than in hay. This advantage may be of importance in winter feeding especially if the ration is otherwise deficient in the vitamin.

Choosing the Crop.—Although corn will probably remain the dominant silage crop in the United States, the better understanding of methods of ensiling grasses and legumes makes it possible to include a long list of these as potential sources of silage.

The list of silage crops may now include the following:

Row crops:
    Corn
    Grain sorghum
    Sweet sorghum
Cereals:
    Oats
    Barley
    Wheat
    Rye
    Emmer and spelt
Grasses:
    Sudan grass
    The millets
    Reed canary grass
    Timothy
    Smooth brome
    Orchard grass
    The rye grasses
    Quack grass
    Johnson grass
    Etc.

Legumes:
    Sweet clover
    Alfalfa
    Red clover
    Alsike
    Ladino
    Crimson clover
    Lespedeza
    Soybeans
    Cowpeas
    Vetch
    Field peas
By-products:
    Sugar-beet tops
    Pea vines

Mixtures of grasses and legumes such as alfalfa and bromegrass or timothy, red clover, and alsike may be, in fact often are, preferable to the separately grown grass or legume.

SILAGE CULTURAL PRACTICES

Stage of Harvest for Forages.—Grasses and legumes have commonly been cut for hay at a fairly advanced stage of maturity to lessen curing difficulties. The later harvests have been associated with a somewhat higher total yield but a lessening of quality. When grown for silage, it is easier to take advantage of the digestibility of the feeding constituents in the less mature forage. Feasible and desirable cutting stages for various crops are as follows: alfalfa at late bud to one-tenth bloom, sweet clover at early to one-half bloom, grasses in blossom, the clovers not later than full bloom, and soybeans when the pods are formed and one-third to two-thirds filled.

Desired Moisture.—When cut at the proper stage of maturity, grasses and legumes contain 65 to 75 per cent water. The crop is ready for the silo when it contains 65 to 70 per cent water. Early-cut alfalfa may well lie in the swath 3 to 8 hours during reasonable curing weather before it is ensiled. On a clear day with temperatures at 70 to 75°F., heavy first-cutting alfalfa will lose about 2 to 3 per cent of moisture per hour in the humid states.

Loading, Unloading, Chopping.—Because green, uncured material weighs 3 to 3½ times as much as cured hay, equipment to handle green forages must be strong. Sweet clover, soybeans, and small grains may be cut with a binder and the green sheaves handled with a fork.

Crops cut with a mower, such as alfalfa, clover, timothy, and others, ordinarily need not be raked. Heavy windrows increase the

FIG. 43.—Cutting sweet clover for silage with the plant in half bloom. The shocks at the right are wheat.

strain on loading equipment and likewise make the labor of handling on the load more difficult. A strong rake-bar type of hay loader will handle the green forage directly from the swath. Very little loading is required because the loads must be relatively small in volume on account of the heavy weight of the green material.

When the loading is done by truck, dumping the load at the filler saves time and equipment. A length of woven-wire fencing, fastened to the back of the truck and laid along the floor and up over the cab, can be used. When the load is in position at the filler, the end of the wire fencing over the cab is hooked by cable to a post back of the truck and, with the load held in this manner, the truck is simply driven out from under it.

It is desirable to use silage cutters particularly designed to handle forage crops, although the larger corn silage cutters usually work effectively on forage material. The machine should be set to cut at ¼ to ½ in. because the finely cut material is more readily packed to secure adequate exclusion of the air.

Field ensilage cutters have been designed for both corn and forage crops. These, operating from a power take-off, cut the material to the proper fineness as it is being picked up in the field. It is loaded directly into trucks from the cutter. Because of the initial large investment, the equipment is suitable only for large-scale operations. It effects a substantial saving of labor.

Silage-corn Varieties.—Growers of corn for silage normally use a later maturing type of corn than would be safe as a grain crop. Sometimes they go the extreme in this respect, planting extremely late varieties that are very deceptive as to yield because of their high water content. Actually these very late varieties possess little if any advantage in acre yield of dry matter, are difficult to ensile properly because of excessive water content, cost more to handle, and make a feed with a much lower grain content.

It is perfectly reasonable to use a somewhat later variety for silage than for grain. A desirable variety is a vigorous one that develops good ears and that normally reaches a stage of maturity, at silo filling time, in which the kernels are well dented and the ear contains about 50 per cent water. The stalks, at this stage, still contain 70 to 75 per cent water; thus, in all, there is ample moisture to ensure good preservation.

According to studies made at East Lansing, Mich.,[1] corn at this stage of development produces its maximum acre yield of total dry matter, with about 50 per cent of the dry matter made up of ears. Corn harvested in the milk stage has only about 25 per cent of its dry matter in the ears.

An acre of corn yielding about 10 tons of green weight will add well over 1,000 lb. of dry matter as the ear matures from 70 per cent moisture content down to 50 per cent. During this period there is very little change in green weight, the additional dry-matter yield being a replacement of water. Most of the added weight is in the ear.

The desirable silage practice, then, is to choose the most productive variety that will get down to 50 per cent ear-moisture content by silo filling time and to delay harvest until this variety is down to 50 per cent ear moisture. Earlier varieties are less productive; later ones make inferior silage.

In the event of a killing frost before the corn has reached desirable silage maturity the crop should be cut and ensiled as rapidly as possible to prevent loss of leaves and nutrients.

Spacing Corn for Silage.—In growing corn for grain, especially if it is to be hand-husked, spacing of the plants to permit the develop-

[1] RATHER, H. C., and A. R. MARSTON, A Study of Corn Maturity, *Mich. Agr. Expt. Sta. Quart. Bul.*, Vol. 22, No. 4, pp. 278–288, 1940.

ment of large ears is of practical importance. In silage, the grain yield can be secured from large numbers rather than from large size, and so silage corn is normally spaced more closely than grain corn. This makes for a somewhat higher acre yield. Corn is commonly planted for grain in 42-in. rows at three kernels per hill or drilled by dropping one kernel every 14 in. Twice this amount of seed can advantageously be used for silage corn by drilling the seed at a spacing of about 7 in. in the row. A 36-in. rather than a 42-in. row may also be used.

Corn and Soybean Silage.—At times, corn and soybeans are planted together for silage. There is very little, if any, advantage in yield from this practice, and the feeding value is changed very slightly; for this combination usually results in about 10 parts corn to 1 part soybeans. The corn-soybean mixture is inconvenient to handle.

Ensiling soybeans with corn when the two crops are grown separately is also practiced. The corn makes more certain desirable fermentation of the soybeans. Otherwise, there appear to be no advantages to the process, and the soybeans normally are less productive than corn.

Sunflower Silage.—Sunflowers will produce higher yields than corn in regions too cold for normal corn production. Cultural practices are the same as for corn. As a feed, sunflower silage contains less total digestible nutrients than immature corn, and the sunflowers are very inferior to well-matured corn silage. The sunflower silage is also relatively low in palatability.

Small-grain Silage.—Any of the small grains can be made into silage if cut in the milk or soft-dough stages. They may be useful as silage crops in regions where corn is not adapted. It is questionable whether the construction of a silo especially for small grains is warranted, for the relatively low acre yields make this silage rather expensive.

At the Michigan Agricultural Experiment Station, excellent stack silage has been made from oats cut in the milk stage with a binder. The sheaves were stacked in a straight-sided stack immediately after the crop was cut. There was a scant 1½ ft. of spoiled material, almost entirely the butts of the sheaves, on the outside. The silage proved very palatable and easy to handle; and the expense of a silo, a silo filler, and power for cutting was eliminated. Incidentally, seedings made with grain cut so early have a vastly improved chance to get established because of removal of competition for soil moisture.

Sorghum.—In the central and southern parts of the western plains, the sorghums are much more productive than corn. The grain sorghums are used for both grain and forage, and sweet sorghums are used for forage and sirup. Some varieties of sweet sorghum, such as Amber cane, are adapted to the North; but most of the grain types require a longer growing season.

Sweet sorghum is more commonly used as a silage crop than the grain types, but either kind can be used. Sorghum seeds should be ripe and hard when the plants are ensiled. Otherwise, the silage is likely to be excessively acid. If too dry, water may be added as the silo is being filled. Sorghum silage is not so valuable as well-eared corn silage but is advantageous where the sorghum is the more productive.

In regions subject to corn allotments under the production-control measures of the Agricultural Adjustment Administration, sorghum has been substituted for corn as a silage crop. This substitution is neither good crop control nor good soil conservation. In the northern corn belt, reports indicate sorghums to be around 80 per cent as valuable as corn as a silage crop and evidently somewhat harder on the productivity of the land.

Silage from Beet Tops.—Sugar-beet tops make a valuable by-product of the sugar-beet industry. Ordinarily, they can be fed most economically in the field. However, when sufficient numbers of livestock are not available either to pasture the tops during the early autumn or to consume them in the dry lot, it may be desirable, if extra feed is needed later, to store them for winter use.

Fresh beet tops contain too much water to be ensiled alone. To make good silage the material should contain at least 30 per cent dry matter, whereas fresh beet tops usually contain about 11 or 12 per cent dry matter. Before ensiling them, either they must be dried until they contain 30 to 35 per cent dry matter, or enough dry material such as chopped cornstalks or straw must be added to bring the dry-matter content of the mixture to the desired 30 per cent. If too wet, the silage will be too acid; if too dry, it will heat and mold. By using 1 ton of cornstalks to 2 tons of fresh sugar-beet tops, it should be possible to make good beet-top silage. Beet-top silage if fed in too large amounts without dry feed is likely to prove unduly laxative.

Types of Silos.—Silage is preserved in all manner of containers or in no container whatsoever. The most common type in the United States is the tower silo built of wood, concrete, tile, or metal. It is designed to keep out air and to be of a size such that a layer may be fed off each day, spoilage of the material at the top which is exposed to the air each day being thus prevented.

Pit or trench silos are also common in the United States. These are merely excavations, preferably tile-drained to carry away seepage.

If the soil is loose, the walls may have to be lined with wood, concrete, or blocks. Trench silos are inexpensive, are easily filled, and are suitable for either cut or uncut material. The packing of the silage is improved by slightly sloping walls, with the trench narrowing toward the bottom.

Temporary silos have been built out of such material as snow fencing, lined with Sisalcraft or other impervious material, or wire fencing similarly lined. Baled straw built in circular form and held in position with wire bands has also been used for temporary silo construction. In the case of the baled straw the silo is fed up with the silage or converted into manure by the animals in the feed lot.

Stack silos consist merely of stacked green material. The outside, exposed to the air, spoils, but the inside of the stack may provide good silage. With low-cost feed material the spoilage on the outside may be less expensive than the overhead on a permanent silo.

Silos constructed of thin metals, especially when of small diameter, have been influenced by outside changes in temperature. During the summer the outside of the silage may dry out excessively from the heat, a condition permitting spoilage, and in the winter difficulties from freezing may be encountered.

Filling and Sealing the Silo.—In Europe, it is common to seal the silos with dirt, weighted covers, and other devices. Most of these methods are impractical with the tower-type silos most commonly used in this country.

Throughout the filling process the silage should be evenly spread and packed to exclude air. Intermittent filling is advantageous. If a layer is put in and permitted to heat moderately (75 to 100°F. but no higher), proper fermentation is encouraged. As the next layer is added, the mass is compressed and does not heat further. The settling permitted by intermittent filling is advantageous in securing an even pack. If two silos are being filled, harvest operations may be kept continuous by putting material in each on alternate days. If too long a break is permitted in the filling process, a layer of mold is likely to develop even though it may not show at filling time.

In sealing the silo, it is desirable to level the material and tramp it thoroughly at intervals for 2 or 3 days. This last layer may well consist of heavier, wetter material, the depth of the spoiled layer that develops on top of the silage being thus reduced.

Properly built trench silos provide access for horses or tractors that may be used to tramp or compact the silage. This is particularly important if the trench silo is to be filled with uncut material, for there is not the great mass of silage on top to compress the bottom layers.

When filling of a trench silo has been completed, it may be covered with a layer of wet straw, green hay, or soil. The soil is most effective in providing adequate exclusion of air.

Silage Valuation.—Numerous feeding trials have indicated that 1 ton of corn silage has approximately one-third the feeding value of 1 ton of good alfalfa hay. The relationship varies, both with the quality of the silage and with the quality of the hay. The one-third rule is commonly used in transactions involving the sale of silage by pricing it at one-third the price of 1 ton of alfalfa hay. The relative value of corn silage high in grain is somewhat greater.

Review Questions

1. Make a list of the crops grown in your community that are suitable for silage making.

2. What are the relative yields of corn silage and alfalfa hay in your community? From this, calculate the relative yields of corn and alfalfa as silage crops.

3. What are the reasons for finely cutting the material being ensiled?

4. What is the function of carotene? Can it be more readily conserved in silage or hay? Why?

5. What organic acid is dominant in good silage? In poor silage?

6. List the advantages of using molasses as an adjunct to silage made from legumes.

7. How may inorganic acids be used in silage conservation? What feeding precautions must be used with silage so acidified?

Problems

1. You wish to put up 100 tons of alfalfa-molasses silage. How much molasses will you buy? How much is this molasses worth as a feed in terms of corn?

2. You wish to use summer silage as a supplement to pasture for beef cattle in a field remote from your buildings. What will your procedure be?

3. Consult the yield records of corn-variety tests in your state, and choose the variety you would use for silage on your home farm. Explain the reasons for your choice.

4. Analyze the conditions in your home locality or on your home farm; in the light of these conditions, make a list of the reasons for and against handling at least a portion of your hay crop as silage.

References

HODGSON, R. E., and J. C. KNOTT: Stack Silage, *Wash. Agr. Expt. Sta. Bul.* 349, 1937.

MORRISON, F. B.: "Feeds and Feeding," 20th ed., The Morrison Publishing Co., Ithaca, N.Y., 1936.

WALLACE, H. A., and E. N. BRESSMAN: "Corn and Corn Growing," John Wiley & Sons, Inc., New York, 1928.

WATSON, S. J.: "Silage and Crop Preservatives," Macmillan and Company, Ltd., London, 1938.

WOODWARD, T. E., and J. B. SHEPHERD: Methods of Making Silage from Grasses and Legumes, *U.S. Dept. Agr. Tech. Bul.* 611, 1938.

CHAPTER XI

PASTURES AND PASTURE MANAGEMENT

A half-billion acres of United States farm land are used for pasture. This pasture is classified by the U.S. Census Bureau as follows:

	Per Cent
Plowable pasture	19
Woodland pasture	21
Other pasture	60

It would appear from this classification that much of this pasture land is not very good. The woodland pasture may or may not be on good land. It is occupied by trees or young growth, of potential wood or timber value; hence, grass production is in competition with trees. Much of the woodland classified as pasture is unsuitable for plowing even if cleared. The "other" pasture may be stony; it may be growing brush of no possible wood value; it may be marshland or land that otherwise is neither woodland nor plowland but that does furnish some grazing. It includes immense acreages of range land insufficiently watered for the production of field crops.

As for plowland pasture, some of it is on well-managed, productive land on which good pastures are grown in sequence with other field crops. Some of it is sloping land, moist land, or land otherwise difficult to plow and till, and its use as more or less permanent pasture provides the most practical cropping program. Still other plowland is called "pasture" as a convenient, though inappropriate, designation for that phase of soil depletion which lies between the poorly managed culture of field crops and eventual abandonment.

What Kind of Land Should Be Pastured?—Chief interest in pasture improvement is centered in plowland pastures. Woodlands and range lands do not offer opportunity for intensive improvement measures although the management of grazing on such areas is a vital factor in their maintenance. The proper use for woodland areas that may provide some pasture is also an important consideration in the determination of land policies. But it is land that can be enclosed, plowed, fertilized, and seeded that has commanded the attention of those who are attempting to effect a major improvement in pastures and pasture management.

Farm-management records have often indicated that farms with the highest proportion of their plowland acreage devoted to pasture had the lowest labor incomes. This has been interpreted by some to mean that pasture is fundamentally a low-income, low-profit crop. A more logical interpretation might be that these farms have poor pasture crops on land depleted by tillage, erosion, and grazing and that this land would yield low returns if planted to almost any of the usual field crops. When in a depleted condition, such land is managed with least effort by using it for poor pasture. There is much evidence to

Fig. 44.—Many sloping soils are subject to excessive erosion when plowed and tilled. The area at the right shows how a 160-acre Tennessee field looked before pasture improvement was started. The area at the left carries a dense cover of white clover and bluegrass, the result of hard work and phosphate. (*Courtesy of U.S. Dept. Agr. Soil Conservation Service.*)

indicate that, on good land, well-managed pasture, for good livestock, yields returns fully equal to those secured from the major field crops.

This does not imply that the best lands should be used for pasture and the poorer lands for field crops. One writer states, "Medium to heavy soils well supplied with moisture are better for pasture purposes than are the lighter, drier soils." This obviously is true. It may be stated with equal emphasis that medium to heavy soils well supplied with moisture are better for corn, wheat, oats, barley, soybeans, tame hay, and many other crops than are the lighter, drier soils. It seems reasonable to assume that plowland still too useful to be abandoned or planted to trees and too unproductive to pay for the tillage expense of regular field crops will continue to be used for pasture though the acre income be low. Eventually, unless restorative measures are applied, even pasture usage may become impractical, for the productivity of land is not static even under grazing.

It also is reasonable to expect that some of the better plowland, primarily used for row crops and grain, can be used for highly productive pasture with the expectation of returns that fully justify this type of land use. The pasture usage of the better lands may well be in rotation with other crops, to the substantial benefit of the soil if proper management practices are followed. There are also many sloping soils that are capable of producing good crop yields but that are subject to excessive erosion when plowed and tilled. Such soils may be used effectively for improved pastures that are justified on the basis of income and that, at the same time, protect the land from destructive erosion.

PRINCIPLES OF PASTURE IMPROVEMENT

There are three basic principles involved in the production of better pastures. The principles are broadly applicable, though the details vary under the influence of local physical, climatic, and economic environment. The broad considerations are as follows:

1. Improvement of the land itself.
2. Utilization of suitable pasture plants.
3. Effective grazing management.

Land Improvement.—The best pastures are produced on land well supplied with all the essential plant nutrients. Soil-improvement principles and practices have already been discussed in Chap. IV. They apply to the growing of better pastures as well as to the effective production of other crops.

The best pasture legumes, the clovers and alfalfa, make their most satisfactory growth when the soil contains abundant calcium for plant nutrition and when it is no more than slightly acid. Lespedeza is an acid-tolerant legume, but it benefits from applications of lime to acid soils. Alfalfa, red clover, and sweet clover make a poor growth when the lime content of the soil is low. Wherever the better legumes grow poorly because of an acid soil, an application of 1 to 3 tons of lime to the acre is the first step in pasture improvement.

A satisfactory growth of legumes is also contingent upon there being in the soil liberal amounts of available phosphoric acid and potash. Potash is most likely to be deficient in the lighter sandy soils and in mucks and peats. Phosphorus is widely lacking. Some of the most marked yield increases due to pasture fertilization have resulted from applications of phosphatic fertilizers, always provided that there is a good admixture of legumes in the pasture, for the grasses themselves make little direct response to phosphate. The grass response comes from increased nitrogen made possible by the more vigorous legume growth.

Cornell University[1] recommends the application of 600 to 800 lb. of 20 per cent superphosphate, used as a top-dressing, every 4 years to pastures based on white clover.

Where clovers are being seeded on soils low in fertility, the Iowa Agricultural Experiment Station[2] recommends an application of 200

Fig. 45.—Studying pasture management on rocky, practically untillable land. The Connecticut Agricultural Experiment Station developed good bluegrass-white-clover turf on such land with limestone and superphosphate. (*Courtesy of B. A. Brown, Connecticut Agricultural Experiment Station.*)

to 300 lb. of 20 per cent superphosphate or its equivalent to be applied at the time of seeding.

The Michigan Agricultural Experiment Station[3] used lime, in the form of marl, and 300 lb. an acre of 0-8-24 fertilizer in establishing a highly productive alfalfa-brome-grass pasture on a Fox sandy loam soil.

[1] JOHNSTONE-WALLACE, D. B., Pasture Improvement and Management, *Cornell Ext. Bul.* 393, 1938.

[2] CHENEY, H. B., Pasture Improvement and Management, *Iowa Agr. Expt. Sta. Bul.* P8 (new series), 1940.

[3] RATHER, H. C., C. M. HARRISON, G. A. BROWN, and R. E. HORWOOD, A Mixture of Alfalfa and Smooth Brome Grass for Pasture, *Mich. Agr. Expt. Cir. Bul.* 159, 1939.

A Wisconsin publication states:

Best and quickest results from [lime, phosphate, and potash] are obtained when these elements are applied and worked into the soil either before or at the time of establishing the pasture. Benefits from these nutrients, when they are used as a top-dressing on established sods, are slow as it takes several years for them to penetrate the soil deeply enough to be beneficial. Their greatest value is to the legumes which in turn can fix nitrogen from the air so that it is available for use by the grasses.[1]

Nitrogen for Pastures.—Legumes make a twofold contribution to pasture improvement. They contribute directly to the pasture herbage by way of protein and mineral-rich feed; and the nitrogen, fixation of which is made more abundant by the presence of legumes, makes for a more prolific and nutritious growth of grasses.

Nitrogen can be supplied directly to the grasses in the form of any one of the numerous nitrogen-carrying fertilizers. This practice has certain practical limitations. In the case of grasses that characteristically become dormant with the advent of dry, hot weather an application of nitrogen does not prolong growth during such periods; hence, nitrogen fertilizers, for the most part, offer no solution to the summer grazing problem. Nitrogen fertilizers do stimulate spring grass growth, usually with a resultant tendency to suppress any legumes that may be present. The annual applications of nitrogen needed to get a response each year are expensive. Hence, if nitrogen fertilizer is to be used effectively, its place would seem to be under circumstances where suitable legumes are not available, where a spring shortage of pasturage exists, and where a good market for livestock products is available. The livestock load must be great enough to utilize all the extra spring growth, lest the stimulating effect of the nitrogen on this growth be wasted. This, of course, increases the need for summer feed.

Beef growers sometimes defer grazing steers on certain of their grass pastures until the grass is mature in midsummer. In such circumstances the extra yield caused by a nitrogen application would be consumed, whether profitably or not being largely dependent on the increased gains made by the steers and the price of beef. Such mature grass is not highly regarded for milking animals.

PASTURE CROPS AND THEIR MANAGEMENT

The selection of plants to be used for pasture and managing them under grazing are two different steps in pasture culture though it is

[1] BURCALOW, F. V., and G. BOHSTEDT, Plan Wisconsin Pastures, *Wis. Ext. Cir.* 298, 1940.

difficult to dissociate them. The type of grazing management that should be practiced is governed to a major extent by the growth habits of the plants that make up the pasture and by the nutritional needs of the livestock.

Close vs. Moderate Grazing.—In the quest for desirable pasture plants, emphasis is often placed on their ability to endure close grazing. Close grazing is undoubtedly necessary for the maintenance of a pasture based on white clover. The English farmer with his white-clover and perennial-rye-grass pastures has an old adage that states, "A cow must eat in May what grows in May." Not only do English pastures depend on white clover as the chief legume, but the British

Fig. 46.—Studying pastures in small paddocks. (*Michigan Agricultural Experiment Station.*)

Isles have temperate summers and frequent misty rains, conditions that tend to keep short grass green and productive. In many sections of the United States, if a cow should eat in May that which grew in May, she would not eat at all in July and August—at least not on the same pasture. Many of our most widely used pasture plants become brown and dormant with the hot, dry weather that prevails in midsummer.

Nor is close grazing in favorable growing periods advantageous with all pasture crops. Ladino, the giant white clover, is relatively unproductive and soon disappears if subjected to continuous close grazing. Nevertheless, it is a valuable pasture crop. This is also true of alfalfa, timothy, smooth brome, crested wheat grass, and many others that have excellent pasture value for the regions to which they are adapted. On the other hand the bent grasses do endure close grazing, but they are not among the most useful of pasture grasses.

One kind of pasture may be made up of species that endure extremely close grazing without satisfying either the appetites or the nutritive requirements of the livestock that are supposed to convert it into economic returns. On the other hand, livestock may thrive, at least temporarily, on a closely grazed pasture, of a different kind, that eventually is destroyed or completely changed in botanical composition as a result of close grazing. The ideal management regulates grazing in accordance with the growth habits of desirable, adapted plant species, naturally present or seeded in the pasture, in order to enhance their survival; grazing management is also modified in accordance with the kind, age, and condition of the animals, in order to achieve effective production of livestock products. These concepts provide a place in the pasture program for plants like white clover, where adapted, which is benefited by close grazing, and also for some of the taller growing, highly productive forages, like alfalfa, Ladino, timothy, and smooth brome, which must be grazed more moderately if they are to endure.

Rotation Grazing.—As a result of a system of grazing and pasture fertilization developed near Hohenheim, Germany, there has been much interest on the part of pasture technicians in rotation grazing. The Hohenheim system involved heavy annual applications of nitrogenous fertilization as well as rotation grazing.

The rotation grazing of this system called for division of the pasture into several smaller fields, each with access to shade and water. With dairy cows the highest producing animals were turned in first. The pasture was stocked heavily enough so that they could consume most of the best appearing herbage in a few days. These cows when moved to the next pasture were followed by lower producing members of the herd, dry cows, and stock cattle. When one period of grazing on a given area was completed, the unconsumed herbage was mowed, the droppings were spread with a chain harrow or other device, and the field was rested until the grass had made sufficient recovery growth for the next round of grazing. In Great Britain, somewhat comparable rotation grazing is recommended for white clover and perennial ryegrass pasture heavily phosphated each year rather than fertilized with commercial nitrogen.

Rotation grazing seeks to correlate grass management with the nutritional management of livestock, a logical goal. It would appear to be best suited where land values are high, the market for livestock products very favorable, and climatic conditions such as to encourage grass growth throughout the season. It involves extra labor, extra fencing, and additional water facilities.

In the United States, rotation grazing as tested by Woodward, Shepherd, and Hein[1] of the U.S. Department of Agriculture resulted in only moderately better milk production than continuous grazing—not enough to warrant the expense of normal extra fencing but possibly enough to warrant cheaper fence construction. This trial is illustrative of many that have been conducted in this country, most of which have shown either a very modest advantage for rotation grazing or no essential difference as compared with continuous grazing. In some trials, production has been less from the rotation-grazing system.

It seems reasonable to suggest that the unusually high protein content of the very young herbage produced under rotation grazing is greater in percentage than is actually required even by dairy cows, thus giving it no material nutritional advantage over forage a little more advanced in maturity. Also, the repeated close grazing and consequent fairly complete defoliation of the plants reduce their productive capacity. A further consideration, at least with respect to some kinds of pasture, may be the greater opportunity for selective grazing in a moderately stocked, continuously grazed pasture, whereas, under rotation grazing, herbage is all of essentially the same maturity and may or may not be in optimum nutritional condition for the livestock.

White-clover Pastures.—White clover is one of the excellent pasture legumes under conditions of temperature and moisture that keep pastures green throughout the season. In the United States, white clover is most commonly associated with Kentucky bluegrass although it is often seeded in complex pasture mixtures.

White clover is widespread throughout the northeastern quarter of the United States and is used moderately for winter pasture in the South. It benefits greatly from applications of phosphate. On potash-deficient soils applications of this nutrient may be advantageous.

If white clover is to be maintained, close grazing must be practiced to enable this clover to spread by stolons and compete successfully with associated grasses. Hence, the grasses grown with white clover must be able to endure close grazing. Because Kentucky bluegrass does withstand the close grazing essential for the maintenance of white

[1] WOODWARD, T. E., J. B. SHEPHERD, and M. A. HEIN, The Hohenheim System in the Management of Permanent Pastures for Dairy Cattle, *U.S. Dept. Agr. Tech. Bul.* **660**, 1938.

clover, it often replaces other grasses sown in a white-clover mixture that are not able to compete under this type of grazing management.

Best results in maintaining white clover continuously in pasture in this country are reported from eastern and northern New York and New England. White clover also does well on the heavier moisture-retentive soils of northern Michigan and Wisconsin. In many regions, however, white clover is elusive and undependable. When late summer and early autumn rains provide an abundance of moisture, the white-clover seed in the soil germinates profusely and the next season, if reasonably moist, is a "white-clover year." Such an occurrence is infrequent on sandy soils and intermittent on the heavier soils except

Fig. 47.—Herefords thriving on a northern Michigan bluegrass-white-clover pasture, the result of phosphate and close grazing. (*Courtesy of E. B. Swingle.*)

in the areas providing most favorable climatic conditions. Most regions in the United States need legumes that root more deeply and are far more drought resistant than white clover.

If environmental conditions are really suitable for white-clover pasture, it is seldom necessary to seed this legume. Seed has already been so widely disseminated in favorable white-clover areas that top-dressing with phosphate and close grazing will develop excellent volunteer stands. If conditions are unfavorable to the white clover, sowing the seed is useless. There are strain differences due to locality of production and to some breeding work. Volunteer stands probably represent locally adapted strains resulting from years of natural selection.

The Bluegrasses.—Kentucky and Canada bluegrass are the most important of the bluegrasses in American pastures. On soils low in organic matter and consequently low in nitrogen, Canada bluegrass often predominates. When the productivity of such soils is raised by the successful introduction of legumes or by nitrogen fertilization, the Kentucky bluegrass tends to replace the Canadian species.

These bluegrasses make their best growth in the spring when soil moisture is abundant and the weather is cool. They mature early when undergrazed; and, regardless of the kind of grazing management, they turn brown and cease growth with the advent of hot, dry weather.

Two ways are suggested as a means of getting the most out of bluegrass pastures under conditions in which they make but little summer growth and therefore do not provide season-long pasture. According to one system the pasture may be heavily stocked in the spring to consume this lush growth as fast as it is produced. This necessitates shifting the livestock to other pastures when bluegrass growth ceases. Under this procedure, white clover will grow with the bluegrass under favorable circumstances. Another system is to defer grazing and thus permit the bluegrass to make a full growth. This mature herbage is considered by many to make excellent pasturage for nonmilking animals. Under deferred grazing of bluegrass, white clover has little chance to get under way.

Renovating Bluegrass Pastures with Legumes.—In Wisconsin, considerable work has been done in the renovation of bluegrass pastures with lime, fertilizers, and legumes. The steps in renovation suggested by Burcalow and Bohstedt are as follows:

1. Select for renovation a moderately sized portion of the pasture with the poorest sod.
2. Have the soil tested.
3. Apply lime and fertilizer as needed.
4. Cut up the sod thoroughly with a disk, spring-tooth harrow, or field cultivator as soon as the land is dry enough to work in the spring.
5. Level and smooth with a harrow.
6. Sow as early as possible in the spring unless weeds are bad, in which case seedings should be delayed until the young weeds are killed by several diskings.
7. Use either a mixture of 10 lb. of alfalfa and 5 lb. of red clover or 12 lb. of sweet clover and 5 lb. of red clover with 3 or 4 lb. of timothy.
8. Harrow or Cultipack after seeding.
9. Fence the seeded area, as legume seedlings must be protected while they are becoming established.[1]

[1] Burcalow and Bohstedt, *op. cit.*

The fertilization of these pastures plus the establishment of such vigorous legumes as alfalfa, sweet clover, and red clover has doubled the productivity of Wisconsin pastures where this scheme of renovation has been practiced. It not only enhances productivity of the grasses, through the use of legumes, but is a potent means of eliminating weeds and white grubs. Renovation, as developed in Wisconsin, is designed primarily for the improvement of hillside and other thinly sodded, unproductive pastures which if plowed would incur serious hazards of erosion.

Alfalfa and Smooth Brome Grass.—One of the very effective pasture-plant combinations is a mixture of alfalfa and smooth brome grass where these plants are adapted. Both alfalfa and smooth brome

Fig. 48.—Smooth brome and alfalfa make up an excellent pasture mixture where these plants are adapted. (*Michigan State College.*)

grass are palatable, nutritious, drought-resistant perennials. The mixture not only grows vigorously in the spring and early summer but has been unusually effective in the production of pasturage during the heat and drought of July and August when so many pastures are dormant and produce little, if any, green forage.

More than 100,000 acres were seeded to alfalfa and smooth brome in Michigan in the single season of 1940. There are also extensive acreages in Nebraska and Iowa, and several of the middle-western and northwestern states are finding this combination advantageous. The mixture appears to be effective wherever alfalfa grows well in northern and corn-belt states. Smooth brome has been grown from the Dakotas westward to Oregon for many years because of its drought resistance. In recent years, it has been found equally valuable farther east even though drought periods there are of much shorter duration.

Cultural Practices.—In growing the alfalfa-brome-grass mixture for either hay or pasture the cultural practices most effective for alfalfa production are equally effective for the mixture. Hence, the lime, phosphoric acid, and potash requirements of alfalfa need to be met. The nitrogen for both the alfalfa and the brome grass is supplied by the nodule-forming bacteria that work with the alfalfa. Brome grass is unusually demanding in its nitrogen requirements. If grown alone, in a year or two it takes on a sod-bound unthrifty appearance. This difficulty can be overcome and a very vigorous growth induced by large applications of nitrogen fertilizer. Fortunately, however, brome grass growing in association with well-inoculated alfalfa gets nitrogen in abundance and does not show the lack of vigor often found in old pure stands.

In Michigan, the customary rate of seeding is 7 lb. of brome grass and 8 of alfalfa to the acre. During the first crop year, this usually results in a mixture consisting of 75 per cent alfalfa and 25 per cent brome grass. If cut only for hay, these proportions change slowly; but if pastured for part or all of the season, the proportion of brome grass in the mixture tends to increase rapidly. In well-managed pastures the alfalfa contributes substantially to the herbage for 3 to 5 years. Even after the alfalfa has largely disappeared, the brome grass remains vigorous for a year or two longer, after which it may show the effects of a diminished nitrogen supply.

Because brome-grass seed is light and chaffy, it is difficult to sow it with a drill. This difficulty is largely overcome by mixing the brome seed with oats and sowing it through the grain box of a drill. Brome grass may be seeded at any time that is advantageous for alfalfa and also in the fall when it is too late for alfalfa. Thus, some growers mix brome-grass seed with wheat, sow it in the fall, and apply the alfalfa seed the next spring. A firm seedbed and relatively shallow (¾-in.) planting are desirable.

Management of Alfalfa-Brome Pastures.—Both alfalfa and brome grass are eaten readily by livestock at rather advanced stages of maturity as well as when the plants are young. The leaves of brome grass remain green and nutritious even after the seed is dead ripe. According to Michigan[1] experiments, a simplified management is effective. This work has indicated no need for keeping alfalfa-brome-grass closely grazed to keep it palatable. In fact, undergrazing may be practiced in May and June, which makes possible continued pasturage later in the season when growth is less rapid. In these trials a normal carrying capacity was three dairy cows, receiving grain supple-

[1] RATHER, HARRISON, BROWN, and HORWOOD, *op. cit.*

ment, to two acres of alfalfa-brome pasture from mid-May to September or five Shropshire ewes and their lambs to the acre, without grain, for the same period.   It has been customary to lighten or discontinue heavy grazing for 4 to 6 weeks before killing frost to permit the alfalfa to restore its root reserves before winter.   During this period, livestock can be grazed more moderately on the aftermath of hayfields or pastured on fields that are to be plowed up.   Rotation grazing of alfalfa-brome-grass pastures has shown no advantage either in yield or in nutritive value.

Fig. 49.—Straight alfalfa (left), grazed for three years had become very weedy; the alfalfa-brome mixture (right), similarly grazed, still provided good clean pasture though much of the alfalfa had disappeared.   (*Courtesy of E. E. Patton.*)

One marked advantage of this mixture is its value for both hay and pasture.   Thus, it may be pastured throughout the grazing season, or a first crop may be cut for hay or silage and the subsequent growth pastured.   This second growth in particular is in excellent condition for pasture when less drought-resistant crops are brown and dormant.

Ladino.—Ladino, the giant white clover, is increasing in popularity as a pasture legume.   In the United States it first became very popular in the far west where it is grown under irrigation.   Later it was found to be well adapted in New England and other areas where moisture was usually not a serious limiting factor.   The plants tend to remain green and succulent throughout the season unless subjected to drought. They do not endure close grazing but make their best recovery if not pastured off more closely than 4 to 6 in.   Under conservative management, Ladino should last 4 or 5 years in a pasture. If grown in association with grass, the Ladino is most likely to be injured by a close sod-forming species like Kentucky bluegrass. Where fields are variable with respect to moisture, subsoil formation, and lime content, as many are, it is possible that a mixture of Ladino and alfalfa might make a better legume base for the pasture than either grown as the only legume.

Ladino seed is small, and 3 to 4 lb. an acre provide a dense stand if sown shallow on a clean firm seedbed.

Lespedeza.—Lespedeza has become very important as a southern hay and pasture legume. The largest acreages are reported from

Fig. 50.—The third continuous year of a one-year wheat, Korean lespedeza rotation. The wheat was removed for grain in late June and the cattle in this picture were grazing the volunteer lespedeza July 20. (*Courtesy of C. A. Helm, Missouri Agricultural Experiment Station.*)

Tennessee, Missouri, Kentucky, North Carolina, Virginia, and Arkansas. Although the most widely used varieties are annuals, they give best results where left on the land year after year to make self-seedings.

In pasture improvement, lespedeza is used in two general ways. It may be established in permanent grass pastures as a source of nitrogen for the established grasses, or it may be grown under culture as the chief source of late-summer and early-fall pasturage. If grown alone, it makes inefficient use of the land; for it starts late in the season, reaches its maximum growth in late August, and ceases growth with the first killing frost.

C. A. Helm[1] of the Missouri Agricultural Experiment Station suggests the following system of management:

Winter wheat, winter rye, or winter barley where it is adapted may be sown in the fall after lespedeza has matured seed. Oats may be used in place of fall grain by preparing the land and seeding in the early spring before the lespedeza seed in the soil has germinated. The grain crop may be pastured off, cut for silage or hay, or left to mature. Where the grain crop containing volunteer lespedeza is pastured, the lespedeza usually will carry the livestock by the time the small-grain pasture has been fully consumed.

Following harvest of the grain crop the lespedeza develops its full growth at a time when it is exceedingly useful for summer pasture. Even though heavily grazed, enough seed is produced and shatters to the ground to provide the seed for the next year's lespedeza crop.

Regardless of the method of using the small-grain crop, its presence in the spring and early summer checks excessive weed growth and allows the lespedeza to use the land during the latter part of the growing season. The seeding of small grains also makes practical the yearly applications of fertilizer on a relatively cheap and profitable basis.

PLANNING A PASTURE PROGRAM

The foregoing discussion of the management of several representative types of pasture suited to different regions has been presented to illustrate the principles and procedures in pasture improvement. There are a great many legumes and grasses described in Chaps. VI, VII, and VIII that are useful in pasture mixtures in the various areas to which they are adapted. No one crop is universal in adaptation, and no one crop is at its best throughout the entire season even under circumstances to which it is perfectly adapted.

Pasturage need not all come from permanent pasture fields or from the plants usually regarded as of special merit for pasture purposes. A mixture of timothy, red clover, and alsike is highly productive of pasturage for its first crop season though the life of these clovers is relatively short. Sweet clover is very productive in many places. Rye, wheat, oats, and Sudan grass may have some place in the pasture program designed to furnish adequate grazing from early spring until late autumn. The aftermath in hay meadows commonly makes excellent summer pasture for a limited period.

A Pasture Calendar.—A pasture calendar suggested by the Iowa Agricultural Experiment Station is presented in Fig. 51 to illustrate

[1] HELM, C. A., Management of Korean Lespedeza, *Mo. Agr. Expt. Sta. Cir.* 210, 1940.

the opportunities for planning a complete succession of crops, whereby animals perform the labors of harvest, leave much of the fertility in

PASTURE CALENDAR

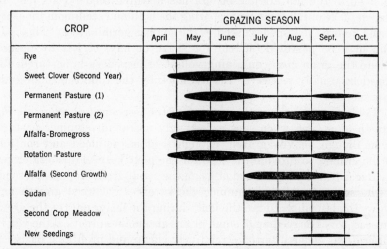

CROP	GRAZING SEASON						
	April	May	June	July	Aug.	Sept.	Oct.
Rye							
Sweet Clover (Second Year)							
Permanent Pasture (1)							
Permanent Pasture (2)							
Alfalfa-Bromegross							
Rotation Pasture							
Alfalfa (Second Growth)							
Sudan							
Second Crop Meadow							
New Seedings							

FIG. 51.—The pasture calendar suggests crops that can be used to provide good grazing for livestock during different parts of the season and indicates their relative productivity (wide bar indicates much feed, narrow bar little feed) or carrying capacity.

It is of prime importance in planning a pasture program to ensure the availability of palatable, nutritious pasturage for as long a period as is practically possible. The value of a good pasture is largely lost if during a part of the season the grazing is of poor quality or is insufficient to keep the animals thrifty and growing. (*Courtesy of H. B. Cheney, Iowa Agricultural Experiment Station.*)

the field, and in all make for one of the most convenient and efficient means of producing farm products.

SPECIAL PROBLEMS WITH GRAZING ANIMALS

There are some problems associated with the management of livestock on pasture that are not satisfied by a consideration of the nutritional value of the forage and its carrying capacity.

Nutrient Deficiencies.—An objector to reed canary grass as a pasture complained that his cows did poorly on this crop; besides, he could not find his herd in time for milking. Reed canary grass that is grossly undergrazed may grow tall enough to hide the herd and, in this condition, may even be too coarse and fibrous for good hay; it certainly does not have the balance of nutrients characteristic of a well-managed pasture. This condition may develop in many species if they become too advanced in maturity. It should be remembered, too, that reed canary grass is usually grown on low-lying muck or peat soils naturally very low in potash and frequently deficient in other essential minerals.

Calcium and phosphorus are the two mineral constituents most likely to affect the nutritive value of pastures. The fact that legumes are usually high in these two elements is one of the reasons why livestock tend to thrive better on a pasture containing a good legume mixture. Where phosphorus is deficient in the soil and consequently in the pasture, animals often exhibit a depraved appetite and are afflicted with bone weaknesses. Other evidences of this deficiency are lessened growth, decreased milk production, and lowered capacity for reproduction. Phosphorus deficiencies in forages and pastures are more likely to occur under conditions of severe drought.

The deficiency of other minerals is of rare occurrence but is receiving consideration for the unusual circumstances under which it does occur. Certain Florida soils have been found lacking in copper and iron. Cattle grazing the pastures growing on these soils do not grow and mature normally, for copper and iron are both necessary in animal metabolism to form hemoglobin of the blood.

A very unusual mineral deficiency, first reported from New Zealand, is one in which the lack of a slight trace of cobalt in what appeared to be perfectly normal pasture plants caused deficiency difficulties with sheep. Where cobalt is present in soils in excess of only 5 to 10 parts per million, the plants take up enough for livestock needs; but difficulties have become evident in the case of livestock grazing on the natural vegetation of soils having less than 2 to 3 parts per million of this element. Very much smaller concentrations of cobalt in the plant tissues are adequate.

Poison Plants.—Difficulties encountered when livestock eat poisonous plants are more common in occurrence than are minor element deficiencies. The potential poisonous properties of darnel, stink grass, and sleepy grass have already been mentioned (page 115). Water hemlock is one of the most dangerous of all weeds. A piece of its fleshy root the size of a walnut is said to be enough to kill a cow. Water hemlock is most likely to be eaten in early spring, possibly because this and related species start early growth in wet ground before the regular pasture plants are well under way. Cattle, forced to low sheltered areas by spring storms, sometimes trample or pull out the roots and eat them. The roots and young top growth contain a very poisonous substance called *cicutoxin*.

Most poisonous plants are relatively unpalatable and are not very likely to be eaten by livestock if the pasture is well managed so as to provide abundant feed of the desirable grasses and legumes.

As for the prussic acid that may be encountered in pastured sorghums and Sudan grass (page 138), proper grazing management again should eliminate nearly all the danger. A tall (2 ft. or more in height) vigorous growth of the plants is rarely if ever dangerous. The occurrence of prussic acid in dangerous quantities is much less likely in the case of Sudan grass than of the sorghums. Errors in attributing instances of livestock poisoning to Sudan grass have also been made. Too often, carelessly discarded paint pails, potential sources of lead poison, or poisoned grasshopper bait spread in a pasture have been the unnoticed cause of animal deaths.

The Bloat Problem.—The bloating of cattle and sheep results from the rapid fermentation of forage in the paunch, causing the production of gas, chiefly carbon dioxide, faster than it can be eliminated. In

Fig. 52.—Pasturing alfalfa. Bloating hazards are greatly reduced if grass is grown with legume pasture and animals are kept continuously in the pasture and are well supplied with water and salt. (*W. K. Kellogg Farm of the Michigan State College.*)

extreme cases, death of the animal results. The consumption of excessive quantities of young succulent clover or alfalfa is most likely to cause bloat difficulties. The more mature forage is less dangerous. The sowing of grasses with these legumes tends greatly to reduce bloat hazards. The other precautions involve largely the management of the livestock and are based on preventing excessive consumption of these legumes in the young succulent condition most conducive to rapid fermentation.

The precautions that appear to have been most effective are (1) to make sure that the stock are not hungry when first turned on a legume pasture; (2) to provide plenty of salt and water in the pasture so that animals do not quench their thirst by eating too much wet herbage;

(3) to confine the animals to the pasture so that they eat moderately at any one time rather than greedily.

The last precaution is the one most often neglected. Animals with free access to legume pastures may also have access to shade and water in some other field. Under such circumstances, they often stay in the shade all day, go into the pasture at night when the herbage is wet, eat too much succulent clover or alfalfa, and bloat. If the stock are really confined to the pasture and the other precautions are observed, bloating hazards should be materially reduced.

Off Flavors in Milk.—Dairymen have the problem of managing their producing cows in such a manner as to reduce the possibilities of tainting the milk with undesirable plant flavors. Milk is affected in flavor by the herbage the cows eat just before or during the milking period. Garlic, rape, rye, and some other plants give a strong undesirable flavor to the milk. When milk is adversely affected, the difficulties with most pasture plants can be alleviated if the cows are turned into the pasture immediately after they are milked and brought back into the barn 3 hours or more before next milking time. This permits plenty of time for a cow to obtain her fill on good pasture.

RANGE PASTURES

The vast range-land grazing areas present a problem of management quite different in detail from that of plowland pastures. The grasses here are largely native, though crested wheat grass, an introduced species, is one of the best for range reseedings. Moisture is limited; hence, growth is sparse, and carrying capacity of the range is light compared with the better plowlands. The problem is to manage as effectively as possible that which nature has provided.

Range Management.—The Great Plains region is described by Allred[1] as an area about 1,300 miles long and 200 to 700 miles wide, with grazing and forage-crop resources for 12 million animal units per year. It has been grazing land since remote geologic ages. White men found it occupied by millions of buffalo and antelope. Shortly after the Civil War, it became cattle country and later much of it was broken by the plow, some of it ill-advisedly.

The pasture problem on the semiarid range is largely one of grazing management. When grazing is too intense, the most palatable forage species are thinned out, eventually to be replaced by certain weeds and shrubs. With less favorable protective cover the land then becomes subject to destructive erosion. The loss of palatable species as a

[1] ALLRED, B. W., Range Conservation Practices for the Great Plains, *U.S. Dept. Agr. Misc. Pub.* 410, 1940.

result of overgrazing is due to constant removal of leaf area by grazing animals, thus retarding the plants in carrying on photosynthesis and the storage of reserve foods necessary for their continued growth.

The practices recommended by Allred to ensure perpetuation of desirable range grasses and thus make possible profitable livestock production and conservation of range resources are as follows: (1) stocking within the normal grazing capacity of the range; (2) lighter grazing during the critical period of leaf and seed production in order that plants may achieve their maximum development; (3) occasional deferred grazing of areas to permit recovery and increase of desirable forage species; (4) stocking with the kind of livestock most suitable to a particular range, *i.e.*, grass range for cattle and horses, browse for sheep and goats. The latter also do better than cattle on rough mountainous areas. Other desirable range-management practices include keeping the livestock well spread over the range by fencing or herding and by distribution of salting and watering places, and the production of supplementary feed from such crops as alfalfa, clover, small grains, sorghums, root crops, and silages where their production is feasible. These supplementary feeds are suggested, not as a means of providing for additional stock to add to the burden of overloaded ranges, but rather to provide more adequate feed, especially in periods of emergency, for the amount of stock the range can normally carry and still be kept in good condition.

Review Problems

1. The total acreage used for pasture in the United States, according to the Census Bureau, is

    a. About the same as the corn acreage.
    b. About half as great as that in corn.
    c. Equal to the combined acreage of corn, oats, and wheat.
    d. Approximately five times the acreage in corn.

2. A springtime top-dressing of a nitrogenous fertilizer on a mixed pasture tends to do all but one of these:

    a. Stimulate the spring growth of the grasses.
    b. Suppress growth of legumes.
    c. Makes grasses more leafy and darker in color.
    d. Prolong the growth of fresh herbage during hot, dry weather.

3. Close grazing of a pasture is necessary for the best development of which of the following legumes?

    a. White clover.
    b. Ladino.
    c. Alfalfa.
    d. Red clover.

4. One of the grass-legume mixtures that is both palatable and drought resistant is

    a. Kentucky bluegrass and white clover.
    b. Redtop and alsike.
    c. Ladino and orchard grass.
    d. Alfalfa and smooth brome.

5. Ladino is a large type of

    a. Alfalfa.
    b. Trefoil.
    c. White clover.
    d. Bluegrass.

6. Korean lespedeza is

    a. An annual legume.
    b. A perennial legume.
    c. A summer annual grass.
    d. A perennial grass.

7. Crested wheat grass has been found to be best adapted as a pasture plant in

    a. The northern Great Plains.
    b. The cotton belt.
    c. The middle-western dairy states.
    d. New England.

8. All but one of these practices are recommended as a means of ensuring perpetuation of desirable grasses on the semiarid ranges:

    a. Stocking within the normal grazing capacity of the range.
    b. Lighter grazing during the critical period of leaf and seed production.
    c. Top-dressing with commercial fertilizers.
    d. Occasional deferred grazing.

9. Given a 40-acre field in the corn belt that is subject to erosion, how should you proceed to establish this as a bluegrass pasture as economically and effectively as possible?

10. Outline the procedure for growing winter barley and lespedeza in sequence for pasture in southern Missouri.

11. Under conditions suitable for the growing of a mixture of alfalfa and smooth brome, how might this mixture be managed so as to provide a full season of nutritious pasture for a herd of dairy cows?

12. With soil and climatic conditions suitable for the maintenance of white clover, give seeding, fertilizer, and grazing-management recommendations for a bluegrass pasture that already contains a light admixture of white clover.

13. You have a rolling area covered with bluegrass under conditions in which white clover is not dependable. How should you utilize this as a pasture for dairy cows in order to secure effective, economical returns?

14. Develop a pasture calendar for your community that includes a sequence of crops to provide pasture throughout the entire grazing season.

15. If alfalfa or a grass-alfalfa mixture is being used as the chief source of pasture in an area where the alfalfa must build up an abundant storage of root reserves

in the fall in order to survive the winter, what pasture can be provided for the livestock during this critical fall period?

16. Review literature on rotation grazing, and prepare a discussion on the suitability of this system of management to the more important pastures of your locality.

17. What are the arguments for and against using some of the better plowland for pasture?

18. What is rotation grazing?

19. Why is it usually desirable to prevent pasture plants from reaching maturity?

20. What kind of livestock can utilize mature bluegrass to best advantage?

21. How is lespedeza fitted into the cropping program for pasture?

22. What are some of the livestock nutrient deficiencies that have been encountered with pastures?

23. What is the relationship between grazing management and occasional difficulties with poison plants?

24. What precautions should be observed to prevent bloating of sheep and cattle on clover pasture?

25. Indicate whether each of the following statements is true (T) or false (F).

a. _____Lespedeza benefits from applications of lime to acid soils.

b. _____Under rotation grazing, the repeated, fairly complete defoliation of plants tends to reduce their productive capacity.

c. _____Canada bluegrass is likely to replace Kentucky bluegrass on soils high in organic matter.

d. _____The leaves of smooth brome remain green after the seed is fully mature.

e. _____Sudan grass 4 in. high is less likely to contain dangerous quantities of prussic acid than Sudan grass 20 in. high.

f. _____The growing of grasses with legumes in a pasture tends to reduce bloat hazards.

g. _____The use of land for pasture ensures the upbuilding of its productivity.

h. _____The top-dressing of a grass-legume pasture with phosphatic fertilizers tends to suppress the growth of the legumes.

i. _____Deferred grazing tends to increase the percentage of protein in pasture plants.

j. _____To be useful for pasture a plant must be able to withstand close grazing.

References

ALDOUS, A. E.: Management of Kansas Permanent Pastures, *Kans. Agr. Expt. Sta. Bul.* 272, 1935.

ALLRED, B. W.: Range Conservation Practices for the Great Plains, *U.S. Dept. Agr. Misc. Pub.* 410, 1940.

BLACK, W. H., A. L. BAKER, V. I. CLARK, and O. R. MATHEWS: Effect of Different Methods of Grazing on Native Vegetation and Gains of Steers in Northern Great Plains, *U.S. Dept. Agr. Tech. Bul.* 547, 1937.

BLASER, R. E., and F. T. BOYD: Winter Clover Pastures for Peninsular Florida, *Fla. Agr. Expt. Sta. Bul.* 351, 1940.

BROWN, E. M.: Some Effects of Temperature on the Growth and Chemical Composition of Certain Pasture Grasses, *Mo. Agr. Expt. Sta. Res. Bul.* 299, 1939.
CHENEY, H. B.: Pasture Improvement and Management, *Iowa Agr. Expt. Sta. Bul.* P8 (new series), 1940.
COOPER, H. P., *et al.:* Permanent Pastures for South Carolina, *Clemson Agr. Col. Ext. Bul.* 99, 1937.
HEIN, M. A., and A. C. COOK: Effect of Method and Rate of Grazing on Beef Production and Plant Population of Pastures at Beltsville, Maryland, *U.S. Dept. Agr. Tech. Bul.* 538, 1937.
HELM, C. A.: Management of Korean Lespedeza, *Mo. Agr. Expt. Sta. Cir.* 210, 1940.
JOHNSTONE-WALLACE, D. B.: Pasture Improvement and Management, *Cornell Ext. Bul.* 393, 1938.
LEUKEL, W. A., J. P. CAMP, and J. M. COLEMAN: Effect of Frequent Cutting and Nitrate Fertilization on the Growth Behavior and Relative Composition of Pasture Grasses, *Fla. Agr. Expt. Sta. Bul.* 269, 1934.
ODLAND, T. E., and R. S. SHAW: Pasture Improvement Practices in Rhode Island, *R.I. Agr. Expt. Sta. Bul.* 270, 1938.
PRINCE, F. A., G. P. PERCIVAL, P. T. BLOOD, and P. N. SCRIPTURE: Pasture Top Dressing in New Hampshire, *N.H. Agr. Expt. Sta. Bul.* 320, 1940.
RATHER, H. C., C. M. HARRISON, G. A. BROWN, and R. E. HORWOOD: A Mixture of Alfalfa and Smooth Brome Grass for Pasture, *Mich. Agr. Expt. Sta. Cir. Bul.* 159, 1939.
SAVAGE, D. A.: Grass Culture and Range Improvement in the Central and Southern Great Plains, *U.S. Dept. Agr. Cir.* 491, 1939.
SEMPLE, A. T., H. N. VINALL, C. R. ENLOW, and T. E. WOODWARD: A Pasture Handbook, *U.S. Dept. Agr. Misc. Pub.* 194, 1937.
STAPLEDON, R. G.: "The Land, Now and Tomorrow," Faber & Faber, Ltd. (The Scientific Press), London, 1936.
STEWART, GEO., and R. H. WALKER: Reseeding Range Lands of the Intermountain Region, *U.S. Dept. Agr. Farmers' Bul.* 1823, 1939.
WOODWARD, T. E., J. B. SHEPHERD, and M. A. HEIN: The Hohenheim System in the Management of Permanent Pastures for Dairy Cattle, *U.S. Dept. Agr. Tech. Bul.* 660, 1938.

CHAPTER XII

THE PRODUCTION OF FORAGE SEED

The production of seed of forage crops is a special enterprise. In the case of cereals, seed is the principal objective of normal production, and a portion of the regular crop is set aside for future planting. With forages the normal objective of the crop enterprise is the production of leaves and stems. In order to secure seed for propagation of new crops, certain fields, or certain cuttings, if more than one is produced in a season, are handled so that seed is produced. Seed production is often localized in favored areas. Problems of culture, crop management, and plant nutrition may be quite different for seed production from those for the production of maximum forage yields.

MAJOR FORAGE SEEDS PRODUCED IN THE UNITED STATES

The most important forage seeds produced commercially in this country are alfalfa, red clover, alsike, sweet clover, lespedeza, and timothy. As seed crops these six species involve the full- or part-time use of approximately 2½ million acres of United States land. The five leading states, with each crop, are given in Table 11.

TABLE 11.—LEADING STATES IN THE PRODUCTION OF SIX MAJOR FORAGE-SEED CROPS*

(1929–1938 average)

Alfalfa	Red clover	Alsike	Sweet clover	Lespedeza†	Timothy
Kansas........	Indiana	Ohio	Minneosta	Missouri	Iowa
Idaho.........	Illinois	Minnesota	North Dakota	North Carolina	Missouri
Arizona.......	Ohio	Oregon	South Dakota	Tennessee	Illinois
Oklahoma.....	Michigan	Michigan	Nebraska	Kentucky	Minnesota
Montana......	Idaho	Wisconsin	Kansas	South Carolina	Ohio

* Adapted from *U.S. Dept. Agr. Crops and Markets*, Vol. 17, No. 12, 1940.
† 1940 crop.

Alfalfa Seed.—Alfalfa-seed growing is associated with hay production, but the seed industry has developed to the greatest extent in regions of relatively low rainfall and low humidity. Highest acre yields are secured under irrigation. . Seed production is highly variable both in humid and in arid states.   Within a 10-year period, production in both Utah, where seed is grown under irrigation, and Michigan, a humid state, has ranged from as low as 18,000 bu. to as high as 105,000 bu.   The short crops come from a much lower harvested acreage owing to the fact that much of the alfalfa intended for seed did not set enough to warrant harvest.

The 1928–1937 average total production of alfalfa seed in the United States was 941,000 bu., and the average yield 1.96 bu. an acre.[1] Much higher seed yields are often secured.   Five to 10 bu. is a large crop.

Pollination.—The alfalfa flower may be either self- or cross-pollinated.   The staminal column, containing both the male (stamens) and female (pistil) parts of the alfalfa flower, grows inside a structure called the *keel*.   This column is held in a tense position; and when the tension is released by mechanical pressure near the base of the keel, or otherwise, the staminal column snaps against the opposite flower petal, called the *standard*, and its pollen is scattered.   This tripping also ruptures a membrane protecting the female parts of the flower so that pollination may take place.   Tripping may be caused by certain insects such as bumblebees and leaf-cutter bees (Megachile); or if environmental conditions are favorable, it may be automatic.   Far less frequently, pollination may occur without the flower being tripped. When tripping occurs in the presence of pollen from other alfalfa plants, the foreign pollen is considered more effective in respect to rate of growth and cross-pollination is likely.   In the absence of pollen from other plants, self-pollination occurs.   Self-pollination occasions a reduction in vigor of the alfalfa plants grown from such inbred seed. If pollination does not occur reasonably soon after the alfalfa flower attains full development, the flower drops off.   This is called *stripping*. Effectively pollinated flowers develop a seed pod containing one or more seeds.

Although instances of alfalfa setting seed without tripping have been reported, work done by E. E. Down in Michigan[2] indicated strongly that lack of tripping is one of the chief factors limiting alfalfa seed production.   From work done in Nebraska, Tysdal[3] likewise concludes that, in general, alfalfa flowers must be tripped to produce

---

[1] *U.S. Dept. Agr. Agricultural Statistics,* Superintendent of Documents, Government Printing Office, Washington, D. C., 1940.

[2] Down, E. E., Alfalfa Seed Production Studies in Michigan, *Jour. Amer. Soc. Agron.,* Vol. 23, No. 12, 1931.

[3] Tysdal, H. M., Is Tripping Necessary for Setting Seed in Alfalfa?, *Jour. Amer. Soc. Agron.,* Vol. 32, No. 8, 1940.

seed and that ordinarily there is not sufficient automatic tripping to produce satisfactory seed crops. Tysdal emphasizes that tripping alone does not ensure a good seed crop, and he points out that under some conditions all the flowers might be tripped and cross-pollinated and still might set very little seed.

Many devices for the mechanical tripping of alfalfa flowers have been tried; but, thus far, none has been commercially successful. Low humidity and high temperatures are supposed to favor tripping. If effective tripping is largely the work of certain insects, *viz.*, bumblebees and leaf-cutter bees, environmental conditions favoring the growth and

Fig. 53.—Larger seed yields are usually secured from alfalfa drilled in rows than from broadcast seedings. (*Michigan Agricultural Experiment Station.*)

activities of these insects are essential to alfalfa-seed production and this adds to the complexity of the problem. To date, extensive research has yielded very little information that can be applied effectively to make alfalfa-seed production more dependable.

Cultural Practices.—Most alfalfa seed is harvested from crops that have been grown from broadcast seed. However, the work of Carlson and Stewart[1] and of other investigators has indicated that larger seed yields are secured from alfalfa drilled in rows than from broadcast seedings and that yields are still larger from alfalfa grown in hills rather than rows. Thin broadcast stands are better seed producers than thick ones.

[1] CARLSON, J. W., and GEO. STEWART, Alfalfa Seed Production, *Utah Sgr. Expt. Sta. Tech. Bul.* 226, 1931.

These facts still do not solve the problem of dependable production; for the growing of alfalfa in thin stands, rows, or hills is no guarantee that there will be any setting of seed at all. Seed setting still depends on factors of environment not readily subject to manipulation.

Where alfalfa is grown under irrigation, a limited water supply that produces a slow, even top growth is regarded as being most desirable for seed production. Various methods of cultivation have produced no marked differences in seed setting, but very thorough harrowing of established broadcast stands has value in thinning the stand and controlling weeds. Clipping of immature alfalfa at various stages of growth has generally been detrimental to seed production. High clipping, which has been tried as a means of delaying blossoming, has resulted in greatly decreased blossom production although alfalfa fields moderately grazed in early spring have produced good seed crops when other conditions were favorable.

Much of the alfalfa seed is harvested from the second or, in the Southwest, from the third cutting. In such cases, cutting the hay crop after the alfalfa is in bloom rather than cutting it at a prebloom stage is the preferred practice.

If seed setting is likely to be poor, it is important that this be known as soon as possible so that the crop can be cut for hay. Forecast of seed cannot be made with certainty. However, a rank top growth accompanied by much lodging seldom produces a profitable seed crop. Nor is seed setting likely if the weather is cool and wet during the blossoming period. If the blossoms quickly blast and strip off, there is little chance for a good seed crop; but if this condition is recognized soon enough, the alfalfa can still be made into fair hay.

Which Cutting to Save.—The question of which cutting to save for seed has no definite answer that is broadly applicable. In the extreme North, if seed is to be harvested it must be from the first growth, possibly delayed somewhat by spring tillage or pasturage. If the first crop is cut for hay, the second does not have time to mature seed before frost.

Where a first cutting can be taken for hay in time for seed development on the second crop, the choice depends on weather and economic considerations. Usually the heavier first cutting is removed to supply needed hay and the second is left for seed or hay depending on whether or not a favorable setting develops. However, a dry, hot spring and early summer may cause the development of an unusually heavy seed crop on the first growth.

Seed Harvest.—The alfalfa seed pods do not all mature at the same time. Sometimes an individual seed plant will contain two settings markedly different in maturity owing to alternation of weather periods favorable and unfavorable to effective pollination. The seed grower must choose a time when about two-thirds the seed pods have turned brown as the best time to cut the crop.

Occasionally, when the seed crop is uniform in maturity, the seed may be harvested directly from the standing plants with a combine. It is usually better practice to windrow the crop when most of the seed pods are brown and allow a few days for the immature seed to dry out.

FIG. 54.—Harvesting alfalfa seed in Ohio by means of a binder with the tying mechanism removed. The windrows made in this manner are threshed with a combine. (*Courtesy of E. E. Patton.*)

The combine may then be used to thresh the seed from the windrow, or the crop may be cured in small piles and hauled to a thresher. Alfalfa straw is brittle and fibrous and has very little feeding value.

Alfalfa-seed Insects.—Bumblebees and other wild bees such as Megachile and Nomia are beneficial to alfalfa-seed production by their aid in tripping and cross-pollination. Close observers have seldom seen a honeybee trip an alfalfa flower. There are some other insects that are decidedly injurious to seed production. Certain species of bugs of the genus *Lygus* work on the young alfalfa flower and cause it to strip off. They have been reported as an important cause of stripping in certain areas when conditions otherwise seemed favorable for a good setting of seed.[1]

[1] CARLSON, JOHN W., Lygus Bug Damage to Alfalfa in Relation to Seed Production, *Jour. Agr. Res.*, Vol. 61, No. 11, 1931.

The chalcid fly, which works on the seeds of clover, bur clover, and alfalfa, can also be very destructive. Its extremely small eggs are deposited through the pod directly into soft immature seeds. The larvae feed on the interior of the seed and leave only a little of the shell. Control measures involve destruction of refuse from fields that have set seed, keeping fence lines and ditchbanks clean, thorough cleaning of the seed plus destruction of infested screenings, and fall or winter tillage of seed fields to cover infested pods and thus prevent emergence of the adults.

Red-clover Seed.—Red-clover seed is produced in association with culture of the crop for hay. As a rule, the first cutting is taken for hay and the second for seed. Production of a million bushels a year has been about normal for this country, and the 1927–1938 average acre yield was 1.17 bu. Four to 6 bu. an acre is a very good crop although higher yields are fairly common under irrigation as in Idaho where the 1927–1938 average acre yield was 4.5 bu.

Pollination.—Red clover must be cross-pollinated to set a commercial seed crop. The pollen must come from a separate plant, pollen from different flowers of the same plant usually proving ineffective. Cross-pollination is brought about by bumblebees and honeybees which are attracted to clover blossoms by the nectar secreted at the bases of the stamens.

When Megee and Kelty[1] caged bees out of red clover, almost no seed was produced whereas that growing in the open or inside cages containing bees set 40 to 100 seeds per head. Beekeepers often place their colonies in blossoming clover fields where they are very effective in increasing the set of seed.

Managing the Seed Crop.—Occasionally the first crop of red clover is saved for seed, but it is usually less productive than the second. This may be due in a large measure to the lack of a sufficient number of bees to effect thorough pollination of the early blossoms. The first cutting also has the heaviest vegetative growth, and rank-growing clover plants are not the best seed producers. An economic consideration of importance is that, should the first growth be saved for seed, the subsequent growth would produce very little hay, whereas the first growth of a good crop produces an excellent yield of hay and the much smaller growth of the second crop is entirely adequate for seed.

In order to secure maximum seed yields from the second cutting, the hay crop should be cut when the clover is well in bloom but before

---

[1] MEGEE, C. R., and R. H. KELTY, The Influence of Bees upon Clover and Alfalfa Seed Production, *Mich. Agr. Expt. Sta. Quart. Bul.*, Vol. 14, No. 4, 1931.

the earliest heads have matured and turned brown. If cut before this time, the hay yield of the first crop and the seed yield of the second may both be reduced. Early cutting of the hay crop, especially early June cutting, is an effective control measure for the clover leaf midge, for it destroys most of the larvae attacking the flowers of the first crop. The blossoms of the second crop will then be too far advanced to be susceptible to injury by the time the next brood of the midge is ready to attack them. The midge works only on the clover flowers. Delayed cutting of the hay crop not only is conducive to damage by the clover leaf midge but tends to slow up the recovery

Delayed cutting is unfavorable

Fig. 55.—Curing red-clover seed in the cock before it is hulled. (*Michigan State College.*)

growth of the second crop to the point where seed yields are materially reduced.

Estimating the Seed Crop.—Clover-seed growers are accustomed to estimating the probable set of seed from the condition of the early blossoms. If these early blossoms, as they approach maturity, show 25 to 30 seeds to the head and if there is a good stand with plenty of bloom, the crop is considered satisfactory for seed and should make 1 or 2 bu. an acre. Sometimes when the weather has been clear and warm but not too hot and bee activity has been great, the individual clover heads will contain 50 to 80 seeds to the head. When there are less than 20 seeds to the head, seed prospects are considered poor and the crop may be cut, pastured, or plowed under.

Mammoth Clover.—Mammoth, or bull, clover is a single-cut type of red clover that is much larger and coarser than the medium-red type.

It is not possible to harvest both a hay and a seed crop with mammoth clover because of its late maturity. Sometimes mammoth-clover-seed growers clip the crop or pasture it moderately in the spring to reduce the bulk of material to be handled when the seed ripens. The early clipping or grazing is also intended to increase seed yields, but such increase does not necessarily follow. When late-spring and early-summer weather is dry so that the weather itself reduces the vegetative growth of the mammoth clover, a further reduction is brought about by clipping, particularly if the clipping is carried on after the clover is more than 6 in. high. In this case the seed yields of the subsequent growth

TABLE 12.—INFLUENCE OF CLIPPING ON SEED YIELDS OF MEDIUM RED, MAMMOTH, AND ALSIKE CLOVER, MICHIGAN EXPERIMENTS, 1938–1940*

Treatment	Range of seed yield, bushels an acre		
	Medium red	Mammoth	Alsike
Not clipped......................	1.0–3.0	3.5–3.8	2.6–6.0
Clipped:			
May 23......................	1.9–2.3	3.0–4.3	0.5–3.4
June 1......................	2.3–3.1	1.2–4.5	0 –3.1
June 8......................	2.9–3.3	0 –4.0	0 –0.9
June 15......................	2.7–2.9	0 –3.8	0 –0.5
June 23......................	0 –1.7	0	0
July 1......................	0 –2.0	0	0

* Adapted from C. R. Megee, The Influence of Clipping Treatments and Rolling on the Yield of Clover Seed, *Jour. Amer. Soc. Agron.*, Vol. 34, No. 9, 1942.

are reduced. However, should the season favor an excessive vegetative growth, the preclipping is advantageous to seed production.

Inasmuch as the conditions influencing growth cannot be accurately predicted, the safe procedure is to avoid any preclipping after the clover is 6 in. high because of its minor advantages and potentially great disadvantages.

Some growers roll their mammoth clover just before bloom. The advantages are largely mechanical. The stems bearing heads turn up, and it is possible to harvest a seed crop with a combine without handling the bulk of the top growth. Rolling also destroys a few stemmy weeds. However, if it is done too late, the clover may not turn up but may merely lie in a mass conducive to the development of molds and mildews.

Harvesting Clover Seed.—In the past, both medium and mammoth clover were usually cut for seed with a mower having an attachment that rolled the clover into windrows out of the path of the horses and mower for the next round. The cutting was usually done when the clover heads were brown rather than black and fully ripe. Curing was completed in the windrow or cock, the material was handled as little as possible to prevent shattering, and it was finally threshed with a clover huller.

With the development of the combine harvester, this implement has been widely used for harvesting and threshing clover seed. The method most conservative of seed is to cut and windrow the clover in the usual manner and, after the seed has dried out, thresh it from the

FIG. 56.—Michigan alsike clover in heavy blossom being saved for seed. (*Courtesy of C. M. Harrison.*)

windrow with a combine having a pickup attachment. When clover seed is combined from the standing crop, it must be dry before harvest is started and losses due to shattering are increased.

Alsike Clover. *Seed Habits.*—Alsike clover, like mammoth red, does not produce both a hay crop and a seed crop in the same season. The fact that seed growers must save the first growth for seed, usually without preclipping, makes both alsike and mammoth clover very susceptible to contamination with sweet clover and many annual weed seeds, largely eliminated from medium red clover when the first crop is cut for hay. As may be noted in Table 12, preclipping of alsike in Michigan trials was very detrimental to seed production. The possible exception to this might be the growing of alsike on unusually rich bottom land which, without early preclipping or grazing, might produce an excessively rank top growth.

The average yield of alsike is about two-thirds greater than that of red clover. Yields of 3 to 4 bu. an acre are common, 6 to 8 bu. is very good, and yields of above 10 bu. an acre are exceptional. The highest yields have been secured under irrigation.

The harvest practices for alsike are very similar to those for red clover.

Sweet-clover Seed. *Seeding Habits.*—Sweet clover grows big, blossoms profusely, and produces seed abundantly. It is a great honey crop, and beemen were the first to bring about its general distribution. It is cross-pollinated, and the seed production of special strains requires careful isolation to keep them pure. It has become increasingly difficult to obtain pure seed of different varieties owing to both cross-pollination and mechanical mixture.

Sweet-clover seed yields an average of above 3 bu. an acre, but the price to the grower has been largely $2.50 to $3.50 a bushel. Thus the acre income from this crop has not been large.

Production Methods.—The first growth of sweet clover may be saved for seed; or a second growth may be thus used following clipping treatments, early pasturing, or harvest of the first growth as hay or silage. Whenever a first cutting precedes a seed crop, this cutting must be above the lower leaf axils, for new growth comes from these rather than from the crown. The later this cutting is taken, the higher it must be, to avoid cutting below live buds and thus eliminating any second growth whatsoever.

The first growth is the largest, the most prolific seed producer, and by far the most difficult to handle mechanically. Seed maturity is indeterminate; and when the later blossoms have matured seed, the first set of seed will have become overripe and much of it will have been lost by shattering. Direct harvest of the first growth for seed with a combine is very wasteful and difficult because of shattering losses and also because of the mechanical difficulties of running such bulky, woody material through a machine. If cut with a binder when two-thirds the seed has matured, then shocked until the balance of the seed is dry, and threshed with a grain thresher, more seed will be saved.

Early clipping tends to reduce the bulk of material and make seed maturity more uniform without materially reducing seed yields. The crop as a whole is probably more valuable if pastured for a time or cut for hay or silage in really early bloom, with the second growth saved for seed, than if grown strictly as a seed crop. The smaller second crop can be combined directly if the harvested seed can be spread out to dry; or it can be windrowed, dried in the windrow, and threshed from the windrow with a combine. The old method of binder harvest is still widely used.

Lespedeza Seed. *Seed Yields.*—One of the characteristics making for the popularity of the annual lespedezas in the regions to which they are adapted is their ability to produce seed, even on closely grazed plants, and to shatter this seed to the ground for natural reseedings.

In order to seed new areas, some seed must be harvested; thus, there is commercial production of lespedeza seed in most of the southeastern states and as far north as southern Indiana and Illinois. One of the largest crops was produced in 1938 when 780,000 acres were harvested and a production of 205,700,000 lb. was secured.[1] If lespedeza seed were hulled, its weight per bushel would be not far from 60 lb., the same as that for clover seed. However, most of it is not hulled, and a bushel of unhulled seed varies considerably in weight, 25 lb. being a fair average. The general range of seed yields is 100 to 500 lb. an acre.

Harvest Practice.—Lespedeza seed is cut with a mower when the leaves have turned brown or after a heavy frost. The seed shatters easily; and, to reduce this loss, cutting is usually done early in the morning. The common and Tennessee No. 76 strains of *Lespedeza striata* are usually harvested with a pan attached to the mower bar to catch the seed. If the price is high enough the straw is threshed out and this may contain about half as much as is ordinarily gathered in the pan. Kobe, also a strain of *L. striata*, and Korean lespedeza (*L. stipulacea*) do not shatter so readily as the common, according to Pieters,[2] and so the pan is unnecessary, though it is sometimes used in case the seed has become overripe. Ordinarily the seed is cut with a mower, bunched, and, when dry, threshed with a grain thresher. Windrowed lespedeza is also threshed with the combine.

Timothy Seed. *Yields.*—About half the timothy seed grown in the United States is produced in Iowa. The rest of it is largely grown in other corn-belt states. The 1927–1938 average[1] production was 1,713,730 bu. and the average acre yield 3.36 bu. The standard weight of a bushel of timothy seed is 45 lb. The farm price for seed has seldom exceeded $2.50 a bushel and is often under $2. A very short crop in 1934 resulted in an average farm price of $6.54 a bushel.

Seeding Habits.—Timothy is normally open-pollinated and subject to cross-pollination by wind-blown pollen. Most of the seed produced in this country is commercial timothy, a mixture of types resulting from no special breeding work. Different varieties have been developed in this and other countries, but as yet none of the selected lines

---

[1] *U.S. Dept. Agr. Agricultural Statistics*, 1940.

[2] PIETERS, A. J., "The Little Book of Lespedeza," published by the author, Washington, D. C., 1934.

has come into very wide use. If their maturity is similar to that of ordinary timothy seed, production of these special lines would necessarily have to be in isolation, to avoid pollen contamination. If the time of pollination of two lines is markedly different, they may be grown adjacent to each other without serious crossing.

Usually the original seedings of timothy are made with red clover, and the crop is cut for hay the first and second crop year. The third year, the clover is essentially all gone, but the timothy under normal conditions still shows some nutritional benefits from having been associated with the clover. This third year is regarded as the best for seed production. The yield the fourth year might be improved by top-dressings of nitrogen; but, as a rule, the value of the seed hardly warrants this additional expense.

Harvest.—The customary method of harvest used to be to cut the crop with a binder, cure it in shocks, and thresh it with a grain thresher. Harvest of the seed with a combine from thoroughly ripe standing timothy is entirely feasible even though some loss from shattering occurs.

MISCELLANEOUS FORAGE LEGUMES FOR SEED

White Clover.—Most of the white-clover seed in United States trade channels is used in lawn-grass mixtures. From 1930 to 1938, imports of this seed ranged from 768,000 to 2,385,000 lb. annually, most of it from Europe. These European imports are greatly curtailed or cut off entirely when intercontinental commerce is disrupted by war. Domestic production of white-clover seed has been substantial in Idaho, Wisconsin, Louisiana, Mississippi, and Oregon.

White-clover-seed production is carried on in connection with utilization of the crop for pasture. Liberal phosphate fertilization stimulates growth of the clover, and close grazing for a short time in early spring reduces grass competition. A yield of 100 lb. of seed to the acre is usually profitable, but yields of over 400 lb. are often secured in the West. In 1941, the Idaho crop averaged 460 lb. an acre.

White clover needs moist weather early in the season to develop a vigorous growth. During the blossoming period, clear, warm weather favoring insect activity is desirable for seed production. As with red and alsike clover, cross-pollination is the rule, and this is carried on by bees of various kinds. Colonies of honeybees placed in white-clover-seed fields help greatly in pollination.

The crop is cut with a mower, preferably with a bunching attachment, cured in small piles, and threshed with a thresher or clover huller.

Ladino.—Nearly all seed production of Ladino, the large white clover, is carried on under irrigation in the far west. Frequently, the first growth is put into the silo and the next crop saved for seed. In the West, conditions may permit the harvest of two seed crops a year in the case of both Ladino and the ordinary white clover. The seeds of alsike, timothy, and sorrel cannot be separated from either white- or Ladino clover seed with ordinary cleaning equipment, and their presence results in severe price discounts.

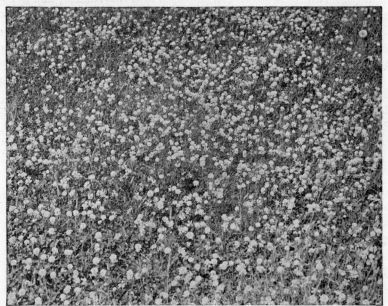

Fig. 57.—Domestic production of white-clover seed has been substantial in Idaho, Wisconsin, Louisiana, Mississippi, and Oregon. (*Courtesy of E. B. Swingle.*)

Strawberry Clover.—The suitability of strawberry clover for highly alkaline soils in the West has made seed production of this legume a worth-while enterprise. The flowers of this clover are self-fertile, but visitation by bees helps ensure effective pollination. Hollowell[1] reports that the crop yields 40 to 300 lb. of seed an acre, with best yields coming from thick stands. With a good stand, harvest practices are the same as for white clover. The crop should be cut when the seed capsules are light brown. If cut too early, the immature seed will be shriveled; if cut too late, much of the seed will shatter off. To reduce shattering, the seed crop should be handled while it is a little damp.

[1] HOLLOWELL, E. A., Strawberry Clover, *U.S. Dept. Agr. Leaflet No.* 176, 1939.

Crimson Clover.—Crimson-clover seed is grown in the Maryland-Virginia section and in states farther south. It, too, shatters easily and must be cut before it is too ripe, preferably when the heads have turned nicely brown. Growth of the clover and seed production are materially benefited by phosphate fertilization. Good crops yield from 4 to 8 bu. an acre. One to five million pounds of crimson-clover seed is normally imported annually from central Europe.

Hairy Vetch.—Hairy-vetch seed harvested as a by-product of small grain culture in Europe is imported into this country and is used in the South for the sowing of this crop for green-manure purposes. Normally, this imported seed is cheap. When the supply of imported seed is low, hairy-vetch-seed production becomes profitable in such states as Oregon and Michigan, which grow the crop on light sandy soil.

Hairy vetch is a winter annual with a vinelike growth. If sown alone, the matted growth of these vines will not produce much seed. Hence, the custom is to sow 10 to 15 lb. of vetch with a bushel of rye. Heavier vetch seedings do not set seed so well as moderately thin stands. The rye supports the vetch vines, and the two crops are harvested together by the methods used in the locality for small grain.

Separation of the two seeds is readily accomplished by a spiral-column machine through which the mixture is poured. The round vetch seed rolls faster and because of centrifugal force works to the outside while the flat-kerneled rye moves much more slowly and stays on the inside.

Some northern Michigan farmers have used quack grass to support the vetch vines. Their practice is to work a quack-grass sod with a field cultivator sufficiently to fit a seedbed without killing out the quack grass, which, incidentally, does not kill out easily. Vetch is seeded in this seedbed in late August or early September and, supported by quack-grass stems, produces a seed crop the next July. Often enough, vetch reseeds voluntarily to produce the next crop.

Vetch-seed yields range from 100 to 700 lb. an acre. When grown with rye, the rye yield is not materially affected by the presence of vetch.

Common vetch seed is grown in Oregon either from pure stands or in mixtures with small grain. September plantings are ready for harvest the next summer. When planted alone, 40 to 80 lb. of seed an acre is used. The lower pods mature first, and the crop is usually cut with a mower when these are ripe and the upper ones are fully formed. A special attachment to the mower facilitates getting the seed into windrows for curing. Ten to 25 bu. of common vetch seed to the acre represents usual production.

MISCELLANEOUS GRASS-SEED PRODUCTION

Kentucky Bluegrass.—The Kentucky bluegrass seed of commerce is used largely in the lawn-grass-seed trade, but a portion of the crop is used for the reseeding of pasture lands.   Most of this seed is produced in two areas, one in Kentucky, the other including parts of Missouri, Iowa, northeastern Kansas, and southeastern Nebraska.   There is minor production in other near-by areas in some years.

Fig. 58.—Curing Kentucky bluegrass seed in Bourbon County, Kentucky.   The seed is placed in windrows and turned daily until it is completely cured.   The normal time required is 2 to 3 weeks.   (*Courtesy of U.S. Dept. Agr. Soil Conservation Service.*)

The production of Kentucky bluegrass seed is a side line to the utilization of this grass for pasture.   It is confined for the most part to farms with large acreages.   The general sequence is to establish a seeding, usually in mixture with timothy and clover.   The first crop year, this mixture is cut for hay.   From then on, it is used for pasture. The timothy and clover will usually have disappeared in 3 years, nearly pure Kentucky bluegrass being left.   Usually, stands that are 10 years old or more tend to become thin and weedy.

If weather conditions and fall-grazing management favor storage of reserve food in the plants, the bluegrass is in best condition to make a vigorous spring growth.   If seed production is intended, spring grazing must be very light or discontinued entirely until after seed harvest.

Kentucky bluegrass seed cannot be separated from the chaff with the usual threshing equipment; therefore, seed harvest is carried on with stripping machines that comb or pull the seed from the standing grass. Harvest begins when the heads begin to turn yellow and the seed is still high in moisture. Overripe seed shatters badly. Because of its high moisture content at harvest, Kentucky bluegrass seed must be dried. The harvested seed is taken to the drying place and piled in windrows 2 to 3 ft. high; these must be turned several times a day to prevent heating. The curing-out process requires 2 to 3 weeks of good weather. The dried seed is then put through machinery that loosens it from the chaff by a rubbing process and cleans it for the market.

In general, seed yields range from 5 to 15 bu. an acre, yields above 20 bu. being exceptional. The weight of a bushel of this seed varies with the thoroughness of rubbing and cleaning to remove the chaff. When finally ready for the market, the seed is graded in accordance with its weight per measured bushel. A current wholesale list quotes Kentucky bluegrass seed as follows:

Grade	Price per Hundredweight
28 lb.	$25.00
24 lb.	21.00
21 lb.	19.50

Following stripping of the seed, Kentucky bluegrass fields are pastured for the balance of the season. Seed production has not been an intensive enterprise, and no special fertilization practices appear to have attained widespread commercial use.

Smooth Brome.—In the early years of smooth-brome culture, nearly all the smooth-brome seed came from states west and north of Kansas and Nebraska. A great deal of the seed used in the United States also came from western Canada. By 1938, work in Michigan, Ohio, and other of the more humid corn-belt states had shown that there, too, seed production of this grass was perfectly feasible; and considerable seed production has been undertaken well east of what was formerly considered brome-grass country. This seed production was associated with a greatly increased use of this grass in the Middle West for forage and pasture purposes.

Seed is produced both in rows and from broadcast seedings, the better yields coming from row plantings. Brome grass is a voracious consumer of nitrogen, and old broadcast seedings become sod-bound owing to insufficient nitrogen to promote a vigorous top growth. Such stands are low seed producers. Rowed brome grass shows evidence of this lack of nitrogen much less quickly than does a solid stand, but even rowed stands more than 1 year old give a very marked response to nitrogen in both forage and seed yields.

In work conducted by Harrison and Crawford,[1] 2-year-old brome grass top-dressed with sulphate of ammonia in April gave the following seed yields as compared with the yield of such grass not fertilized:

Fertilizer, Pounds	Yield, Pounds per Acre
None	356
100	436
250	523
500	789
750	663
1,000	742

At $0.10 a pound for seed the 500-lb. application increased the acre income by $43.30 at a fertilizer cost of approximately $10.

Fig. 59.—Smooth brome grass produces best seed yields when grown in rows and fertilized liberally with nitrogen. (*Michigan Agricultural Experiment Station.*)

Stands older than 2 years appear to have gradually deteriorated in seed-producing ability despite fertilization. Further studies of the nutritional requirements of this unusual grass are in progress.

The most satisfactory harvest procedure appears to be to let the seed fully mature on the standing grass and harvest it with a combine, cutting as high as possible. For this and other light-seeded grasses the wind of any threshing equipment must be almost completely shut off to prevent blowing the seed away. The leaves of brome grass are still

[1] HARRISON, C. M. and W. N. CRAWFORD, Seed Production of Smooth Brome Grass as Influenced by Applications of Nitrogen, *Jour. Amer. Soc. Agron.*, Vol. 33, No. 7, 1941.

green when the seed is fully ripe, and after seed harvest this grass still makes good pasture.

The standard weight of a bushel of brome grass seed is 14 lb. In general, seed yields range from 100 to 700 lb. an acre.

One of the important seed-production considerations with respect to smooth brome is to avoid fields infested with quack grass. The seeds of quack grass cannot be cleaned out of smooth-brome seed, and the latter if badly infested with quack grass becomes entirely unsalable.

Orchard Grass.—Kentucky, Virginia, and Missouri grow much of the orchard-grass seed produced in this country. The 1935–1939 average production for the country was 3,094,000 lb. Seed yields in general range from 100 to 400 lb. an acre. Commercial seed production is from broadcast seedings made with winter wheat or spring-sown oats or barley. The orchard grass is seeded at 10 to 14 lb. an acre.

According to Helm[1] the seed is best harvested by topping the stand, *i.e.*, cutting it with a grain binder set to cut the crop with just enough straw to make bundles. At the proper stage the heads are dry enough to shatter easily when struck across the hand, though the stems are still green. If cut too early, the seed will be light and of low germination. To reduce shattering, cutting ought to be done in the morning while the plants are still damp.

It takes about a week of good drying weather to cure out the sheaves enough so that they can be hauled from the field and stacked, after which the balance of the forage can be cut for hay or pastured.

Redtop.—Most of the world's supply of redtop seed and 95 per cent of that produced in the United States is grown in a dozen counties of southern Illinois.[2] Most of the land growing this seed crop is very acid and poorly drained and has an impervious subsoil lacking lime. It is unsuited for most cultivated crops but maintains redtop stands for several years.

The average acreage of redtop harvested for seed in Illinois is in excess of 200,000, with annual average yields ranging from 30 to 75 lb. an acre.

The Illinois Agricultural Experiment Station report on this crop states that redtop-seed yields were improved by the use of organic manures and lime. The crop is sown broadcast at 8 to 15 lb. an acre, usually in the fall. Fall seedings become established more quickly than those made in the spring. Stands are kept for 3 to 15 years. The seed is cut with either a mower or a binder, cured in the cock or

[1] HELM, C. A., Orchard Grass in Missouri, *Mo. Agr. Expt. Sta. Cir.* 172, 1934.

[2] BURLISON, W. L., C. L. STEWART, R. C. ROSS, and O. L. WHALIN, Production and Marketing of Redtop, *Ill. Agr. Exp. Sta. Bul.* 404, 1934.

shock, stacked, and finally threshed with a properly adjusted grain thresher. The preferred time of harvest is not later than about a week after blooming is completed. As with many grasses, ripe seed shatters and is readily lost.

FIG. 60.—Redtop stacks such as those in (a) are a common sight over much of the redtop area in southern Illinois. These stacks may be threshed or fed as roughage without removal of the seed. The seed crop is commonly harvested with a binder (b). Threshing (c) may be done directly from the shock or after stacking, suitable time being allowed for the stacks to go through a sweat. (Courtesy of W. L. Burlison, Illinois Agricultural Experiment Station.)

Rye Grass.—The rye-grass seed grown in the United States is nearly all produced in the Willamette Valley in Oregon. It consists of a mixture of annual and perennial forms, and the mixture may be both genetic and mechanical in character. It is generally known to the trade as *domestic rye grass*, but Schroth and Hein of the U.S. Department of Agriculture[1] use the name *common rye grass*. The seed competes with imported Italian and perennial rye grass. The Italian is usually an annual, but the crop grown from commercial Italian rye-grass seed often contains both annual and perennial farms. For the years 1929 to 1938, average annual rye-grass-seed imports were as follows:[2]

Type	Imports, Pounds
Italian	192,000
Perennial	719,000

In 1937, over a million pounds of each was imported. Utilization of the rye grasses for pastures and lawns has increased. The annual forms have been found particularly useful for winter lawns in the South and as annual pastures.

The seed is harvested in the hard-dough stage with a binder, cured in the shock, and threshed with a grain thresher; or it may be allowed to mature and then is harvested from the standing grass with a combine. Sometimes it is windrowed before being threshed with a combine. Ripe seed readily shatters. An average yield is 600 to 700 lb. an acre; but 1,200 to 1,500 lb. of seed may be secured under favorable conditions.

Crested Wheat Grass.—The demonstrated value of crested wheat grass for northwestern dry lands has brought about the development of domestic seed production of this introduced species. Crested wheat grass is a prolific seed producer; but, as in so many grasses, the seed shatters easily at maturity and must be harvested with care. The seed crop is ready for binder harvest when the heads change from green to a light straw color. Seed yields in the West are somewhat larger than those secured from smooth brome. The weight of a measured bushel is usually from 20 to 24 lb., and recleaned seed should have a purity of about 90 per cent. The growing of the crop in 36- to 42-in. rows is favored for seed production.

The Fescues.—The production of meadow-fescue seed has developed to some extent in Kansas where the crop is harvested much like small grain.

Chewings fescue, a variety of red fescue, has been imported from New Zealand in quantities exceeding a million pounds annually. A limited quantity is grown in Oregon. This grass is useful for shady

[1] SCHROTH, H. A., and M. A. HEIN, The Ryegrasses, *U.S. Dept. Agr. Leaflet No.* 196, 1940.

[2] *U.S. Dept. Agr. Agricultural Statistics*, 1940.

lawns, on light soil for golf courses and roadside seedings, and as an orchard cover crop to prevent erosion. Trial plantings in Michigan in 1940 yielded 400 lb. an acre and were easily harvested with a combine.

Sudan Grass.—Sudan grass seed is produced in the southwestern United States. The Texas Agricultural Experiment Station[1] reports that best seed yields are secured when the crop is drilled in 3-ft. rows at 10 lb. an acre. The rowed Sudan grass has consistently out-yielded that which was broadcast. The seed crop can be cut most conveniently with a corn binder. It is shocked in large shocks to cure

FIG. 61.—Chewings fescue seed in Michigan being harvested very economically with a combine.

and is threshed with a grain thresher with the air blast greatly reduced to prevent blowing the seed away with the straw. Harvest starts when the seeds in the main, or first, heads are ripe.

Wild Grasses.—The reseeding of western ranges as a soil-conservation measure has occasioned much interest in harvesting seed of native wild grasses. The revolving spike-cylinder seed stripper, used in harvesting Kentucky bluegrass seed, has been used to gather the seed of blue grama grass.[2] Similar equipment, modified to meet special requirements, is used to gather seed of grama and drop-seed grasses. Taller species like western wheat grass are harvested with the binder or combine.

[1] KARPER, R. E., J. R. QUINBY, and D. L. JONES, Sudan Grass for Hay Seed and Pasture, *Tex. Agr. Expt. Sta. Bul.* 396, 1929.

[2] HOOVER, M. M., Native and Adapted Grasses for Conservation of Soil and Moisture in the Great Plains and Western United States, *U.S. Dept. Agr. Farmers' Bul.* 1812, 1939.

Because much of this native grass seed is light and may have hairy glumes, many sterile florets, or heavy awns, special processing is needed to condition it for seeding with mechanical equipment. A type of scarification with rubbing machines of various sorts removes awns and glumes so that the seed can be fanned and screened and got into condition to flow normally through a seed drill.

SOME GENERAL CONSIDERATIONS IN GRASS-SEED CULTURE

For the most part, grass-seed culture has been carried on as an extensive enterprise with but little attention to special cultural practices and the use of commercial fertilizers. However, the normal prices for many of the grass seeds are high enough so that reasonable increases in yield can more than pay for special treatments.

Fertilizers for Grass Seed.—There is, no doubt, a considerable variation among grass species in their response to fertilizers. The unusual response of smooth brome to nitrogen has already been mentioned. Nitrogen is unquestionably the plant food that can influence seed production to the greatest degree. Phosphorus and potassium are needed for grasses, but the requirements for these nutrients are less marked.

If too much nitrogen is applied, grasses develop too much top growth, lodging is severe, and seed yields are reduced. According to work done in Wales,[1] stiff-strawed species such as cocksfoot (orchard grass) and timothy are less susceptible to lodging than rye grass and the fescues, and larger quantities of nitrogen can be applied to them for production of seed. With stoloniferous species like creeping red fescue and Kentucky bluegrass, Evans states that applications of nitrogen may result in as much as a 50 per cent decrease in seed yield as often as it may show an increase. Fall applications of nitrogen for such grasses are more likely to prove beneficial than those made in the spring, according to the Welsh work.

Grasses that are broadcast in pure culture for seed evince a greater demand for nitrogen than rowed plantings of the same species. This may be due in large part to the fact that the interrow cultivation stimulates release of the plant nutrients. Rowed plantings are easier to keep clean, which is likewise important.

The extent to which grazing, clipping, and other management treatments in the fall may affect the subsequent seed crop has not received adequate study in the United States.

[1] Evans, Gwilym, Technique of Grass Seed Production at the Welsh Plant Breeding Station, *Imp. Bur. Plant Genet., Herbage Pub. Ser. Bul.* 22, 1937.

WEED PROBLEMS IN RELATION TO FORAGE-SEED PRODUCTION

To be marketable, not only must forage seeds be of good appearance and high germination, but they must not contain weed seeds and objectionable crop mixtures. In fact, almost any mixture reduces the market price of the seed. Red clover is often mixed with alfalfa in forage seedings, and yet alfalfa seed containing a mixture of red clover is not nearly so salable as pure alfalfa seed. Noxious-weed seeds are, of course, the most objectionable admixtures. Each state has its own list of legally noxious weeds; and their presence in crop seed, even to a seemingly slight degree, may make the crop seed legally unsalable.

Cleaning Losses.—Every lot of seed must be cleaned before it is ready for the ultimate sower. The charge for cleaning and the loss of some good seed in this process are a normal charge against seed handling. When the crop seed contains too many weeds or kinds that can be removed only with difficulty, the cleaning charge and shrinkage losses become excessive.

In a Michigan study[1] of seed cleaning losses, quality seed from clean, well-cared-for fields shrunk but little in being prepared for the market, the low shrinkage in the lots examined being 3.72 per cent for alsike, 3.88 per cent for mammoth, and 5.15 per cent for medium red clover. With other lots, low-quality seed, inert matter, and weed seeds made necessary the use of different screens and a stronger wind blast, even for the first cleaning, so that one 1,700-lb. lot of alsike shrunk 45 per cent, an 8,600-lb. lot of mammoth containing a heavy infestation of bracted plantain shrunk 23 per cent, and several smaller lots of medium red clover shrunk more than 50 per cent.

The reduction of cleaning losses and price discounts for objectionable seed involves thorough preparation of seedbeds at intervals so as to destroy weed seeds in the soil and the careful avoidance of planting seed that contains weeds.

Troublesome Weed Seeds.—All weeds are troublesome, some more so than others. Most states have laws specifying that the seeds of certain weeds are legally noxious and restricting the sale of seed containing such weed seeds. The Michigan law is typical. If legally noxious weed seeds are present in crop seed in excess of 1 in 5 g. of crop seed, the presence of such noxious-weed seeds must be distinctly shown on the label. If noxious-weed seeds are present in excess of 1 to 2,000 crop seeds, the seed is legally unsalable.

---

[1] RATHER, H. C., Weed Problems in Relation to the Production and Marketing of Farm Seeds, *Jour. Amer. Soc. Agron.*, Vol. 22, No. 5, 1930.

Under the terms of the Federal Seed Act of Aug. 9, 1939, seeds of the following plants shall be considered noxious-weed seeds when in imported seed:

Whitetop—*Lepidium draba* L.
Canada thistle—*Cirsium arvense* (L.)
Dodder—*Cuscuta spp.*
Quack grass—*Agropyron repens* (L.) *Beauv.*
Johnson grass—*Sorghum halepense* (L.) *Pers.*
Bindweed—*Convolvulus arvensis* L.
Russian knapweed—*Centaurea picris Pall.*
Perennial sow thistle—*Sonchus arvensis* L.
Leafy spurge—*Euphorbia esula* L.

A few weeds, the seeds of which cannot be removed from certain crop seeds at all or only with considerable expense, deserve special comment.

Buckhorn and other closely related members of the plantain family are especially common in clover seed. They can be destroyed readily by plowing and tillage, but once in a clover field there is no satisfactory control except by hand labor. Special cleaning mills that take advantage of the sticky character of buckhorn seeds or their difference from clover seed in specific gravity can effect a good separation but at considerable added expense.

Wild mustard and members of the mustard family (Brassicaceae) in general owe their troublesome character to their profuse production of seed and the fact that the seeds retain their viability in the soil for a long time.

Field dodder is a parasitic vine that lives on alfalfa, clover, and occasionally other plants. The seed is very objectionable in clover and alfalfa and once in the soil may retain its vitality and provide a new source of infestation for many years. Badly infested fields should be plowed, thoroughly tilled, and planted to a row crop and then to a nonlegume.

White campion, sleepy catchfly, bladder campion, and night-flowering catchfly, all members of the pink family (Caryophyllaceae) reproduce by seeds that are hard to remove from alfalfa, red clover, and alsike. A few plants can be rogued out of seed fields; but if the infestation is severe, the field should be mowed early to prevent seed production, plowed, and planted to a cleanly cultivated row crop or summer-fallowed before it is reseeded to alfalfa or clover.

The buckwheat family (Polygonaceae) includes several weeds that may cause heavy shrinkage losses in the cleaning of forage seeds,

Among the more common are field sorrel, curly dock, and lady's-thumb. *The goosefoot family* (Chenopodiaceae) includes lamb's-quarters (pigweed) and Russian thistle, a common pest in western alfalfa.

Canada thistle, quack grass, field bindweed, and other persistent perennials (see Chap. V) may be spread by seed as well as by underground stems and must be guarded against in the production and dissemination of crop seed.

SEED LAWS

Many grass and legume seeds are difficult to identify. When this problem is complicated by the seeds of hundreds of weeds, the job is one for experts. The seed business cannot be operated on the principle of *caveat emptor*—"Let the buyer beware." The sowers of seed cannot be expected to be familiar with all the weed seeds, not even all the crop seeds, they encounter.

Some crop seeds are indistinguishable one from another. Mammoth-clover seed is identical in appearance to that of medium red clover. Ladino-clover seed and ordinary white-clover seed look just alike. Furthermore, the value of seed may depend on its origin; yet Italian clover seed, unadapted in the United States, is identical in appearance to the hardiest of red-clover seed grown in northern states.

Seed laws are designed to reduce the gamble a farmer takes when he buys seed. They are based on labeling procedure. Each lot or parcel of seed exposed for sale carries a label that gives the purchaser pertinent information he might otherwise be unable to secure.

Name of Seed.—First, the seed must be identified. The seed label ordinarily goes no further than giving the commonly accepted name of the kind of seed, *e.g.,* timothy, red clover, or alfalfa. Varietal names are usually not required by seed laws, but seed-certifying agencies do provide assurance of varietal genuineness.

Purity.—The purity of seed shown on a seed label is the approximate percentage by weight of pure seed present. The percentage of purity is important, but it may be not nearly so important as the character of the impurities. When impurities consist of inert matter, they are relatively harmless; when they consist of noxious-weed seeds, they are dangerous.

Impurities.—The impurities consist of inert matter, weed seeds, and other crop seeds. Most seed laws require that the seed label show the percentage by weight of inert matter and the percentage by weight of "foreign seeds," *i.e.,* all seeds other than the agricultural seed that constitutes the lot being offered for sale. Definite limits are placed on the number of noxious-weed seeds that may be present.

Origin.—For the several crops for which origin of production is of agronomic importance the place where the seed was grown may be required to be shown on the label. Seed-law-enforcement officials may use shipping records to aid in administration of this provision, but sometimes the seed tells its own story. For example, Idaho alfalfa seed will not contain the seeds of Johnson grass. When Johnson grass seeds are present, the alfalfa seed is either of southwestern origin or a blend containing southwestern-grown seed.

Seed Staining.—A Federal law requires that all red-clover and alfalfa seed imported into the United States be identified by staining at the port of entry. Red-clover and alfalfa seed grown in Canada is widely useful in the United States and is stained 1 per cent violet. If imported alfalfa or red clover is of unknown origin or comes from an area the seed of which has been found generally unsatisfactory in the United States, it must be stained 10 per cent red or 10 per cent orange-red. By a 1941 ruling of the Secretary of Agriculture, it was determined that the seed of alfalfa and red clover from any foreign country other than the Dominion of Canada was not adapted for general agricultural use in the United States. Under this ruling, 10 per cent of the seeds in each container of such alfalfa and red-clover seed, or any seed containing 10 per cent or more of such alfalfa and red-clover seed, admitted into the commerce of the United States shall be stained red or an orange-red color.

The presence of red- or orange-red-stained seed in any lot of red-clover or alfalfa seed is a warning to the buyer that such seed is imported and has been found not to be adapted for general agricultural use in this country.

Germination.—Obviously, to be of value, seed must grow; therefore, seed labels show the approximate live-seed content of the lot. Germination tests are conducted in many ways, and the rate of germination is by no means the same for all species. The United States official germination test for alfalfa seed is conducted between blotters or in soil, at 20°C., and the final count is read in 7 days. Canada bluegrass is tested in Petri dishes with two thicknesses of blotters, one thickness of absorbent cotton, or five thicknesses of paper toweling, at a temperature of 20 to 30°C., with the final count made in 28 days.

The U.S. Department of Agriculture publishes the Rules and Regulations under the Federal Seed Act which contains official methods for conducting laboratory germination tests for all crop seeds.

Hard Seeds.—The hard seeds normally found in alfalfa, the clovers, sweet clover, and other small-seeded legumes are live seeds that fail to sprout in a short period of time because they absorb moisture very slowly. The germination of such seeds is greatly hastened by scarification, a process of scratching the seed coat, as by rubbing it against sandpaper, so that moisture can penetrate more readily. At one time, seed scarification was widely advocated for alfalfa, sweet-clover, and red-clover seed. However, seed so treated is more subject to deterioration in storage; and, at the usual rate of planting, stands are just as good from unscarified seed as from that which has been scarified.

A seed label may report alfalfa germination as follows:

> Germination—54 per cent.
> Hard seed—41 per cent.
> Probable live seed—95 per cent.

Such seed should be entirely satisfactory for planting in a good seedbed at 10 lb. or more to the acre. It is not unreasonable to expect some benefit from the hard seed which eventually germinates and may thereby thicken a stand injured by frost, drought, or otherwise. The hard seeds of red clover are harder than those of alfalfa, but they too may prove beneficial in the long run. Sweet-clover hard seeds are very hard. Scarification may be advisable to secure quick germination of spring-seeded sweet clover. Hard seeds are responsible for the volunteering of sweet clover in subsequent crops of alfalfa or red clover that may be seeded several years later. This volunteer sweet clover is especially undesirable in clover and alfalfa fields intended for seed. It is controlled by harvest of the first crop for hay in the case of alfalfa and medium red clover but cannot be readily eliminated from mammoth- and alsike-seed fields, for no hay crop is harvested.

Seed Analysis.—In the usual seed analysis, determinations are made beyond the requirements for labeling. Such determinations include the approximate number per pound of each weed or other crop seed present. Farmers and seedsmen in most states may obtain this seed-analysis service from state seed laboratories. The larger seed companies employ their own seed analysts. The analysis work is carried on by uniform methods worked out by the Association of Official Seed Analysts of North America.[1]

Review Problems

1. Consult the latest issue of U.S. Agricultural Statistics, and fill out the following table for the United States:

[1] Rules and Recommendations for Testing Seeds, *U.S. Dept. Agr. Cir.* 480, 1930.

Seed crop	Acreage harvested		Yield per acre		Production		Price for last crop
	10-year average	Last year	10-year average	Last year	10-year average	Last year	
Alfalfa.........							
Red clover.....							
Alsike.........							
Sweet clover...							
Lespedeza......							
Timothy.......							

2. Which of the following statements is true?

 a. The alfalfa flower is normally self-pollinated.
 b. Alfalfa may be either self- or cross-pollinated.
 c. Most alfalfa flowers are self-sterile.
 d. Cross-pollination of alfalfa flowers seldom occurs under natural conditions.

3. Which of the following statements is most widely accepted?

 a. The automatic tripping of alfalfa flowers is most commonly responsible for a good seed crop.
 b. Tripping is unnecessary for a good set of seed.
 c. Tripping resulting from the activities of certain wild bees and other outside agencies is one of the essentials for a good setting of alfalfa seed.

4. If environmental conditions in general favor a good setting of alfalfa seed, the largest acre yields may be expected from

 a. Alfalfa planted in rows or hills.
 b. Thin broadcast seedings.
 c. Thick broadcast seedings with a very heavy top growth.

5. A good setting of alfalfa seed is most likely when the weather during the blossoming period is

 a. Cool and rainy.
 b. Hot and humid.
 c. Moderately hot and clear.
 d. Extremely hot and dry.

6. In some areas a large amount of stripping of alfalfa flowers is caused by injury to the young blossoms. This is the work of

 a. Chalcid flies.
 b. Bumblebees.
 c. Megachile bees.
 d. Lygus bugs.

7. Which of the following statements is false?

    a. Good clover-seed crops are the result of a large amount of both cross- and self-pollination.

    b. Nearly all clover flowers are self-sterile.

    c. Cross-pollination is necessary for the setting of a clover-seed crop.

8. When the second crop of medium red clover is to be saved for seed, the best time to cut the first crop for hay is

    a. When the first buds begin to show.

    b. When the clover is in early bloom.

    c. When the first flowers are brown.

    d. When nearly all the flowers are brown and mature.

9. Clipping mammoth clover when it is 8 to 12 in. high

    a. Is always detrimental to seed production.

    b. Is likely to prove beneficial to seed production when subsequent weather conditions favor an unusually rank top growth.

    c. Is always beneficial to seed setting.

10. When sweet clover is cut for hay, a seed crop may be harvested from the second growth

    a. Under no circumstances.

    b. Provided that the first crop is cut high so that new growth may develop from the axils of the lower leaves.

    c. Provided that the first crop is cut low so that new growth will start from the crown.

11. Nearly half the timothy seed grown in the United States is produced in

    a. Oregon.

    b. New York.

    c. Iowa.

    d. Illinois.

    e. Minnesota.

12. Stands of white clover are most likely to be thickened and seed yields increased by liberal fertilization with

    a. Nitrogen.

    b. Barnyard manure.

    c. Phosphate.

    d. Potash.

13. Hairy-vetch seed production is favored by

    a. Light seedings made with rye.

    b. Heavy seedings made with rye.

    c. Moderate seedings of vetch in pure culture.

14. Kentucky bluegrass seed is harvested

    a. With a combine at full maturity.

    b. With a binder when two-thirds the seed is ripe.

   c. With a mower and windrower.
   d. With a special seed stripper when the seed is still relatively high in
   moisture.

15. Smooth-brome-seed yields are likely to be greatest

   a. With light applications of nitrogen.
   b. With heavy applications of nitrogen.
   c. If no nitrogen is applied.

16. Most of the commercial redtop seed is grown on

   a. Very acid, poorly drained heavy soils.
   b. Nearly neutral clay loams high in organic matter.
   c. Well-drained sandy loam soils.
   d. Muck.

17. Seed production of the finer stemmed grasses, such as red fescue, is most
likely to be improved by

   a. Avoiding nitrogen fertilization.
   b. Liberal spring applications of nitrogen.
   c. Applications of nitrogen just before heading.
   d. Applications of nitrogen the fall preceding seed harvest.

18. Red-clover and alfalfa seed of unknown origin that is imported into the
United States

   a. Must be stained 10 per cent red at port of entry.
   b. Must be stained 1 per cent violet.
   c. Must be stained 1 per cent green.
   d. May enter commercial channels without staining.

19. Make a list giving the common and scientific names of the weeds that are
legally noxious according to the seed laws of your state.

20. Make a table from the official Rules and Regulations under the Federal
Seed Act, giving the accepted procedure for testing the germination of the following
crop seeds:

Kind of seed	Sub-strata	Temperature, degrees centigrade	First count, days	Final count, days	Remarks
Alfalfa...............					
Kentucky bluegrass....					
Smooth brome.........					
Red clover............					
Korean lespedeza......					
Orchard grass..........					
Timothy..............					

References

Cox, J. F., and G. E. STARR: "Seed Production and Marketing," John Wiley & Sons, Inc., New York, 1927.

EVANS, GWILYM: Technique of Grass Seed Production at the Welsh Plant Breeding Station, *Imp. Bur. Plant Genet., Herbage Pub. Ser. Bul.* 22, 1937.

MUENSCHER, W. C.: "Weeds," The Macmillan Company, New York, 1935.

PIPER, C. V.: "Forage Plants and Their Culture," The Macmillan Company, New York, 1924.

Rules and Recommendations for Testing Seeds, *U.S. Dept. Agr. Cir.* 480, 1938.

Rules and Regulations under the Federal Seed Act, *U.S. Dept. Agr. Serv. Regulat. Announc.* 156, 1940.

CHAPTER XIII

CORN

"Corn is king," so it has been said. Most certainly this tall and leafy grain-bearing grass, developed to something approaching its present state in the most ancient days of a primitive American agriculture, has come to play a leading role in the drama of current civilization, whether as master or servant. Directly or indirectly, corn contributes in a major way to the food supply of mankind in every land. Five million acres are grown in South Africa, 20 million acres in the Danube River basin, 9 million in Russia, 8 million in India, and 2 million in Egypt. Mexico, Argentina, and Brazil each grow 7 to 10 million acres.

Yet corn is particularly a North American crop—a crop of the United States, with nearly five million American farms participating in its culture, growing half the world's corn acreage, and numbering its bushels by the billion. A normal United States corn crop is $2\frac{1}{2}$ billion bushels; $1\frac{1}{4}$ billion dollars is its normal farm value. On two occasions, its farm value has exceeded 4 billion dollars. At times, its value has been great enough to bring prosperity to millions of farms; in darker days, some of it, unmarketable, has been thrown into the furnace. No wonder that the planting, culture, harvest, distribution, and use of corn intimately affect the well-being of so many American people.

KINDS OF CORN

Dent Corn.—Most of the corn now grown in the United States is of the dent-corn type. The yellow dent varieties are most popular; but for certain purposes, notably in the breakfast-food industry, white corn is used exclusively. The denting of the cap, or crown, of the kernel results from the greater shrinkage of the soft starch in the crown as compared with the harder starch that makes up the balance of the kernel. Dent corns may have many rows of narrow kernels or fewer rows of very broad kernels. Standard corn-belt varieties usually carry 16 to 20 rows of kernels, and there is normally one ear to the stalk. Prolific varieties grown in the South may have five, six, or more ears per plant.

239

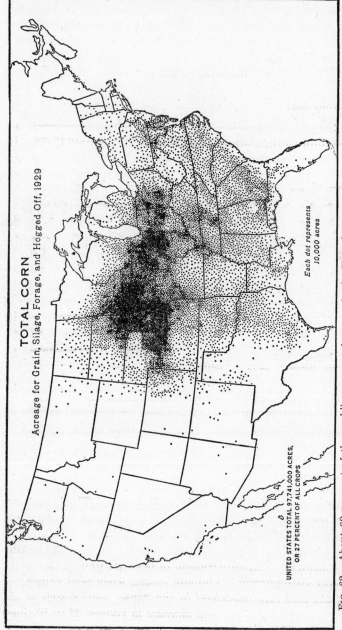

TOTAL CORN

Acreage for Grain, Silage, Forage, and Hogged Off, 1929

Each dot represents
10,000 acres

UNITED STATES TOTAL 97,741,000 ACRES,
OR 27 PERCENT OF ALL CROPS

Fig. 62.—About 60 per cent of the world's corn crop is grown in the United States, nearly all east of the line of 8-in. summer rainfall and south of the line of 66° F. summer temperature. In the corn belt, the area shown as nearly black on the map, production exceeds 3,000 bu. per sq. mile and in some counties rises to 5,000 bu. This is mostly a glaciated region, much of which is characterized by prairie soil, derived primarily from calcareous glacial drift and high in humus and nitrogen. The land is level to rolling, nearly all arable, and adapted to the use of modern machinery. In addition, the winters are dry and cold, retarding soil leaching, and the summers are wet and warm, promoting rapid plant growth. (*U.S. Department of Agriculture.*)

Flint Corn.—Flint-corn kernels are characterized by hardness and the vitreous nature of the outer portions of the endosperm so that no denting occurs as the corn ripens. Some varieties are very early, others are of medium maturity, and tropical flints require a long growing season. The northern flint corns sucker profusely and usually have long slender ears. Eight-rowed varieties are common. The corn meal made from flint corn is of excellent quality.

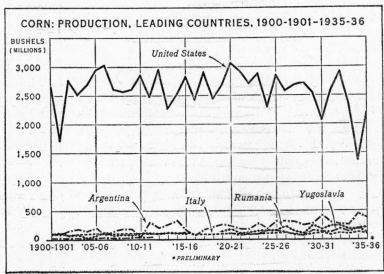

FIG. 63.—The United States is by far the greatest corn-producing country in the world. Since 1900 annual production has averaged about 2½ billion bu., including the estimated equivalent in grain of corn cut for fodder and silage and hogged or grazed off. The general trend has been downward since about 1920. In the drought year 1934 the nation produced the smallest corn crop in more than 50 years. The only competitors of the United States, of consequence, are Argentina and the countries of the Danube valley. (Rumania and Yugoslavia boundaries are prewar prior to 1918.) (*U.S. Department of Agriculture.*)

Popcorn.—Popcorn is really a type of flint corn. The kernels are smaller than those of ordinary flint corn, and the starch is very hard. The hull is tough and thick in proportion to the size of the kernel. Popcorn must be early enough in the area where it is grown to mature fully and dry down to a moisture content of between 10 and 15 per cent in order to pop satisfactorily. Popping results when heat causes the explosion of the moisture contained in the dense, hard starch of the kernel. The best strains of popcorn increase in volume 25 to 30 times on being popped. There is a high correlation between volume increase and crispness, both desirable characters. Failure to pop properly may be due to too much or too little moisture in the kernel, immaturity, a

high percentage of soft starch, and disease.   Desirable popping characteristics are also more pronounced in certain varieties.   These are
divided into three general classes, as follows: hull-less, with shoe-peg-
shaped kernels and very little chaff; rice, with kernels sharply pointed
at the crown; and pearl, with rounded kernels similar in shape to small
kernels of ordinary flint corn.   The greatest kernel expansion is usually
secured with the hull-less types and the least with the larger grained
pearl varieties.

Sweet Corn.—Sweet corn is regarded as a horticultural crop.   It is
one of the most common of home-garden plants, is grown by truck
gardeners for the city market, and is one of the important canning
crops.   It is harvested in immature condition and is esteemed as a food
because its relatively high sugar content gives it a delightful flavor.
When mature the kernels of sweet corn wrinkle and take on a vitreous
appearance.   Such early varieties as Golden Bantam and hybrids
originating from it are very popular for serving on the cob and are
usually available in the home garden and on the city market.   Stowell's
Evergreen and Country Gentleman, larger and later varieties, are more
prominent with the canning trade.   Single-cross sweet-corn hybrids
very uniform as to cob size and shape offer special opportunities for
canning corn on the ear or for marketing to the more critical trade in a
transparent wrapping.[1]

Other Types.—Flour corn, or soft corn, is a type in which nearly all
the starch is soft with only a shell of the more vitreous material.   Some
types dent slightly on reaching maturity; but for the most part
shrinkage of the kernels is uniform, and denting does not take place.
Flour corn is not commercially important.   Pod corn is something of a
curiosity.   Each kernel is enveloped in its own pod, or husk, the entire
ear also being enclosed in a husk as are those of the more common corns.

The discussion in this chapter deals largely with dent corn, but
essentially the same cultural practices are used for the production of
the other types of corn.

THE USES OF CORN

General.—Corn is first of all a grain crop.   Nevertheless, it is also
the foremost crop for silage, a fairly substantial acreage is used as
forage without being husked, and the stover after husking is an important winter roughage for livestock.   In 1940, 88 per cent of the United
States corn acreage was harvested for grain, 5 per cent was ensiled,

---

[1] BARRONS, K. C., Marketing Husked Sweet Corn, *Mich. Agr. Expt. Sta. Quart.
Bul.*, Vol. 23, No. 4, 1941.

and 7 per cent was hogged off, pastured, or used for forage as a soiling or fodder crop.

Corn and Hogs.—The chief use of corn in the United States is for pork production. In the leading corn states, Iowa and Illinois, corn utilizes 30 to 35 per cent of all land available for crops. This is in the very heart of the corn belt and also at the center of intensive pork production. Hogs in the United States eat as much corn as all other livestock put together. The process of converting corn into income through hogs is so direct and so important with respect both to corn and to hogs that the prices of corn and of hogs in Chicago tend to maintain a very close relationship known as the *corn-hog ratio*. When this relationship is normal, 11½ bu. of No. 2 corn is equal in value to the price per 100 lb. for heavy hogs.

At farm points some distance from Chicago the quantity of corn needed to equal in value the price per hundred for hogs is greater than 11½ bu. largely because of higher transportation costs of the corn in relation to its value. The corn-hog ratio changes with the relative scarcity or abundance of either corn or hogs but seldom remains out of line for more than 1 or 2 years; as a long-time average, it adheres very closely to the normal relationship.

Corn and Other Livestock.—Although approximately 40 per cent of the United States corn crop is fed to hogs, its use as a feed for dairy and beef cattle, sheep, poultry, horses, and mules is highly important. The concentrates in a good dairy ration commonly consist of 30 to 50 per cent ground corn properly balanced with protein-rich feeds and more bulky concentrates such as wheat bran and oats. Corn is much more important than any other concentrate for fattening beef cattle and lambs and is used in lesser proportions for growing and breeding animals.

The 1929–1938 average production is shown below with that of the other two leading feed grains, oats and barley.

Feed Grains	Production, Tons
Corn (grain basis)	64,000,000
Oats	16,000,000
Barley	5,000,000

The Nature of Corn as a Feed.—Corn is very palatable, and it is rich in digestible carbohydrates and fats. Feeds high in protein must be fed with it to provide balanced rations. There is a justified preference for yellow corn over white as a livestock feed, for yellow corn provides vitamin A whereas white corn does not. The vitamin A in yellow corn largely comes from xanthophyll, a compound related to carotene, the source material for vitamin A in most feeds. If white corn is fed with good hay or any other feed which adequately provides carotene it may be substituted for yellow corn with equally good results.

Corn By-products as Feed.—In the processing of corn for other purposes, several by-products are derived that are used for feed. Hominy feed consists of the corn germ, the seed coat, or bran, and some of the starch as a by-product obtained in the processing of corn meal or corn grits. Corn meal is the ground endosperm of the corn, with germ and bran removed. Corn grits are made up of the flinty endosperms broken into medium-sized particles, likewise separated from the germ and hull. Most of the oil in the corn kernel is in the germ. After this is extracted the remaining material is known as *corn-oil meal*. Corn gluten is a high-protein by-product of the manufacture of cornstarch. Gluten feed contains corn bran and is often partly corn-oil meal whereas gluten meal, much higher in protein than standard gluten feed, is the corn gluten separated from the starch in milling and containing essentially none of the seed coat, or hull.

In the manufacture of alcohol and distilled liquors, barley malt is mixed with ground grain to provide the material for fermentation and distillation. After distillation the solid residue is strained off, dried, and marketed as distillers' dried grain. The feeding value of this material depends to some extent on which grain predominates. The by-product of alcohol and distilled liquor made predominantly from corn is distillers' corn dried grain, a fairly bulky concentrate high in protein and fat, high in digestibility, but of only fair palatability, a slight disadvantage readily overcome by using this feed in mixtures.

Industrial Uses of Corn.—Chemically, the corn kernel has six different substances that can be separated, starch, protein, oil, fiber, inorganic minerals, and water. In milling and manufacturing processes the protein is associated with by-products that eventually return to the farm as feed, the oil may be considered as an industrial by-product, and other industrial products are derived from the starch. Cornstarch and its derivatives, sirup and sugar, accounted for the use of over 85 million bushels of corn in 1927, but this quantity varies widely in different years, in part because of competing products. Cornstarch is used in the food, chemical, textile, paper, laundry, automotive, fuel, and plastic industries. Corn sugar, or dextrose, is a basic chemical product and is used in making several acids, alcohols, resins, and similar chemicals. It also has certain medicinal uses. This sugar, resulting from the hydrolysis of cornstarch, is not so sweet as cane sugar, has lower solubility, forms smaller crystals, and caramelizes more readily. Corn sirup is of importance in the manufacture of confections, jams, and jellies. Corn sirup and pancakes make a favorite old-time farm breakfast.

Corn is a source material for alcohol. Industrial alcohol as well as that in distilled liquors is of importance in corn utilization. The possibilities of using corn and other farm crops as a source of alcohol for power fuel have occasioned much discussion and some commercial experimentation. That certain kinds of alcohol can be used for power has been demonstrated. A blend of around 10 per cent anhydrous ethyl alcohol with gasoline can be used in present-day engines if they are properly adjusted. When gasoline is abundant and relatively low priced, the use of such blends is uneconomical and would require some form of subsidy. However, the possibility of developing types of motor fuel from farm products, which can eventually be used to replace in part the gradually diminishing supplies of present-day fuels, is foreseen as a potential means of utilizing millions of farm acres.

As Human Food.—Corn, of course, is important as a direct source of human food. Without expensive processing, corn meal can be prepared in many ways for human consumption. Corn bread is tasty and substantial, and corn mush as a cooked cereal or fried and sweetened with sirup is a pleasing and nutritious food. The processed starch and sugar have many food uses, and grits is also an esteemed food product.

The use of corn as food probably received its greatest stimulus with the development of corn flakes as a breakfast cereal. These flakes are made from the rolled and toasted endosperm of pure white corn.

Corn as a Cash Crop.—Corngrowers are not dependent on only the industrial and food uses of corn as a cash-crop outlet for their crop. The corn-hog price relationship has already been noted. This close price relationship exists because the corn sold by farmers is, for the most part, eventually purchased by other farmers—farmers who fatten hogs, steers, and lambs or who produce dairy or poultry products—hogs providing the major market.

The data on corn production and prices by 10-year periods since 1900 are given in Table 13.

Statistics for the country as a whole show good, bad, and intermediate conditions. From a long-time viewpoint, corn prices appear to have been influenced more by wars, depressions, and general economic conditions than by acres harvested and bushels produced although the supply at any one time is unquestionably an important

TABLE 13.—CORN ACREAGE, PRODUCTION, AND VALUE IN THE UNITED STATES BY
10-YEAR PERIODS SINCE 1900*

Period	Average annual harvested acreage, acres	Average yield per acre, bushels	Average annual production in grain equivalent on entire acreage, bushels	Average farm price per bushel, cents	Average acre value
1900–1909	95,818,000	27.3	2,613,216,000	47.7	$13.02
1910–1919	101,553,000	26.0	2,635,384,000	95.0	24.70
1920–1929	100,368,000	26.8	2,695,277,000	77.1	20.66
1930–1939	98,085,000	23.5	2,309,153,000	58.5	13.75

* Adapted from *U.S. Dept. Agr. Agricultural Statistics*, 1940.

market factor. The low yield for the 10-year period 1930–1939 is probably due more to widespread droughts recurring during this period than to any downward trend in yield occasioned by less effective production practices.

Certain areas and, of course, individual growers secure far more than the average yields given in Table 13. The 1928–1937 average acre yield in Iowa, the leading corn state, was 35.5 bu., the Iowa crops of 1938, 1939, and 1940 were estimated at 46, 52, and 51 bu. an acre, respectively. Although yields of more than 100 bu. an acre must be regarded as exceptional, such yields are produced in a few fields under very favorable conditions almost every year.

Excessive total production in relation to effective demand together with generally adverse economic conditions in the early 1930's resulted in very low corn prices. The Agricultural Adjustment Administration of the U.S. Department of Agriculture has sought to bring about better prices by means of corn-acreage limitations and corn loans. In the interest of soil conservation a concerted effort has been made to secure the diversion of a part of the corn acreage to the production of sod-forming, soil-improving crops. The harvested-corn acreage for 1934–1940 averaged 91,717,000 as compared with an average harvest of 103,059,000 acres a year for 1927–1933, the 7 years immediately preceding the program of the Agricultural Adjustment Administration. The 86,449,000 acres harvested in 1940 represented the smallest harvested-corn acreage in the United States from 1894 to 1940.

Standards for Corn.—To facilitate the marketing of corn, the U.S. Department of Agriculture has established market classes and grades and an inspection service to supervise the grading work. The general classes cover yellow, white, and mixed corn; special classes, likewise based on color, cover flint varieties.

Grade divisions within the various classes are based on quality, the considerations being test weight, moisture content, and the percentage of damaged corn and foreign material. The most common price quotations are based on U.S. No. 2 corn. Corn of this grade must weigh at least 53 lb. per bushel and must not contain over 15.5 per cent moisture, 3 per cent cracked corn and foreign material, and 5 per cent damaged kernels, with a limit of 0.2 per cent heat-damaged.

CORN CULTURE

Corn in the Rotation.—In an experiment conducted on the soils and crops experiment farm of Purdue University,[1] corn grown continuously on the same land from 1919 to 1940 gave much lower yields than that grown, for example, in a commonly used 3-year rotation of corn, oats, clover. The corn yields secured under the two systems were as follows:

Crops	1916–1927 yield, bushels	1928–1940 yield, bushels
Corn in corn, oats, clover rotation....................	60.4	66.7
Continuous corn*......................................	55.1	40.7

* Experiments started in 1916. Continuous corn plots started in 1919.

The practice of continuous corn culture is very unusual. However, it is not at all uncommon to grow corn after corn for one or two seasons. In Indiana trials already referred to, corn was grown 2 years in succession in several rotations. Invariably, the second-year corn crop gave substantially poorer yields than the first. The drop in yield of second-year corn tended to be about 5.5 bu. an acre compared with the yield of the first crop following clover or alfalfa. This was under conditions where corn generally was yielding above 60 bu. an acre.

It should not be inferred that planting corn after corn is never justified. For example, according to the 1935 agricultural census, 44 per cent of the land available for crops in Pottawattamie County, Iowa, grew corn. There were 67,000 more acres used for corn than the combined acreage of tame hay and plowable pasture. Obviously, growing corn after corn for a year or two must be widely practiced where corn growing is such a major enterprise.

[1] WIANCKO, A. T., R. R. MULVEY, and S. R. MILES, Progress Report of the Soils and Crops Experiment Farm from 1915–1940, *Ind. Agr. Expt. Sta. Cir.* 242 (revised), 1941.

Corn, oats, clover, or corn, wheat, clover, where corn is cut in time to put in wheat, are widely used 3-year rotations. They are often modified into 4-year rotations by growing corn two seasons in succession. Two years of corn, 1 year of small grain, and 3 years of alfalfa make a 6-year rotation for a livestock farm requiring large amounts of both grain and forage.

Fig. 64.—Corn planted and harvested along contour lines in Ohio as a soil conservation measure. (*Courtesy of U.S. Dept. Agr. Soil Conservation Service.*)

For the major corn-growing regions it may be said, in general, that corn for 1 or 2 years follows the forage legumes in a rotation, small grain follows the corn, and the legume seeding is reestablished in the small grain. Such a rotation might require anything from 2 to several years, but the 3- and 4-year rotations are most common.

Corn and Fertilizers.—The providing of suitable soil conditions for corn involves much more than making applications of barnyard manure and commercial fertilizer directly to the corn crop, helpful as such applications sometimes may be. An effective program of soil management provides for a vigorous growth of legumes, protection of the soil from destructive erosion, the return of manure and crop residues to the soil, and the planting of crops in suitable sequence. Applications of lime, phosphoric acid, and potash which may be required for the establishment of a full and vigorous stand of alfalfa or clover are sometimes more significant than the direct fertilization of corn.

Specific fertilizer requirements for any crop depend on the condition of the particular parcel of land on which the crop is to be grown. Under some conditions, applications of fertilizer for corn may result in no yield increase or in increases of only 2 or 3 bu. an acre. Under other circumstances the yield increase may be 10 or 12 bu. an acre or more. These very marked responses are most often secured when the content of some particular nutrient, in available form in the soil, is unusually low or when nutrients are decidedly out of balance.

Corn is considered by soil scientists to be a good indicator of plant-nutrient deficiencies although it is often difficult to interpret symptoms of such deficiencies in the field because of the complicating effects of many environmental factors. In general, corn plants starved for nitrogen are stunted and spindling, with pale yellowish leaves. The older leaves are affected first, with yellowing along the midrib from the leaf tip. The tip and later the whole leaf dry up. In some cases, phosphorus-deficiency symptoms are evinced by a similar yellowing although young plants poorly supplied with phosphorus may be dark green and there is a tendency for the leaves and stems of certain strains to become purple. Phosphorus-deficient corn is often imperfectly pollinated, according to Hoffer.[1] This is due to delayed emergence of the silks and gives rise to irregular or dropped rows of kernels. Corn plants deficient in potassium grow very poorly and are likely to appear short in proportion to the leaf growth. As the shortage becomes more severe, the leaves are streaked with yellow and their edges dry out, or "fire." The ears are likely to be small, chaffy, and poorly filled.

In order to determine the nutrient requirements more accurately, plant-tissue tests and tests of the soil are used to supplement the visible evidences of nutrient deficiencies exhibited by the plants. The final proof of the value of any remedy is the growth of healthy vigorous corn on the land when the nutrients in which it appeared deficient have been adequately supplied.

[1] HOFFER, G. N., Deficiency Symptoms of Corn and Small Grains, "Hunger Signs in Crops," American Society of Agronomy and National Fertilizer Association, Washington, D.C., 1941.

Planting and Spacing.—In early corn-growing days, farmers used to mark their cornland in small squares and plant it in hills by hand or with hand planters. The modern checkrow planter accomplishes the same thing mechanically. A large proportion of the corn-belt corn crop is planted in hills 42 in. apart. The effort is usually made to get three plants to the hill.

Under any given conditions, corn planted in a relatively thin stand produces the larger ears whereas the more thickly planted corn produces more but smaller ears. The larger ears are advantageous in respect to hand picking and husking. Some experiments have shown that corn planted 36 by 36 in. slightly outyielded that planted in wider spacings. Closer spacings than this have usually appeared advantageous only for smaller early varieties or on exceptionally productive soil. In Iowa experiments[1] a 21- by 21-in. spacing had an insignificant advantage in yield over a 42- by 42-in. spacing. The more widely spaced corn had a distinct advantage in lodging resistance. In both spacings the rate of planting was adjusted to give an expected stand of 14,224 plants an acre, a planting rate of four kernels to the hill in the standard 42- by 42-in. spacing. This was at a slightly heavier rate than that most commonly used; but, on the basis of other experimental work, the heavier planting was considered advantageous for most of Iowa. Further work at the Iowa Agricultural Experiment Station[2] indicated that a 21- by 21-in. single-kernel spacing had approximately a 15 per cent yield advantage, as an average for 7 years, over a 42- by 42-in. four-kernel planting.

Modern corn planters can plant corn in continuous drills as well as in checkrows. That corn which is rowed in both directions is obviously easier to cultivate and keep free from weeds. In the absence of serious weed growth, corn in continuous drills yields as well as that which is checkrowed if the numbers of plants are comparable. Corn planted in 42-in. rows with a kernel every 14 in. requires the same amount of seed and should produce the same number of plants as that checkrowed in 42- by 42-in. hills with three kernels to the hill. With average-sized kernels these spacings require about 8 lb. of seed an acre. Corn for silage is usually planted in continuous drill rows, 50 to 75 per cent more seed being used than is customary if the crop is to be harvested for grain.

Furrow Planting.—In some of the drier sections of the country, corn is planted in furrows rather than on the surface. The furrows

---

[1] BRYAN, A. A., R. C. ECKHARDT, and G. F. SPRAGUE, Spacing Experiments with Corn, *Jour. Amer. Soc. Agron.*, Vol. 32, No. 9, 1940.

[2] Fifth Annual Report, Iowa Corn Research Institute, 1940.

may be opened with special attachments for the corn planter or with a lister. The lister is a double moldboard plow that throws the soil both ways. Sometimes the land is double-listed in preparation for planting, but the double listing has shown no notable advantages in experiments comparing these methods. In regions of limited rainfall, better corn yields are secured following listing than from surface planting. The listing method also has a lower labor requirement. It has been observed that surface-planted corn has a greater stalk and leaf development than listed corn even though the listed corn is its equal or superior in grain yield. Listing and furrow planting have not been found advisable on the cooler and wetter soils.

Corn Germination.—As a general rule, corn is planted so accurately with respect to number of kernels per hill and spacing that moderate differences in germination are likely to have a significant effect on the stand. A lack of uniformity in the stand of corn does not appear to be a serious yield deterrent, but a decrease in percentage of stand occasioned by planting seed of low germination is associated with a definite decrease in yield. Corn of 90 per cent strong germination or better is regarded as very satisfactory. If the rate of planting of low-germinating seed is increased, difficulties may be partly overcome although the percentage of seedling losses due to disease and other factors in corn of low germination makes it decidedly preferable to plant strongly germinating seed whenever it is available. Corn that produces only 80 per cent of a perfect stand, if planted at normal rates, may be expected to result in nearly a 10 per cent reduction in yield.

Testing seed corn for germination may be carried on effectively in many ways. The percentage of strong, disease-free germinating kernels, producing both roots and sprouts, is a good indicator of the planting value of the seed. Suitable conditions for carrying on a corn-germination test include the following: (1) Moisture soaked in an absorbing medium such as soil, paper toweling, or even a roll of newspaper. This medium should be free from mold-producing organisms. (2) Air to provide oxygen for the increased respiration of the germinating kernels. (3) Satisfactory temperature. The corn-germination tests of official seed-testing agencies are conducted at a temperature of 20 to 30°C. Such tests are given their first reading in 4 days and the final reading in 7 days.

Time of Planting.—Corn must be planted late enough to avoid injury from spring frosts and early enough to mature before autumn frosts. If the variety used has the opportunity to mature fully, it appears to make little difference just when it is planted during this safe period.

In Nebraska experiments,[1] during one 9-year period 1925–1933, corn planted as early as Apr. 25 yielded highest during 3 years but produced essentially the same average yield as that secured from later plantings. During the 7 years 1922–1928, corn planted as late as June 14 yielded highest only once and was materially less productive on the average. The results were quite different, however, during the next 5-year period 1929–1933, when corn planted June 10 yielded highest in 4 of the 5 years and averaged materially higher in yield than corn planted at the earlier dates. The Nebraska investigators pointed out that, by spreading the planting season over a considerable period of time, the likelihood of low yields resulting from any brief period of unfavorable weather becomes less. Losses from immaturity and inferior grain quality may be expected to increase with undue delay in planting.

In Michigan,[2] with its much shorter growing season, it was found that the yield of very early varieties for the locality was not nearly so greatly influenced by time of planting as that of larger varieties which used essentially all the average growing season. These were markedly curtailed in yield by early June planting as compared with the most

TABLE 14.—INFLUENCE OF TIME OF PLANTING ON THE YIELD OF FULL-SEASON, EARLY, AND VERY EARLY CORN VARIETIES AT MONROE, MICH., AVERAGE RESULTS FOR 4 YEARS

Varietal class	Yield, bushels per acre at uniform moisture			
	First planting, Apr. 28–May 8	Second planting, May 12–20	Third planting, May 25–June 4	Fourth planting, June 9–18
Varieties normally requiring full growing season	40.9	46.9	44.7	34.0
Early varieties	30.3	37.0	33.6	28.2
Very early varieties	23.2	27.4	27.0	24.4

favorable dates for that area, which ranged from May 12 to May 20. Incidentally, the varieties using the full growing season were substantially more productive than the earlier lines (see Table 14). Corn planted at the earliest dates in these experiments was usually somewhat injured by spring frosts.

[1] KIESSELBACH, T. A., A. ANDERSON, and W. E. LYNESS, Cultural Practices in Corn Production, *Nebr. Agr. Expt. Sta. Bul.* 293, 1935.

[2] MARSTON, A. R., and C. B. DIBBLE, Investigations in Corn Borer Control at Monroe, Michigan, *Mich. Agr. Expt. Sta. Spec. Bul.* 204, 1930.

For the United States as a whole, corn planting begins in late February in Florida and continues progressively until early June in the most northern states. Harvest for nearly all regions begins in September and continues throughout October. In some cases, corn is picked from standing stalks in November and early December. Shocked corn is often husked throughout the entire winter.

Cultivation.—The general principles involved in cultivation have already been discussed in Chap. V. The major considerations as they affect corn culture deserve some reemphasis here. Corn cannot compete with weeds. Cultivation, sometimes supplemented with hand hoeing, is the only practical way effectively to control weeds.

Fig. 65.—Freedom from weeds is essential to good corn yields.   (*Courtesy of John Deere, Moline, Ill.*)

The Illinois Agricultural Experiment Station studied corn cultivation in experiments covering three periods and totaling 21 seasons. From these comprehensive studies it was concluded:

Since cultivation is the only practical method of controlling weeds, the depth and frequency of corn cultivation should be determined by their growth. The growth of weeds should be prevented insofar as possible by shallow rather than by deep cultivation.

Deep cultivation of corn may result in root injury and decreased yields in comparison with shallow cultivation. The effect of excessive and deep cultivation seems comparable to that of actual root pruning. Proper cultivation should kill the weeds with minimum injury to the corn roots; obviously, this is more easily accomplished when the weeds are small.

The need for cultivation seems to be no greater in dry than in wet years; it may, in fact, be less. However, on heavy soils which check badly, cultivation may be necessary in order to fill the large cracks and thus stop the direct loss of moisture from the deeper strata.[1]

Corn Development and Maturity.—Immature corn is slightly higher in protein than that which is fully developed; but the kernels tend to be lighter, more chaffy, and less desirable as feed. Corn that has been harvested or killed by frost before it has reached maturity has not attained its full productive possibilities. But the greatest disadvantage of handling immature corn is the difficulty of keeping it satisfactorily in storage.

Corn may be considered ripe when, without frost or similar interference, it has completed translocating dry matter into the kernels. This completion of growth is not attained until the ears contain not more than 40 per cent moisture.[2] When the ears are down to 40 per cent moisture, the grain of dent varieties is fully dented and hard enough so that the kernels cannot be easily cut with the thumbnail. The moisture content of the stalk at this stage may range from 60 to 70 per cent, depending on the variety. Subsequently the husks and then the leaves and stalks dry out, lose their green color, and become subject to considerable breakage and disintegration.

As corn, having a potential yield of 60 bu. an acre, matures from the milk stage when its ears contain 70 per cent or more water, it is producing grain dry matter at the rate of approximately 1 bu. an acre each day. The grower who cuts and shocks his corn during the ripening process, *i.e.* when the ears are in the early dent stage and still have a 50 per cent moisture content, may thus readily lose 10 bu. an acre. He can make excellent wages when corn is at this stage of development by staying out of the cornfield until the crop is fully mature.

When the ears of corn are down to 40 per cent moisture, the corn is mature and can be cut and shocked. It is not ready to be husked or picked. To be cribbed with safety, ear corn should be down to approximately 25 per cent moisture. Shelled corn containing 17 per cent or more moisture may heat and spoil in storage, especially in warm weather. The top moisture limit for U.S. No. 2 corn is 15.5 per cent. The maximum total dry matter in corn, considering stalks and leaves as well as ears, is reached at the early dent stage when the ears still contain 50 to 55 per cent moisture. This is the proper time to put corn

[1] WIMER, D. C., and M. B. HARLAND, The Cultivation of Corn—Weed Control vs. Moisture Conservation, *Ill. Agr. Expt. Sta. Bul.* 259, 1925 (reprinted 1938).

[2] RATHER, H. C., and A. R. MARSTON, A Study of Corn Maturity, *Mich. Agr. Expt. Sta. Quart. Bul.*, Vol. 22, No. 4, 1940.

into the silo. The stalks should still contain nearly 75 per cent moisture so that there is enough water in the entire plant to ensure good preservation. Corn ensiled in the milk or early soft-dough stage has a low proportion of grain growth and makes silage of inferior quality and feeding value.

Corn Moisture in Relation to Freezing Injury.—The moisture content of corn is important with respect to its potential seed value. Corn high in moisture is very susceptible to freezing injury which destroys its ability to germinate.

Kiesselbach and Ratcliff[1] found that corn containing 15 to 20 per cent moisture was injured in germination by exposure to severe cold, 0 to −5°F., for 24 hours. The more moisture the corn contained, the greater the freezing injury and the less severe the cold had to be before causing injury. Corn containing 60 per cent moisture could not withstand even a light freeze. However, corn dried down to a moisture content of 15 per cent or less proved entirely safe from any freezing injury. Because of this condition, commercial seed-corn growers have found it advisable to dry seed corn artificially so that it would contain no more than 15 per cent moisture.

Corn Harvest.—Each year the National Corn Husking Contest attracts more than 100,000 people to watch the nation's best cornhuskers vie for championship honors. These experts keep a constant stream of ears rattling off their wagon sideboards in 80 minutes of punishing effort with no time out. In 1940, Irvin Barman of Illinois won the contest by husking 46.58 bu. of corn in the allotted time. It takes not only good men but high-yielding corn to make such records possible.

Good corn will always be a major objective, but hand husking is a vanishing art. The mechanical corn picker, one- or two-row in design and picking 7 to more than 15 acres in a 10-hour day, is replacing the seasonal labor that has been taking care of this job by hand. A Federal report[2] issued in 1938 pointed out that general acceptance of the corn picker for 30 million acres of grain corn would probably involve a saving of man labor of about 2 hours an acre, or a total of six million 10-hour days, a sizable reduction in farm labor requirements. In leading cash grain and corn-feeding areas, it has been estimated that 90 to 97 per cent of the corn is husked from standing stalks.

[1] KIESSELBACH, T. A., and J. A. RATCLIFF, Freezing Injury to Seed Corn, *Nebr. Agr. Expt. Sta. Res. Bul.* 16, 1920.

[2] MACY, L. K., L. E. ARNOLD, and E. G. MCKIBBIN, Changes in Technology and Labor Requirements in Crop Production—Corn, *WPA Natl. Res. Proj. Rpt.* A5, Philadelphia, 1938.

In Ohio, Indiana, and other areas where winter wheat follows corn and on farms where the fodder is used as a winter roughage, corn is cut by hand or with a binder at maturity and husked from the stover in the autumn and winter. Husking may be done by hand; but this job, too, has been mechanized with the husker-shredder, an implement that was already in wide use in the early part of the twentieth century. The value of the husker-shredder has been increased in areas having a heavy European corn-borer infestation, for this implement and the ensilage cutter destroy practically all borers that pass through the machinery.

Fig. 66.—Harvesting corn with a mechanical corn picker. (*Courtesy of John Deere, Moline, Ill.*)

Hogging Down and Pasturing Corn.—The easiest way to harvest corn is to open the gate and turn hogs, steers, or lambs into the field. More than 5½ million acres were harvested in this manner in 1940. The corn should be allowed to mature fully before stock is given access to the field; otherwise, development of the maximum potential yield is not attained. Hogs do about as well in the cornfield as in the dry lot if the corn is supplemented by such feed of higher protein content as may be secured by interplanting rape or soybeans in the corn. The rape can be sown at the last cultivation; it will grow fairly well unless the season is too dry. Soybeans can be put in the row with corn at planting time. Lambs and steers likewise need supplemental feed richer in protein than corn. Steers pasturing on ripe corn should be followed by hogs to prevent wasting the crop. This method of corn harvest is best suited for dry conditions, for wastage of the grain is excessive in wet weather.

Silage.—The principles and practices of handling corn for silage have been discussed in Chap. X.

CORN PESTS

Diseases.—It has often been said that corn, in its present highly developed state, could not exist without culture and care by man. One of the corn problems is to combat diseases that threaten the crop from the time the seed is planted through to the storing of the grain.

Seedling diseases cause poor stands and weak plants. There are several seedling diseases caused by fungi that are carried in the seed. When seed corn is gathered at maturity and promptly dried down to 15 per cent moisture or less, kernel infection is greatly reduced. Other organisms are present in the soil. They quickly attack seed with damaged or broken seed coats, seed that germinates slowly, and possibly any seedling delayed in growth by cold, wet weather following planting. Seed-borne infections can be controlled to a large extent by treating the seed with disinfectants of tried and proved value.

One of the most common diseases of the aboveground portions of the corn plant is smut, caused by the fungus *Ustilago zeae*. Varieties and corn hybrids differ in their susceptibility to this disease. The trouble is most prevalent where growing conditions are least favorable. Corn smut is carried over from year to year in the soil and in corn refuse. It spreads from plant to plant by means of air-carried spores.

Bacterial wilt, also called *Stewart's disease*, is particularly destructive to early sweet corn. Field corn is much less commonly infected, but it is not immune. Wet weather and high soil temperature at planting time favor the development of the disease. Sweet-corn plants are subject to attack at any stage. Wilting occurs first in the leaves. Later the entire stalk of young plants may succumb. Infected plants are stunted in growth, and often the tassels have a bleached appearance. Considerable progress has been made in the development of hybrids markedly resistant to this ailment.

Diplodia zeae causes a dry rot of the stalks of susceptible corn plants late in the season. This organism also attacks the roots. Injury to both stalks and roots is a very common cause of serious lodging of the corn so that not only is yield reduced but harvest of the crop becomes extremely difficult. The disease is combated by seed treatment and varietal resistance.

The Diplodia fungus also causes an ear rot that appears first as a dense, white mold. Badly infected ears turn brown and lose much weight. Other ear diseases include a pink rot that develops irregularly over the ear, caused by *Fusarium moniliforme*, and a very conspicuous pink to red moldy disease called *Gibberella ear rot* that starts at the tip of the ear and works downward.

In a discussion of the more important corn diseases, Koehler and Holbert of the University of Illinois[1] emphasized breeding, care of the seed, and seed treatment as important control measures. They pointed out that progress in disease control, not possible by open-pollinated breeding, has been attained by selecting disease-resistant inbred lines and using these lines in the production of hybrids. In caring for the seed, fire drying of seed ears picked at maturity was stressed as a means of checking disease invasion. The recommendation for seed treatment states, "After the seed corn has been dried thoroughly and shelled, it should be treated with a good chemical dust disinfectant to check or retard the development of seedling diseases after the seed is planted. Treated seed may be stored safely in a dry building. A little heat in the building is advisable during very cold or prolonged damp weather."

Corn Insects.—Several insects may cause damage to corn when conditions favor their development. White grubs and wireworms work on corn roots. Cutworms, army worms, and chinch bugs attack the stalks at various growth stages. The ear worm damages the ripening grain, and certain moths and weevils work in stored corn. Their characteristics and life history and effective measures to control them are in the province of special entomological study.

The European Corn Borer.—The European corn borer is so dominantly a corn insect and control measures are so closely linked with agronomic practice that special consideration here is warranted. This insect was introduced from Europe by accident, probably in a broomcorn shipment, and found a favorable environment in the sweet- and grain-corn fields of the northeastern United States and southern Ontario. By the middle 1920's, it had moved as far west as Ohio, Indiana, and Michigan. The infestation was so intense in some Ontario corn-growing counties as to threaten continued production of the crop. The corn crop of wide areas was devastated, and some fields contained as many as 30 to 50 borers per cornstalk.

Vast cleanup campaigns were conducted under governmental supervision, quarantines were established, parasites were liberated, and other means of combating the pest were followed. A succession of very dry years probably did as much as anything to hold this insect in check; the spread into new areas since the late 1920's has been limited. Within the infested areas, however, the European corn borer has become a

---

[1] Koehler, Benjamin, and J. R. Holbert, Combating Corn Diseases in Illinois, *Ill. Agr. Expt. Sta. Cir.* 484, 1938.

definite and important factor in corn production, it has influenced corn-growing practices and corn-breeding work, and it still does substantial damage.

The adult of the European corn borer is a moth yellowish to brown in color and not unlike several other species of moths in appearance. In the Middle West, these moths are active from late June to early August. The females deposit their eggs on the underside of corn leaves after the plants are 1 ft. or more in height. Infestation is likely to be greatest on early-planted corn and on rapidly growing early-maturing varieties. There are over 200 host plants; but, in this country, corn

Fig. 67.—Husking corn with a husker-shredder. This procedure destroys the larvae of the European corn borer that are removed from the field in the stalks. (*U.S. Department of Agriculture.*)

is the preferred host. The females lay an average of about 400 eggs each. These soon hatch into tiny worms, or larvae, which feed first on the leaves and later work into the stalk. Broken tassels often furnish striking early evidence of corn-borer infestation.

The borers grow to nearly 1 in. in length and ⅛ in. in thickness. The head is dark brown or black, the body pale pink to light or dark brown on the surface. The larva is thin-skinned and subject to injury from exposure. As the season progresses, the worms work downward in the stalk, weakening it, causing breakage, and interfering with the development of the plant and ear. Overwintering takes place in the larva, or worm, stage, the borer hibernating in stubble, cornstalks, and trash. In late May or early **June of the** next year, the larva bores an opening to the surface, spins a cocoon, and changes into a pupa. It remains in this resting stage 10 days to 2 weeks and then emerges as an adult moth.

Control Measures.—Most control measures seek to destroy the insect in the larval stage. Ensiling corn or shredding the stover destroys nearly all borers passing through the machinery. If corn is cut low, more of the larvae will be removed from the field in the stalks. Where ensiling or shredding are not feasible, larvae may be destroyed by burning the stalks or by plowing them under. The job of plowing must leave no refuse on the surface. If refuse from stalks used as feed is deeply buried in manure, the borers will be destroyed.

Ordinarily, late-planted corn is less subject to severe attack than that planted early, but the late-planted corn may be less productive (see page 252). Stiff-stalked corn hybrids are better able to withstand borer infestation without breakage than weak-stalked varieties, and some progress has been made in the development of hybrids that are resistant to borer attack and damage. There is still much to be done in this field.

Cleanup measures, involving plowing under and other destruction of corn refuse before the moths emerge in June, must be thorough and must cover a wide area to be fully effective.

Review Problems

1. The normal United States corn crop amounts to how many bushels?

    a. 100 million.
    b. 2 billion.
    c. 2½ billion.
    d. 5 billion.

2. The chief difference between the grain of flint- and dent-corn varieties lies in

    a. Color of the kernels.
    b. Size of the kernels.
    c. Hardness of starch in the kernel endosperm.
    d. Number of kernel rows.

3. With a normal corn-hog ratio prevailing and the price of No. 2 corn in Chicago at 70 cents a bushel, the Chicago price per hundredweight of live hogs should be approximately

    a. $6.
    b. $8.
    c. $10.
    d. $12.

4. The corn sold as a cash crop is used, for the most part,

    a. As feed for livestock.
    b. To make breakfast cereals.
    c. In making industrial products.

5. The standard weight of a bushel of shelled corn is

    a. 35 lb.
    b. 48 lb.
    c. 56 lb.
    d. 70 lb.

6. Where corn is grown 2 years in succession on good corn soil, second-year corn can normally be expected to yield

    a. Somewhat better than first-year corn.
    b. About the same as first-year corn.
    c. Approximately 5 bu. an acre less than first-year corn.
    d. Fully 15 bu. an acre less than first-year corn.

7. Prepare illustrations of suitable 3-, 4-, and 5-year rotations for your locality that include corn, and suggest an effective fertilizer program for each rotation.

8. A farmer in the corn belt is producing corn primarily as a cash crop. Look up current market quotations to determine whether price considerations favor his growing yellow in preference to white corn.

9. Probably the chief advantage of the furrow planting of corn in drier regions is

    a. Saving of labor.
    b. Easier control of weeds.
    c. Conservation of moisture.
    d. Production of larger plants.

10. List three general conditions that must be met in carrying on a satisfactory germination test of seed corn.

11. Under some conditions, corn planted in early June has yielded fully as well as that planted in mid-May. Under other conditions the June-planted corn has been decidedly inferior. Give one explanation for this difference in results.

12. A field of knee-high corn is free from weeds. The weather has been dry. Which of the following appears advisable?

    a. Cultivating deeply to create a soil mulch.
    b. Cultivating lightly.
    c. Avoiding any further cultivation.

13. A farmer wishes to fill his silo by mid-September. What sort of variety should he grow?

    a. A large late variety that will be in the late-milk stage by that date.
    b. A variety that will have nicely dented and begun to harden.
    ι. A variety that will normally be fully mature.

14. Seed corn is not considered safe from freezing injury until its moisture content is down to not more than

    a. 35 per cent.
    b. 25 per cent.
    c. 20 per cent.
    d. 15 per cent.
    e. 10 per cent.

15. Why is the growing of soybeans with corn considered advantageous if the crop is to be hogged down?

16. What are the more important general measures used to combat corn diseases?

17. A field of corn heavily infested with European corn borers has been harvested with a corn picker. How should this field be handled to reduce possibilities of severe corn-borer infestation the next year?

18. Why must corn-borer control measures be thoroughly practiced by all farmers over a wide area in order to have their maximum effect?

References

HUGHES, H. D., and E. R. HENSON: "Crop Production," The Macmillan Company, New York, 1930.

KIESSELBACH, T. A., A. ANDERSON, and W. E. LYNESS: Cultural Practices in Corn Production, *Nebr. Agr. Expt. Sta. Bul.* 293, 1935.

KOEHLER, BENJAMIN, and J. R. HOLBERT: Combating Corn Diseases in Illinois, *Ill. Agr. Expt. Sta. Cir.* 484, 1938.

MORRISON, F. B.: "Feeds and Feeding," 20th ed., The Morrison Publishing Co., Ithaca, N.Y., 1936.

WALLACE, H. A., and E. N. BRESSMAN: "Corn and Corn Growing," John Wiley & Sons, Inc., New York, 1928.

WIMER, D. C., and M. B. HARLAND: The Cultivation of Corn, *Ill. Agr. Expt. Sta. Bul.* 259, 1925 (reprinted 1938).

CHAPTER XIV

WHEAT AND RYE

WHEAT

The Wheat Country.—Westward through Kansas, Nebraska, and the Dakotas lie the Great Plains. An occasional clump of trees, man-planted in a naturally treeless country, marks a farmstead. Otherwise, the plains spread out in an almost unbroken landscape, the ultimate in flatness, extending mile upon mile into the eastern halves of Montana, Wyoming, and Colorado and southward into Oklahoma.

Once this was buffalo country—then range land for thousands of cattle driven over long trails to markets or northern shipping points. Then came homesteads and wheat. In some sections, severe droughts and periods of more than average rainfall recur at irregular intervals. Erosion by both wind and rain is common, for in some localities as much as 15 per cent of the year's total rain may fall in a single hour. Some sections were unduly exploited for wheat under the stimulus of wartime prices in 1917–1919. Dust storms brought havoc to a land that needed grass, and the difficult job of reestablishing cover was begun. Sorghums and other drought-resisting species have become a part of the farming scheme. But still this general region, more than any other in the United States, depends on wheat.

Spring-wheat Belt.—The Dakotas and Montana grow mostly spring wheat, for in much of this open northern country winters are too severe for varieties sown in the fall. The dry climate and the deep, dark soils of this region, which extend into southwestern Canada, favor the production of hard vitreous wheat. This wheat is the equal of any in the world for bread-baking purposes.

The subhumid climate which presents one of the difficult problems with respect to the agriculture of the whole Great Plains region is the chief factor in contributing to the superb quality of its wheat. It is the dry growing season that largely makes for wheat high in protein, high in strength of gluten, and high in test weight.

Very little spring wheat is grown in the more humid regions east and south of Lake Michigan. A little, however, is produced in the Pacific Northwest and some in Nebraska, Colorado, and Kansas, frequently, in the latter states, as a replacement for winter wheat that has failed.

263

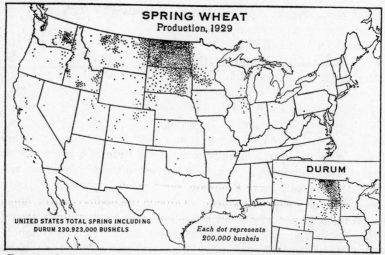

FIG. 68.—Spring wheat constituted nearly 40 per cent of the acreage of all crops in 1929 in the spring wheat belt. A secondary center of production is located in the sub-humid portions of Washington and Oregon. Scattered areas are found in Idaho, Utah, and Colorado. Practically no spring wheat is now grown east or south of Lake Michigan. The southern boundary of the spring wheat belt is determined partly by the northern boundary of winter wheat, which is, in general, more productive and more profitable. (*U.S. Department of Agriculture.*)

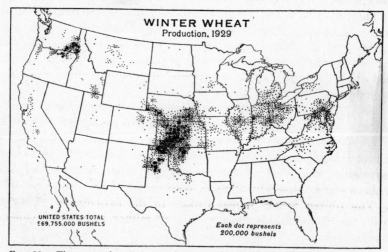

FIG. 69.—There are three winter wheat areas: (1) the hard winter wheat region of Kansas and adjacent parts of Oklahoma, Colorado, and Nebraska, with an arm extending eastward into northern Illinois; (2) the soft winter wheat region which includes all the remaining eastern districts; and (3) the white (very soft) wheat districts of the Pacific coast states. The southern boundary of the eastern belt follows the isotherm of 72°F. during the month preceding harvest (June 15). The northern frontier of winter wheat follows, in a general way, the mean winter isotherm of 17°F. (*U.S. Department of Agriculture.*)

South Dakota, largely a spring-wheat state, raises a substantial acreage of winter wheat as a normal practice.

Durum Wheat.—Within the hard-spring-wheat area, largely in eastern North Dakota and South Dakota, are produced some three million acres of durum wheat. This unusually hard wheat, with a long, amber-colored berry, is used for the manufacture of macaroni.

Hard Red Winter Wheat.—The most important class of wheat in the United States with respect to acreage is hard red winter. Production is most intensive in the central and southern sections of the Great Plains. Kansas alone normally grows over 10 million acres of wheat, largely hard red winter, and in 1938 harvested nearly 15 million acres. North Dakota with over 8 million acres of spring wheat is Kansas' nearest rival as a wheat producer. Outside the plains country, smaller acreages of hard red winter wheat are grown in Iowa, Illinois, Indiana, Oregon, Washington, Idaho, and Montana.

Soft Red Winter Wheat.—In the more humid sections of the country, wheats are of a softer texture. The protein content is lower, and the flour has less strength. Hard-wheat varieties do not maintain their high protein content and superior texture when grown in this region. Likewise, the finer straw of the hard-wheat varieties becomes susceptible to lodging when produced under conditions of high humidity and plenty of water. Where subhumid and humid areas meet, east and south of the hard-red-winter-wheat areas, both soft- and hard-red-winter varieties are grown. Farther east, centering in Ohio and Indiana, is the most intensive area of soft-red-winter-wheat production; but the crop is also important in Pennsylvania, Maryland, Virginia, and North Carolina.

Soft White Wheat.—Soft white wheat yields the weakest flour of any class. It makes a heavy, soggy loaf of bread but is ideal for cakes, crackers, pastries, and special breakfast-food products. In the eastern half of the country, this kind of wheat is grown in southern Michigan and western New York. Chief areas of production, however, are in the western states, especially Oregon, Washington, Idaho, and California.

The United States Wheat Crop.—In the agricultural census for 1934, the United States wheat crop of 61 million acres was divided as follows:

Wheat Crops	Per Cent
Hard red winter	44.6
Hard red spring	23.2
Soft red winter	20.9
White	6.7
Durum	4.6

The 61-million-acre crop of 1934 was not far from the normal harvested acreage for the period since the first World War, although drought from 1934 to 1936 caused abandonment of a vast acreage during that period and left but 43 million acres for harvest in 1934, out of a seeded acreage of 64 million. Production has ranged from 526 million bushels in 1934 to 942 million bushels in 1931, and farm value from $289 million dollars in 1932, a year of record low prices, to over 2 billion dollars in 1919, when quite the reverse was true.

Wheat Prices.—The traditional price at which wheat is supposed to be profitable is $1 a bushel. However, $1 or more a bushel for wheat can hardly be said to be normal. From 1866 to 1940, the season

Fig. 70.—A field of Turkey (hard red winter) wheat near Lincoln, Nebraska. (*Courtesy of F. D. Keim, Nebraska Agricultural Experiment Station.*)

average price a bushel received by farmers has been above $1 for 24 years and below for 50 years.

For 60 years the United States has been an important exporter of wheat, rarely shipping out less than 100 million bushels annually. Peak in exports was attained during the years following the First World War when the average annual exports for 1919–1928 amounted to over 220 million bushels. World-wide depression and a policy of self-sufficiency on the part of leading wheat-buying countries brought a serious curtailment of the international wheat trade so that from 1932 to 1936 the United States exported less than 50 million bushels annually.

Wheat Yields.—The average acre yield of wheat for the United States for the 50-year period 1889–1938 was 13.9 bu. There appears to have been no change in the trend of acre yields, fluctuations from year to year having been due to seasonal influences.

Comparative wheat yields for different wheat-growing areas are typified by the 10-year (1927–1936) average yields for representative pairs of states. These were as follows:

	Average Yields, Bushels
Wheat Areas	
Washington and Oregon	20.1
Ohio and Indiana	18.5
Kansas and Nebraska	13.4
North Dakota and South Dakota	9.9

Acre costs of production are lowest in the plains region, where low-cost seeding and harvest practices are most feasible, and highest in the northeastern part of the country. In general, acre yields well above average are essential if the individual grower is to find wheat growing a profitable enterprise.

Wheat and Moisture.—We have already noted how the broad classification of wheat is closely associated with climatic conditions. The hard spring and winter wheats of the plains country are produced with limited moisture, the soft red winter wheats are grown in the more humid Middle West, and the very soft white wheats are grown under irrigation or on moisture-retentive, heavy soils of lake-tempered eastern Michigan and western New York.

In any given area, hardness or a vitreous texture of the kernel is associated with a higher content of crude protein. In the humid areas, when moisture is below normal during the growth of the plant, protein content of the grain tends to run higher than usual. Conversely, in humid areas, when rainfall is above normal, wheat frequently develops an excessive straw growth, plants lodge, and the grain is light in weight, low in gluten strength, and inferior in quality.

There is greatest concern over moisture in subhumid regions where a moisture deficiency as compared with normal may ruin the crop entirely. In this connection, Cole and Mathews state:

Under the limited precipitation of the Great Plains, the initial water content of the soil, which can be approximated by the depth to which the soil is wet, is a strong determinant of the yield that will be produced.

Frequent failures, low average yields, and very infrequent good yields from spring wheat seeded on soil that is wet only 1 ft. deep or less clearly show that seeding when that condition exists is not warranted. . . .

The highest assurance of good yields is afforded by an initial condition of 3 ft. or more of wet soil.[1]

[1] COLE, JOHN S., and O. R. MATHEWS, Relation of the Depth to Which Soil Is Wet at Seeding Time to the Yield of Spring Wheat on the Great Plains, *U.S. Dept. Agr. Cir. No.* 563, 1940.

Strikingly similar results were secured by Hallsted and Mathews working in dry-land sections of Kansas with winter wheat. These workers state:

When little or no rainfall occurs soon after wheat has been planted on soil moist to only a few inches, the probability of failure is greatly increased. . . .

When the initial soil moisture is deficient and the precipitation is low to Apr. 1, it is probable that abandonment of the crop and the conservation of water in a summer fallow for a future crop will pay far better than allowing the water to be wasted by the poor crop and weeds on the land.[1]

In regions where dry farming is practiced, summer fallowing of wheatland is the chief means of moisture conservation. Summer fallowing consists in keeping the soil free from plant growth throughout the season. Soil moisture is lost during the summer season through plant utilization and by direct evaporation when temperature is high and relative humidity low. It is now well understood that tillage conserves a great deal more moisture by destroying weeds than by preventing evaporation through the formation of a soil mulch. Thus, by summer fallowing, the loss of moisture through plants is prevented, and a portion of the rainfall of one winter is stored in the soil and carried over for the use of the crop to be grown the following year. Summer fallowing also enhances the accumulation of nitrate nitrogen in the soil for use of the future crop.

In experiments at Moro, Ore., the 12-year average yield of wheat was 4.6 bu. an acre greater on land plowed Apr. 1 and summer-fallowed with clean cultivation than on land plowed the same date with no summer tillage.[2]

Irrigating Wheat.—In sections of extremely low rainfall, dry-farming practices are inadequate to produce normal growth and irrigation must be resorted to.

Robertson and his associates,[3] of the Colorado Experiment Station, found that the highest yield and most efficient use of water were obtained by irrigating wheat at the jointing, or heading, stage when only a 6-in. irrigation was used. A higher yield and more efficient use of water were obtained when a small amount of water was applied at frequent intervals, but this method of application is not feasible in field

[1] HALLSTED, A. L., and O. R. MATHEWS, Soil Moisture and Winter Wheat with Suggestions on Abandonment, *Kans. Agr. Expt. Sta. Bul.* 273, 1936.

[2] HUNTER, BYRON, Dry Farming Methods and Practices in Wheat Growing in the Columbia and Snake River Basins, *U.S. Dept. Agr. Farmers' Bul.* 1545, 1927.

[3] ROBERTSON, D. W., et al., Studies on the Critical Period for Applying Irrigation Water to Wheat, *Colo. Expt. Sta. Tech. Bul.* 11, 1934.

practice. Irrigations made one year have a beneficial carry-over effect on the crop the following year, this residual influence being correlated with the moisture content of the soil the previous fall.

Winter Injury to Wheat.—The growing of winter wheat carries with it the problem of winter injury. On heavy, moisture-retentive soils, freezing causes the formation of ice crystals and an expansion that lifts the plants. Subsequent thawing permits the soil to settle down, the roots being thus left exposed. Repeated freezing and thawing frequently cause the commonly observed condition called *heaving* in which roots are broken, the roots and crowns become exposed, and many plants die. Poorly nourished plants with weak root systems are more subject to heaving than vigorous thrifty plants, but under extreme circumstances the best of wheat may be injured.

When ice sheets form on low-lying ground, they may be sufficiently dense to cause the wheat to smother. Smothering may be due to a lack of oxygen, but Sprague and Graber[1] report work indicating that accumulations of carbon dioxide in toxic concentrations is the primary lethal factor.

Overwintering wheat may be killed by the direct effect of low temperatures. When winter approaches, the gradual advent of low temperatures causes the plants of hardy varieties to "harden off" and become very resistant to injury from low temperatures. When warmer temperatures occur, the wheat plants lose their hardened condition and are readily injured by freezes not nearly so severe as may have occurred in midwinter without hurting the stand. Thus winterkilling, both from heaving and from the direct effect of low temperatures, is likely to be much more prevalent in early spring than in the coldest part of the winter, although low temperatures may kill wheat whenever they occur, especially if the wheat is poorly insulated by inadequate snow or vegetative cover.

Preventing Winterkilling.—The chief defense against winter injury to wheat is the selection of a winter-hardy variety. Winter hardiness in wheat is a very complex character, and its expression is greatly influenced by environment. A variety hardy under certain circumstances may prove susceptible to winter injury under others. Nevertheless, winter-hardy varieties have been developed for each of the winter-wheat areas, one of the outstanding being Minhardi. Developed at the Minnesota Agricultural Experiment Station from a cross between Turkey and Odessa, the Minhardi variety has proved more cold resistant than either of its parents.

[1] Sprague, G., and L. F. Graber, Physiological Factors Operative in Ice-sheet Injury of Alfalfa, *Plant Physiol.*, Vol. 15, pp. 661–673, 1940.

To secure the latest in acceptable winter-hardy varieties of wheat, it is desirable for growers to maintain close contact with the work of experiment stations in their own states.

Further, to avoid winter losses, wheat must be planted early enough to develop a strong, well-nourished root system before cold weather sets in. A well-fed plant is possible only if the proper plant nutrients have been adequately supplied.

Where winterkilling due to low temperatures is likely, the planting of wheat in furrows is sometimes used as a preventive measure. Special furrow drills open fairly deep furrows every 12 in., and the grain is planted in the furrows. These hold snow, and extremely low soil temperatures are thus in part prevented.

Wheat Pests. *The Hessian Fly.*—The Hessian fly is primarily a wheat pest; but it also works in winter barley, rye, and spelt. It causes straw to lodge just before harvest, and poor filling of the grain is often the result.

The fly passes the winter as a larva inside its puparium which looks much like a flaxseed. The puparium is tucked in between the leaf sheaths just above the root. In the spring the larvae pupate and finally produce adult flies which lay eggs on the wheat leaves. Maggots from the eggs work down inside the leaf sheaths, usually above the bottom node, or joint, and there feed on the plant juices and on scrapings of plant tissue, weakening the straw and interfering with the development of the head. Frequently several maggots in the "flaxseed" stage are found packed closely together at the base of a weakened or broken stem just prior to harvesttime.

During the summer a number of generations is produced, female flies laying eggs in the autumn on the leaves of young plants and thus producing the larvae which live over winter.

Parasites work on the Hessian fly and tend to keep it in check. However, a cold, wet spring is less harmful to the fly than to its parasites and may indirectly cause a bad fly season.

There is a time in early autumn after which no eggs are laid. If wheat is planted late enough, the plants will not be sufficiently advanced to receive eggs until after the fall egg-laying period is over. "Fly-free" wheat-planting dates are determined by the various state agricultural experiment stations in cooperation with the U.S. Department of Agriculture. They vary somewhat from season to season. They are planned, for each location, to be late enough to avoid the fall egg-laying period of the fly and early enough to permit the wheat to make a good growth before winter sets in.

The breeding of wheat varieties resistant to damage by the Hessian fly has been carried on with promising results, especially by the Kansas Agricultural Experiment Station.

Stem Rust.—The most important wheat disease is stem rust. In severe epidemics, usually associated with warm, humid weather, the whole crop of ravaged areas may be shriveled to the point of worthlessness and the yield cut in half. Even the milder epidemics take a severe toll in yield and quality. The severe epidemic of 1935 is said to have resulted in losses of 100 million dollars in North Dakota alone.[1]

Stem rust of wheat is caused by a fungus organism (*Puccinia graminis tritici*) that passes through the following three stages: A spring stage in yellow pustules on the underside of the leaves of common barberry. A summer (red-rust) stage on the growing wheat. In this stage a new crop of spores may be produced every 10 to 18 days to spread the infection. A winter (black-rust) stage, which develops as the grain matures and leaves its spores on old, infected grain stubble or infected wild grasses to overwinter, germinate, and reproduce the spring stage once more on the common barberry.

The disease is not borne in the seed; hence, no seed treatment is effective. Spraying is impractical because of the character of the crop. Destruction of the common barberry on a wide scale has reduced the number of spring host plants, but the disease in the red-rust stage still spreads from one wheat field to another. Thus, red rust may overwinter south of San Antonio, Tex., and be blown northward from field to field by the wind.

Early planting of spring wheat tends to reduce rust hazards, but the most promising means of combating this disease appears to be the development of rust-resistant varieties.

Stinking Smut.—The stinking smut of wheat, also called *bunt*, is responsible for severe wheat losses. This disease is particularly damaging in the Pacific Northwest where many physiologic forms of bunt complicate the problem.

Stinking smut is not readily detected until the plants are headed. Infected heads are abnormal in shape or size. Often the glumes are spread apart by the growth of the smut balls which replace the normal kernels in the head. When the heads mature, the darker smut balls are easily recognized. The smut has a fetid odor like that of decaying fish. In threshing, the smutted kernels are broken open, and the spores of the fungus are thoroughly scattered over the otherwise clean grain. Clean wheat may be infected in dirty threshers or combines or

[1] *U.S. Dept. Agr. Yearbook of Agriculture*, p. 250, 1936.

from infested soil. Ordinarily, the spores adhere to the wheat kernel and are planted with it, germinating with the wheat to infect the seedling plants.

There are several effective seed treatments, including copper carbonate, formaldehyde, and certain organic mercury dusts. Full directions concerning their use accompany these materials when sold for seed-treating purposes. The proper organic mercury dusts are effective not only against stinking smut but also against certain other

Fig. 71.—Seeding clover on winter wheat in early spring.

seed-borne diseases, including scab. Smut-resistant varieties have also been developed.

Loose Smut.—The disease known as *loose smut of wheat* (*Ustilago tritici*) is mentioned here largely because it is so often confused by growers with the more serious stinking smut. This disease is carried inside what appear to be normal wheat kernels. It is spread when the wheat is in flower. Entire heads are destroyed by being replaced with a mass of black dusty spores. These soon are blown or washed away, barren stems being left. It is doubtful whether an infestation up to 5 per cent actually results in a decrease in wheat yield, but the appearance of this disease when the wheat first heads out is disconcerting.

Loose smut can be controlled only by a complex hot-water treatment that frequently does more damage than the disease. Certain varieties are resistant to this disease.

Wheat in the Rotation.—The most effective crop rotations are those which include a leguminous, soil-improving crop, such as alfalfa, red clover, sweet clover, soybeans, or cowpeas. On the more fertile soils, wheat is likely to develop excessive straw growth and lodge if grown immediately following a legume. Hence, corn or some other row crop logically follows the legume, and wheat follows the row crop. Frequently wheat is used as a companion crop in which to make a forage seeding. In regions of moderate rainfall or on less fertile soils, wheat may follow legumes advantageously, for lodging is unlikely.

In areas comparable with parts of western Kansas, none of the usual legumes is dependable. In such regions the year of fallow is a desirable part of the wheat rotation (see Table 15).

TABLE 15.—YIELDS OF WHEAT AFTER FALLOW AND AFTER KAFFIR AT THE FORT HAYS EXPERIMENT STATION, HAYS, KANS.*

Cropping Method	Average Yield per Acre, 1916–1927, Bushels
Wheat on fallowed kaffir ground	24.2
Wheat after kaffir, in rows of the usual width	12.2
Wheat after kaffir, in rows 80 in. apart	15.1
Wheat after corn, in rows of the usual width	16.2
Wheat after corn, in rows 80 in. apart	17.8

* SALMON, S. C., and R. I. THROCKMORTON, Wheat Production in Kansas, *Kans. Agr. Expt. Sta. Bul.* 248, 1929.

The following are some typical rotations, including wheat, in regions where legumes form the basis of the cropping system:

Northeastern Kansas:
 Wheat, wheat, clover, corn, oats.
Central Kansas:
 Wheat, alfalfa (2 or more years), early-maturing sorghum, corn, oats.
Corn belt:
 Corn, wheat, clover.
 Corn, oats, wheat, clover.
 Corn, corn, wheat, alfalfa.
Northern dairy states:
 Corn, wheat, alfalfa (2 or more years).
 Field beans, wheat, alfalfa (2 years), corn, barley (seeded to sweet clover).

Preparing for Wheat.—Wheat requires a clean, firm seedbed carrying sufficient moisture for good germination and rapid growth of the young seedlings. As has already been noted, in the drier regions the depth of wetting of the soil is all-important. In humid regions, autumn rainfall is usually adequate to start the crop in good condition.

However, a seedbed prepared late or poorly may dry out rapidly or be too coarse or weedy to permit good growth. If the land must be plowed, as after small grain or sod, it is definitely advantageous that the plowing and preliminary fitting be done early. The importance of this was demonstrated in Kansas experiments where land plowed July 15, to a depth of 7 in., produced 9 bu. to the acre more, as a 10-year

FIG. 72.—Tall stiff-strawed white winter wheat in Michigan.

average, than land similarly plowed Sept. 15, shortly before planting time.[1]

Land that has been in row crops such as field beans, corn, or early potatoes may be thoroughly disked for fall wheat. Some soybean growers are using early-maturing varieties that may be combined in time to fit the land for wheat by disking.

In the moisture-deficient regions, early listing has given results second only to fallow as a method of preparing the land for wheat. Early listing is a low-cost operation compared with plowing and does not leave dry soil so loose. The stubble is left at or near the surface where it reduces soil blowing and provides better conditions for the absorption of moisture.

Soil Treatments for Wheat.—A sound cropping program gives due consideration to the maintenance of soil productivity throughout the rotation. When purchased fertilizers must be applied, the time of application is logically determined by the relative values and relative responses of the different crops. Wheat is one of the crops definitely responding to barnyard manure and the proper commercial fertilizers except in the regions where moisture is predominantly the limiting factor.

In portions of the Great Plains and throughout the corn belt and eastern wheat-growing areas, the fertilization of wheat very often serves a two-fold purpose: it directly stimulates the vigor of the wheat,

[1] SALMON, S. C., and R. I. THROCKMORTON, Wheat Production in Kansas, *Kans. Agr. Expt. Sta. Bul.* **248**, 1929.

and it markedly benefits the seedings that are so often made with wheat.

Barnyard manure, which really is a complete fertilizer low in phosphorus but liberally providing nitrogen, potash, and organic matter, is excellent for both wheat and associated seedings. Most corn-belt, northern, and eastern soils are deficient in phosphorus, and so this constituent is of chief importance in commercial fertilizers for wheat. The amount of potash to use depends on the soil and frequently on the seedings to be made with wheat. More potash can be used advantageously if legume seedings are to be made with wheat than if the wheat is to have no seeding with it.

A reasonable amount of nitrogen stimulates fall growth, and application of this constituent is sometimes warranted in the spring as a top-dressing for wheat that has come through a difficult winter.

Application of a complete fertilizer, such as a 2-12-6 or a 2-16-8, at the rate of 125 to 250 lb. an acre, is typical of desirable wheat-fertilization practice. Fertilizers can be applied most advantageously at the time of seeding with a combination grain and fertilizer drill.

The burning of wheat straw is a soil-robbing practice. At Manhattan, Kans., the mere burning of wheat stubble resulted in a yield loss of 2 bu. an acre. Top-dressing the wheat with straw is sometimes desirable for the purpose of preventing soil blowing and to protect wheat from winter injury. Straw can be used to best advantage when accompanied by commercial fertilizer, manure, or a plowed-under legume to prevent the temporary tying up of plant food while the straw is being decomposed by bacterial action.

Cultural Practices. *Time of Seeding.*—The time of seeding winter wheat is governed by two considerations. It is desirable to seed late enough to avoid the Hessian fly, early enough to avoid winterkilling. It is not always possible to do both. The exact dates depend on the locality. The inexperienced grower does well to consult his county agricultural agent or state agricultural experiment station with reference to the preferred local practice.

Spring wheat should be sown as early as weather conditions for the locality permit. Early-sown spring wheat is less subject to severe stem-rust damage and generally produces better yields.

Depth of Seeding.—In humid regions the principle governing depth of seeding is to have a soil so well prepared that a 1½-in. seeding is in moist soil. In dry regions the grain is covered to a depth of 2 or 3 in. At this depth, light showers will not cause it to sprout; and when enough rain falls to reach the seed, there will be sufficient moisture to keep it growing.

Rate of Seeding.—Within fairly wide limits, it makes but little difference how much seed is planted to an acre. Four to 6 pk. an acre is a very common rate throughout much of the more humid wheat area. When wheat is planted later than the normal date for the locality, an increase of 1 or 2 pk. an acre in rate of seeding is considered advisable. In the drier regions, 3 or 4 pk. an acre is considered sufficient.

Pasturing Wheat.—Wheat makes excellent fall or early-spring pasture. However, if yield of grain is the chief consideration, as is usually the case, the pasturing of wheat is normally detrimental to grain yields. The yield of grain is dependent on an abundant leaf area to carry on photosynthesis and develop a thrifty productive plant.

Occasionally, wheat is too thrifty for its own good. Under conditions of high organic fertility and abundant rainfall, wheat may become too vegetative, abundant straw and leaves subject to excessive lodging being the result. If such conditions are evident in the fall or early spring, light grazing may prove beneficial to grain yields. If forage seedings have been made with wheat, light spring pasturage of the wheat when the land is dry enough to stand tramping by stock is likely to prove definitely beneficial to the seeding by reducing the vegetative growth of the wheat and consequently the subsequent competition for moisture. Grain yields will be somewhat reduced unless the wheat had an excessive vegetative growth.

Quality in Wheat.—Quality in wheat depends on what the wheat is to be used for. The pastry-flour miller wants a soft, starchy wheat that the bread-flour miller finds entirely inadequate for his product. Hence, the first market classification based on quality is a broad one, depending on certain general characteristics of wheat closely associated with variety and the general climatic conditions under which the wheat is produced. There are seven official classes of wheat in the United States, *viz.:* Class I, Hard Red Spring Wheat; Class II, Durum Wheat; Class III, Red Durum Wheat; Class IV, Hard Red Winter Wheat; Class V, Soft Red Winter Wheat; Class VI, White Wheat; Class VII, Mixed Wheat. Wheat of any class, except Mixed Wheat, may contain not over 10 per cent of wheat of a different class or classes either singly or combined.

Wheat Classes.—Hard Red Spring and Hard Red Winter wheat are the two most desirable classes for making bread flour. These two wheats contain a large quantity of strong, elastic gluten. This makes for expansion of the dough into large light-textured loaves of bread, the kind in greatest favor in the United States.

Ordinary durum wheat is very hard. It is used for the manufacture of macaroni, spaghetti, vermicelli, and similar products. Red durum wheat is largely used for poultry and stock feed.

Soft red winter and white wheat flours are lower in protein and weaker than hard-wheat flours. Both are used in making pastry, crackers, biscuits, and cakes. White wheat is particularly suitable for the manufacture of special breakfast-food products.

Within each broad market class are certain other grading factors that play a part in the market value of the crop.

Test Weight.—The standard legal weight of a bushel of wheat is 60 lb. Hard vitreous wheat high in protein commonly weighs more than 60 lb. to the bushel. Soft-textured wheat, plump and very good in appearance for its class, usually weighs from 58 to 60 lb. A severe rust epidemic, the lodging of wheat straw before the grain is mature, or a low fertility level may result in wheat lacking in plumpness; sometimes it is severely shriveled. The chief reason a miller pays more for plump wheat of high test weight is that 60 lb. of such wheat yields more flour than 60 lb. of wheat of a lower test weight.

Purity.—From the milling standpoint, everything other than wheat that may be present in a given lot reduces the flour yield. Foreign material includes sand, dirt, weed seeds, chaff, straw, etc. Some kinds are doubly objectionable. Garlic in wheat carries its objectionable odor into the flour and is very damaging to quality. Chess, rye, and cockle, foreign seeds often found in wheat, tend to darken the flour and damage its texture.

Mixtures of classes and varieties that differ in milling qualities make it difficult for a miller to produce a uniform grade of flour. A miller producing a blended flour prefers to blend according to formula rather than to purchase wheat mixed in indefinite quantities. The chief difficulties with mixed wheats arise in areas producing two different classes. Small local elevators without adequate equipment for keeping different classes and grades separate contribute to this difficulty. The problem is further complicated by the fact that the price differential between pure and mixed wheat is often nonexistent or so small as to offer little inducement either to farmers or to local elevators to make any special effort to keep wheat pure.

Freedom from Disease.—Stinking smut, or bunt, is the chief disease affecting wheat quality, and smutty wheat is severely discounted. Such wheat must be washed to remove the smut balls and smutty odor which otherwise would ruin the flour. This, of course, adds to the processing expense. Scabby wheat is likely to be shriveled, and it yields less flour.

Moisture.—Excessive moisture in wheat is objectionable from two standpoints: The miller does not wish to pay wheat prices for water, and excess water is very likely to result in the development of molds, mustiness, or even heat damage. Musty wheat produces musty-smelling flour. A small amount of sprouted wheat, resulting from wet weather during the harvest period, is not serious; but if in excess of 3 per cent, is definitely injurious to milling quality. Heat-damaged kernels, developing in stored wheat of excessive moisture content, impart a bitter taste and dark color to the flour even when present in amounts of less than 1 per cent.

Wheat containing less than 13.5 per cent moisture will not heat or become musty under ordinary conditions, whereas wheat containing over 14 per cent moisture is likely to give trouble. When a grower is forced by inclement weather to harvest wet wheat, he can save its quality and eventually dry it out by moving it from one bin to another, whenever it shows evidence of excessive heating. It is possible to store wheat in ventilated bins with higher initial moisture content than is safe in nonventilated bins if sufficient air movement through the wheat is provided.

The light sweating of wheat in a stack or shock is probably beneficial to its milling quality.

Color.—Bright color in wheat indicates freedom from disease, favorable harvest conditions, and freedom from mustiness or heat damage.

Texture.—A dark, vitreous appearance is favored in the case of hard wheats because of its association with high protein content. The larger markets are equipped to run chemical tests to determine the protein content of wheat; and choice, dark, hard wheat, which is high in protein, has consistently brought a premium.

On the other hand, millers of white wheat find the darker, more vitreous kernels objectionable for their special products. In certain drier seasons favoring the availability of nitrogen in the soil, white wheat takes on an amber appearance rather than the more starchy texture that is preferred for the milling of pastry flour. In Michigan and western New York, pure white wheat has normally brought a slightly better price than mixed or soft red wheat. Production of the most favored quality of white wheat has largely been on heavy, moisture-retentive soils.

Feeding Wheat.—Although considerable wheat is fed to poultry and livestock each year, some farmers hesitate to feed wheat partly because they are not accustomed to doing so and partly because wheat usually brings a higher price than any other grain. Occasionally, however, the price of wheat is low enough in relation to that of other grains to warrant its extensive use as feed.

Livestock-feeding experiments have shown that, in a general way, a pound of wheat is equal to a pound of corn as a feed for farm animals. Because a bushel of wheat weighs 60 lb. and a bushel of corn 56 lb., a bu;hel of wheat is worth a little more as feed than a bushel of corn. Likewise, a bushel of wheat has considerably more value than a bushel of the lighter feed grains, rye, barley, and oats.

If wheat is to be fed, it should be crushed or coarsely ground. When mixed with twice its weight of other feeds, wheat will not tend to form a sticky, pasty mass when eaten by horses or cattle. With feeding wheat, as with other grains, it is important also to feed those additional products which will furnish in proper proportion the nutritive material that the grain lacks.

RYE

Winter rye is the hardiest of all cereals. It is the one winter grain consistently able to live through the extremely cold winters of northern North Dakota and Montana, provided that proved varieties are used. It sprouts more readily and grows more vigorously at low temperatures

Fig. 73.—Long well-filled heads of Rosen rye. (*Courtesy of A. A. Johnson.*)

than wheat, and so it may be planted with some success in winter-wheat areas at too late a date for the sowing of wheat. Rye frequently outyields spring wheat in dry sections on sandy soils and is generally more productive than wheat during severe rust epidemics. Where conditions are favorable for winter wheat, the wheat not only is more productive than rye, as a general rule, but almost always brings the higher price. But where conditions of fertility are adverse, rye, with its ability to use relatively unavailable forms of plant food, has definite advantages.

On the surface, it appears that rye is the least profitable of small grains. For example, the 1929–1938 average acre value of rye in Michigan was but $6.69 compared with $9.88 for oats, $12.45 for barley, and $15.48 for wheat for the same period. Part of this lower value was due to the relatively low price for rye and part to its low acre yield. However, it should be remembered that rye is grown on some of the sandiest land in Michigan, land not at all suitable for barley and on which oats and wheat might make an even less favorable showing than rye.

Thus, for all its low repute as an income-producing crop, rye has a place in American agriculture as a cash grain, a feed crop, a pasture, and a producer of organic matter.

Areas of Production.—From 1900 to 1920, rye production was carried on most extensively in Michigan, Wisconsin, Minnesota, Pennsylvania, and New York. Then production expanded greatly in North Dakota and to a lesser extent in South Dakota and dropped in the middle-western and eastern states. Commercial rye production has definitely shifted to the northern Great Plains. It is one of the minor crops of the Middle West and corn belt and is also grown, both for grain and hay, in the arid and frosty portions of the Great Basin and intermountain regions, particularly in the higher and drier sections of eastern Washington and Oregon, in northern California, and in Wyoming.

The 1929–1938 annual average rye acreage harvested in the United States was 3,246,000; the annual production, 38,043,000 bu. Thus, its importance in this country is less than 5 per cent of that of wheat. From 10 to 20 million bushels of the grain crop are used as livestock feed on the farms of rye producers, and a somewhat larger quantity is sold for cash. Part of the cash-crop rye is also fed.

Rye Uses.—As a feed crop, rye is less valuable than corn, wheat, or barley. It is somewhat unpalatable and is considered heavy and sticky. It should always be mixed with other grains. Rye shorts and other by-products of the milling of rye should also be mixed with other feeds. As a hay crop, rye has its greatest value in dry, frosty regions where other crops cannot be grown. Rye is also of value as a late-fall, early-spring pasture in the North, a winter pasture in the South, a winter cover crop, and a green manure.

The rye bread widely consumed in the United States is made from a mixture of rye and wheat flour, straight rye flour producing too dark a loaf for the American trade. A substantial quantity of the United States rye crop is also used in the distilling of whisky. The residue, after the distilling process has been completed, is dried and marketed as a livestock feed under the name of distillers' rye dried grains.

Rye Culture.—The technique of growing a crop of rye is not very different from that for wheat. It can be seeded later in the fall; but the earlier seedings, made at normal wheat-planting time, are preferable. Rye will respond to the same fertilizers as wheat, but the increase in rye itself seldom pays. Fertilization is warranted in the interest of seedings when such are made with rye; but seedings with rye, on the kind of soil on which rye is so often grown, frequently are not successful.

Under semiarid conditions, 3 or 4 pk. of rye to the acre provide an adequate amount of seed, 5 to 6 pk. being commonly used in the more humid regions. The larger quantity is desirable for late seedings.

Rye Varieties.—The rye flower is open-pollinated, and so it is difficult to maintain pure rye strains. In Michigan, where Rosen rye is best adapted, pure seed of this variety is produced in perfect isolation, by growers on South Manitou Island in northern Lake Michigan. This seed provides parent stock for maintenance of the Rosen variety on a large scale. North Dakota, Montana, and similar regions need very winter hardy varieties. Of this type Dakold is a rye that has proved very satisfactory. In the South, where rye is used chiefly for grazing and winter hardiness is less essential, Abruzzi is the preferred variety. A number of varieties have been selected for local conditions.

Spring Rye.—Spring rye is of minor importance and seldom equals winter rye in yield. It matures quickly even from a late-spring sowing, but early seeding gives best yields. It has produced fair returns on sandy soils in northeastern Colorado and may be used on other dry highland areas of the Great Basin region.

Ergot.—Except in the case of ergot and stem smut, diseases of rye are relatively unimportant. Ergot is the more likely to cause serious losses. It is a fungus disease found on many grasses. That found on some of the grasses will also infect rye. The disease is occasionally present on wheat and barley but seldom on oats. The black bodies resulting from this disease contain poisons that may cause serious difficulties with all classes of farm livestock and are likewise dangerous to man.

Ergot is recognized in ripening grain by the hard, violet or black, hornlike bodies that replace the normal kernels in the head. The fungus may live over winter in the ground, or it may be planted with the seed. Warm temperature with abundant moisture is necessary for the germination of the sclerotia (resting bodies) in the soil. The

germinating sclerotia produce very small stalks just above the ground
from which come spores that are carried by air currents to the flowering
grain.   A secondary spread of the disease is carried on by insects that
may visit infected flowers.   Dry weather during the heading period
greatly reduces infection.

Ergot is controlled by crop rotation that avoids the growing of rye
or susceptible grasses on ergot-infected land for 2 or 3 years.   The
infested seed may be cleaned by pouring the seed into a solution made
by adding 40 lb. of salt to 25 gal. of water.   The ergot bodies and light
kernels will float and may be skinned off.   The pure grain must then be
washed in clean water (to remove the salt), dried thoroughly, and held
for planting.

Review Questions

1. What climatic characteristics of the Great Plains favor the production of
wheat of superior quality for the milling of bread flour?
2. If more than one class of wheat is grown in your state, which class brings
the better price?
3. What varieties of wheat are recommended in your state?   What are their
chief merits?
4. What is the proper time to sow fall wheat in your state?   Spring wheat?
5. What factors determine the best time to seed wheat?
6. In subhumid areas, what effect does soil moisture have with respect to
the advisability of seeding wheat?
7. Why do not farmers in humid areas take advantage of premium prices by
growing high-protein hard wheats?
8. Which should you consider more objectionable, a mixture of 25 per cent
white wheat in a lot of soft red winter wheat or a moisture content of 16 per cent?
9. If, according to state-wide crop reports, rye almost always produces a lower
acre income than wheat, why is rye grown?
10. Describe the rye variety most widely used in your state.

Problems

1. If garlic is a problem in your state, prepare an article discussing control of
this weed in wheat fields.
2. You are seeding wheat on a sandy loam soil in the corn belt and are going
to seed red clover with it.   The land previously grew corn.   What will your fertilizer procedure be?
3. Growing wheat in a humid area, you have a very vigorous spring growth.
The wheat is seeded to alfalfa.   Under what conditions and to what extent might
pasturing this wheat be justified?
4. Make an itemized list of costs you would incur for seed, fertilizer, and seed-
treating material to put in 50 acres of wheat.
5. There have been instances when wheat was a cheaper feed than corn.   If
corn is worth 60 cents a bushel, what price would wheat have to bring to warrant
its substitution for corn in a livestock ration?

6. You wish to use rye as a winter cover after corn. What will your seeding practices be, and how will you handle the rye the next spring?

7. Prepare a short article on the use of rye as a green manure.

References

CARLETON, M. A.: "The Small Grains," The Macmillan Company, New York, 1924.

COMBS, WILLIS B., and FRED G. SMITH: Grain Grading Primer, *U.S. Dept. Agr. Misc. Pub.* 325, 1939.

KELLEY, C. F.: Methods of Ventilating Wheat in Farm Storage, *U.S. Dept. Agr. Cir.* 554, 1940.

PIETERS, A. J.: "Green Manuring, Principles and Practice," John Wiley & Sons, Inc., New York, 1927.

U.S. Dept. Agr. Agricultural Statistics. Superintendent of Documents, Government Printing Office, Washington, D.C.

CHAPTER XV

OATS AND BARLEY

Oats and barley have much in common. They are both small grains or cereals, members of the great grass family. Both are most commonly seeded in the spring and grown as annuals; yet each has varieties that are winter annuals to be sown in the fall. They are grown by essentially identical seeding, cultural, and harvest methods. They fit conveniently into the same sort of crop rotations, have about the same effect on the land and on succeeding crops, and have approximately the same seasonal labor requirements. Their most important use is as feed for livestock; yet each is used to some extent as food for man. It was a Scotchman who is reputed to have said that in England oats makes fine horses and in Scotland it makes fine men.

Distribution in the United States.—More than a million farmers in the United States grow oats; about a third of a million grow barley. More oats are grown because the oat crop is less restricted in soil and climatic requirements than barley. Of the two crops, it is somewhat easier to grow oats well. Iowa is the leading oat state; but the crop is widely grown throughout the corn belt, the Dakotas, the middle-western dairy states, and eastward to New England. The acreage is important in a region extending from eastern Kansas through Oklahoma into north-central Texas, less so in the eastern cotton country, and scattering in the central and northern Rocky Mountain states and on the Pacific coast.

Barley production is most concentrated in North Dakota, South Dakota, and Minnesota. Much good malting barley is produced in eastern Wisconsin and northern Illinois and Iowa. There is another intensive area in western Kansas and Nebraska extending into Colorado. The valleys of California produce malting barley for export and some winter barley is grown in the Southwest partially to replace corn for feed. Practically none is grown in the cotton belt.

Why Oats and Barley Are Grown.—Neither oats nor barley can be regarded as high-income crops. For the 10 years 1930–1939 the average cash value of an acre of oats in the United States was $8.32, and that of an acre of barley just $1 more. Only farmers operating on an extensive basis with low costs or those producing high acre yields

284

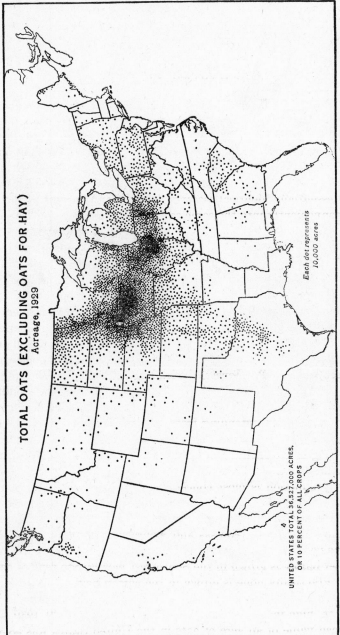

TOTAL OATS (EXCLUDING OATS FOR HAY)
Acreage, 1929

Each dot represents
10,000 acres

UNITED STATES TOTAL 36,527,000 ACRES,
OR 10 PERCENT OF ALL CROPS

FIG. 74.—The corn belt, particularly the northern part, is also the center of the production of oats, and the crop is very important in the spring wheat and dairy belts to the north and east. Oats are adapted especially to a fairly cool, moist climate. Nevertheless, a large acreage extends southwestward across Oklahoma to central Texas. This acreage is partly fall sown. (*U.S. Department of Agriculture.*)

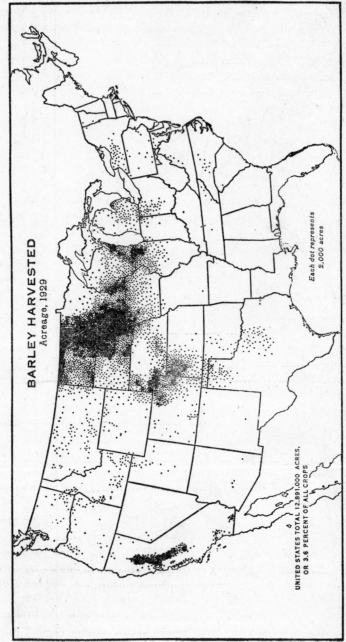

FIG. 75.—A dot on this map represents only one-fifth as much acreage as on the corresponding maps for oats, corn, and wheat. Barley is of minor importance in the United States as compared with these crops except in the spring wheat and hard winter wheat belts and in a few smaller areas. Some varieties of barley are sown in the fall in the Southwest, thus escaping most of the drought and summer heat. These largely replace corn for feed. Other varieties are cold-resistant and replace corn in the Northwest. (*U.S. Department of Agriculture.*)

can afford to sell these crops for cash except in the occasional year of high prices. The answer is that price considerations tell only a small part of the story of the utilization of these two grains.

In Michigan, a typical dairy state, the 1940 oat crop at average farm prices was credited with a value of $18,752,000. However, cash sales amounted to a little less than 10 per cent of this figure. The cash income from barley represented but 19 per cent of the farm value of the crop though malting barley as a cash crop is important in the leading barley counties. In the case of barley, over 80 per cent and, in the case of oats, 90 per cent of the crop was fed on the farm that produced it; and livestock has usually paid more than cash-crop prices for these grains. As a feed, barley can replace corn pound for pound in the dairy ration, it closely approaches corn in value as a feed for beef cattle and sheep, and it is only moderately less efficient than corn for hog feed. Oats carry a little more fiber and are somewhat lower in total digestible nutrients than barley.

But grain production either for feed or for cash is not the only consideration that makes for the wide growth of these crops. The straw, oat straw in particular, is needed for livestock bedding. Bedding may not contribute much to farm income; but it is a necessary item in livestock management during the winters, and it is expensive if the livestock farmer has to buy it. Eventually, of course, it is returned to the land with manure to improve the production of more valuable crops. These straws also provide low-grade roughage for feed.

Another consideration is the convenience of these grain crops in the rotation. Sod-forming forages, the legumes and legume-grass mixtures, are necessary for livestock production and effective soil management. These forages can be established most conveniently and cheaply in most regions by seeding them with oats or barley.

Finally, it must be admitted that many farmers do not have much choice in the matter. The corn-belt farmer cannot grow corn on his land all the time. Such a practice would ruin the land, wreck the corn market, and make for an exceedingly cumbersome distribution of labor. Soybeans have made vast inroads into the oat acreage since 1935; but the fact remains that the growing of spring grains fits in efficiently with corn growing and livestock farming, and their culture will undoubtedly continue to be highly important.

Kinds of Oats.—There are many different kinds of oats. Throughout most of the corn belt and in northern states, spring varieties are grown. Fall-sown varieties are used in the South because their growth is made in the cooler weather which is more favorable to this crop. No winter-oat varieties have been developed thus far that are sufficiently hardy for dependable production where winters are severe.

There are white oats, yellow oats, gray oats, black oats, and red oats. Most oat varieties have hulled kernels, but some varieties are hull-less. Of the spring-sown varieties, some, like the Kherson strains, are early. These are favored in much of the corn belt, especially in its southern part, because they complete growth before the hottest driest part of the season. Varieties that mature in midseason and those that are late have proved most productive where summers are more temperate, including much of North Dakota, northern Minnesota, Wisconsin, Michigan, New York, New England, and irrigated sections of the Northwest. In the extreme north, early varieties are needed in some localities in order that the crop may mature before fall frost. The larger midseason and late varieties are more productive of forage and are preferred where the crop is grown for hay.

Barley Types.—There are several subspecies of barley, one obvious classification being based on the number of kernel rows on a head. Six-row barleys, as the name implies, have six rows of kernels. Common six-row barley has lax or nodding heads, whereas in another type the spikelets are compacted and stand erect. In two-row barley the side spikelets are infertile; only the middle spikelets produce seed, developing but two rows of kernels on each head. An intermediate type appears to have come from a cross between six- and two-row groups.

The common six-row barleys include the Manchuria and Oder-brucker, varietal types grown in the humid-spring regions; Coast barley, adapted to semiarid regions; Trebi, a bluish-kerneled variety highly productive in the Dakotas and similar areas; and a group of winter varieties adapted to humid regions of mild winters.

The hardiest winter barleys resist winterkilling better than any of the present varieties of winter oats, but they are not so winter hardy as the best winter wheats. Michigan Winter barley, released from the Michigan Agricultural Experiment Station in 1916, is still grown in the more favorable locations in that state; but winter barleys are much better suited in such states as Tennessee, where Tennessee Winter and Wintex have been developed, Missouri, and Oklahoma.

Hooded barleys have a hood-shaped appendage instead of the awn. They may be hull-less as in Nepal or hulled as in Success. Himalaya is also hull-less, but it is a bearded variety. These three are all best adapted to semiarid regions.

The two-row barley group includes Chevalier, Horn, and Hannchen, grown in semiarid and irrigated districts; Alpha, developed in New York; and Hanna, a widely adapted variety.

The U.S. Department of Agriculture introduced Lion barley from Russia.   This is a six-row, black variety with beards that are smooth, *i.e.*, practically free from the tiny barbs that make barley beards so irritating.   Many of the barleys now in commercial use have resulted from crosses between the Lion variety and the six-row or two-row types of rough-bearded barley.   A few illustrations will serve to show the influence Lion barley has had in barley improvement.   Spartan is a two-row, white variety selected from a Michigan cross between Lion and a Hanna selection.   The Wisconsin Agricultural Experiment Station developed Barbless, a six-row, white barley, from a Lion × Oder-brucker cross.   Velvon, developed in Utah, involves Trebi parentage on the one hand and a Coast × Lion cross on the other.   All these

Fig. 76.—A field of malting barley in Minnesota, one of the leading barley states. (*Courtesy of H. K. Wilson, Minnesota Agricultural Experiment Station.*)

varieties are smooth-bearded, a feature that makes them less irritating to livestock and more popular with the farmers who have to handle the crop.

Malting Barley.—The term *malting barley* is essentially a quality designation rather than the name of a type or variety.   Malting barley comes from limited areas each of which has its own peculiar influence on the quality and character of the malt.   In California, barley of the Coast type has found favor with maltsters in England.   However, most of the barley for malting in the United States comes from an area including northern Illinois, southern Michigan, Wisconsin, Minnesota, Iowa, eastern South Dakota, and eastern North Dakota.   The best grades are grown on well-drained clay to fine silt loam soil, well supplied with organic matter and the usual plant nutrients.

With respect to varieties, two-row barleys in general are not wanted in this country though they are used by European maltsters. Trebi, a very productive six-row variety for the northwestern states, likewise is considered unsatisfactory. The varieties that are acceptable if meeting other malting quality standards are of the Oderbrucker and Manchuria group and such smooth-bearded strains derived from them as Wisconsin Barbless, Velvet, and Minsturdi.

Malting barley must be clean and undamaged. Mixtures are objectionable, even mixtures of acceptable varieties or of barley from different though approved localities. The barley, in order to malt properly, must be uniform in physical and chemical composition so that it will absorb water evenly, germinate, and malt uniformly. In the better grades the kernels are plump, of good test weight, well matured, and bright in color; they must be mellow rather than steely in texture. Broken kernels will not malt and must be screened out. Grains threshed too closely are even more objectionable because the sprouts may be broken off before the malting process is complete. The capacity for as nearly 100 per cent germination as possible and for even germination is the most important attribute of good malting barley, for malting is a germinating process.

Barley that is to be malted is separately assembled in accordance with varietal type and area of production. The grain is graded for size, steeped until it contains about 46 per cent moisture, and then put in germination drums at a suitable sprouting temperature for about 6 days. Germination is then stopped by drying the grain, the sprouts are removed, and the malted grain is then ready for the market. In the germinating process, development of the enzyme diastase is stimulated. The enzyme is active in the conversion of starch to malt sugar (maltose). Not only is it effective with the starch of the barley kernel, but also it will act on the starch of raw grains that may be mixed with malt. The malt sugar thus produced is readily fermentable.

The standard weight of a bushel of barley malt is 34 lb., and that of the barley 48 lb.

Brewers' Grains.—Brewers' grains are a by-product of the brewing process. In the brewing process the starchy endosperm of corn or rice may be added to barley malt in the form of grits to make up the mash. After the process of converting the starch in the mash to malt sugar has been completed, the liquid and soluble materials that make up the *wort*, used in brewing, are separated from the mash, the remaining material constituting wet brewers' grains. The residue is usually dried, unless fed near the brewery, and goes under the name of brewers' dried grains. This feed is a concentrate ranging from 20 to a little over 25 per cent protein. Its palatability and digestibility are low; but it may be used effectively, especially for dairy cows, if it makes up only 20 to 30 per cent of the concentrate portion of the ration.

Quality in Oats and Barley.—The general attributes of quality in oats and barley are plumpness, purity, and freedom from damage and from disease. Plump grain is indicative of favorable growing conditions and a good harvest. The standard weight of a bushel of oats is 32 lb. Number 2 oats may weigh as low as 30 lb. to the bushel; but oats of superior varieties, grown under favorable conditions, often weigh 36 to 42 lb. Such oats bring premium prices, and they are better as feed. The heavier oats are lower in fiber and higher in total digestible nutrients than light grain. The same is true for feeding barley, and malting barley of superior test weight produces a higher yield of malt extract. A bright color is particularly desirable for both these grains when they are to be used in the processing of human food.

BARLEY AND OAT CULTURE

Adaptation.—Both barley and oats grow best under temperate climatic conditions. Where these grains are produced in the South, the seeding date is such that growth takes place in the cooler part of the season. Oats are grown with fair success on a wider range of soil types than barley; but the best yields of each are secured on fertile, well-drained soils that are loamy in texture. Barley is likely to be troubled more by scab and blight on heavy, poorly drained soils; on light soils, its straw is short, the plants tiller poorly, and yields are low. An abundance of available nitrogen in the soil coupled with wet growing weather often causes excessive straw growth and lodging in both oats and barley. If the crop goes down before it is fully developed, the grain is likely to be shriveled and the yield reduced.

Place in Rotations.—The normal place in the rotation for oats or barley is that immediately following a row crop. Land that has been in corn, beans, soybeans, sugar beets, potatoes, or other row crops usually may be disked rather than plowed, the first step in seedbed preparation for the grain crop being thus simplified.

Common 4-year rotations in the corn belt are as follows: corn (2 years), oats, clover; corn, oats, meadow (2 years); corn, two grain crops, clover. Where sugar beets are grown in the Lake states, barley and oats are suitable following crops. These grains are less likely to lodge after sugar beets than after corn, beans, or soybeans; and, according to work done by Salter and Lill at Holgate, Ohio,[1] oats yield much better after sugar beets than they do after corn or small grain.

In much of the western area where barley growing is most extensive, rotation of crops receives practically no consideration and barley is merely worked into the farming scheme with other grain crops, chiefly wheat. The practice is not conducive to high yields.

Fig. 77.—A Nov. 5 picture of Missouri Early Beardless Winter barley. Winter barley in this region is sown in early fall to provide fall pasture and winter cover. The grain matures in very early summer providing high-grade early feed. The crop is an excellent companion for legume seedings releasing the land early so the seedings may have a long season for growth without competition. (*Courtesy of C. A. Helm, Missouri Agricultural Experiment Station.*)

In the South, fall-sown oats or barley may follow corn or cotton. Sometimes green manures like cowpeas or soybeans, seeded in corn at the last cultivation, are plowed under for grain. On the better soils of humid regions the plowing under of a green manure or legume sod for oats or barley frequently results in excessive lodging of the grain.

Etheridge and Helm[2] state that the most efficient rotation of spring oats in Missouri, from the viewpoint of total annual production per acre and conservation of the soil, is with Korean lespedeza. Oats may be sown in the spring on the last year's lespedeza sod thereby providing

[1] Salter, R. M., and J. G. Lill, Crops Sequence Studies in Northwestern Ohio, *Jour. Amer. Soc. Agron.*, Vol. 32, No. 8, 1940.

[2] Etheridge, W. C., and C. A. Helm, Growing Good Crops of Oats in Missouri, *Mo. Agr. Expt. Sta. Bul.* 359, 1936.

a 1-year rotation of oats and lespedeza, the latter volunteering from seed shattered the previous season. Winter barley is also grown in rotation with lespedeza.

Both barley and oats are useful in cheapening the cost of establishing seedings of alfalfa, sweet clover, red clover, and other perennial or biennial forages. Barley is reputedly a less severe competitor with the forage seeding than oats; but it probably has no advantages in this respect over the earlier maturing, shorter strawed oat varieties.

Fertilizers for Barley and Oats.—Both barley and oats respond well to phosphate and potash fertilizers, with a little nitrogen to give the crop a vigorous start, if these nutrients in available form are not present in the soil in adequate amounts. However, it takes a big increase in grain to pay for the fertilizer. The most profitable returns are made possible if a legume is seeded with the grain so that the fertilizer may help not only the grain but also the forage, the latter often being the more important consideration.

Time of Seeding.—If the time of seeding the oat and barley crops is governed by any one principle, it is that seeding should be done early. This applies to both oats and barley, whether fall- or spring-sown and regardless of variety. Earliness, however, is relative; it is not established by any one calendar date. May 5 is early for seeding spring grain in the Lake Superior country; Feb. 15 is early in Texas and Oklahoma. The best time to sow the spring varieties is just as soon as the seedbed can be well prepared. Spring-sown oats are seldom injured by spring freezes—even rather severe freezes such as may occur in the northern plains after seeding time. The chances of decreased yields due to late planting are much greater than chances of injury due to any reasonably early planting. Experiments in Montana, North Dakota, and South Dakota[1] have indicated that, as an average, the yield of barley is decreased by more than 1 per cent for each day that seeding is delayed after Apr. 25.

The time of seeding spring oats and barley closely coincides and in some important areas is in conflict with the time for sowing spring wheat. As for oats and barley, both are subject to reduced yields if planting is too long delayed. Local considerations, the comparative value of the two crops to an individual farm, and the condition of the fields for each crop will determine which crop to sow first.

Early sowing of the winter varieties of these grains is prior to Sept. 20 for the northern part of the area in which they are used, *viz.*, Virginia to southern Missouri, and by Nov. 1 along the Gulf coast. In

[1] HARLAN, H. V., Barley; Culture, Uses, and Varieties, *U.S. Dept. Agr. Farmers' Bul.* 1464, 1925.

California, oats are seeded from October to February, most of the crop being put in in November.

Rates of Seeding.—The most usual rate of seeding oats with a grain drill in the United States is 3 bu. an acre; that for barley is 2 bu. If the seed is broadcast, the rate of seeding is increased by 25 per cent to make up for less even distribution and coverage. The most marked exception to these rates is the practice in the arid Great Plains of sowing either of these crops at 1 to 1½ bu. an acre because the water supply usually is insufficient to support the increased number of plants that should develop from a heavier seeding rate. Where the winter varieties are sown for forage in the South or the spring varieties are so used elsewhere, the quantity of seed to the acre is increased by 25 or 30 per cent. A greater measured quantity of seed must be sown with large-seeded varieties than with smaller seeded ones in order to secure the same number of plants.

Obviously the amount of seed used can be too small; but if the seed-bed is well prepared, the rates of seeding suggested above are more than adequate. Two bushels of oats or 1½ bu. of barley should be entirely sufficient if the seed is of average size. If the productive environment is favorable, an increase in tillering of the plants will make up for this reasonable decrease from the average seeding rate; if the environment is unfavorable, a higher rate of seeding cannot be expected to correct for the deficiency.

In a detailed Michigan study[1] of the rate of seeding barley, certain advantages were found in using reasonably lower rates of seeding, aside from the lesser cost for seed. As the rate of seeding was increased from ½ to 3 bu. an acre, the number of plants per unit area increased; but tillering, length of straw, length of head, number of kernels per head, and weight of 1,000 kernels decreased. The quantity of seed that gave maximum acre yields was not a single rate but a wide range covering 1 to 2½ bu. for six-row varieties and 1½ to 3 bu. for the larger seeded two-row varieties. An increase in rate of seeding beyond this optimum range was associated with so great a reduction in tillering, length of head, and number of kernels per head that acre yields were reduced. There was also an increased tendency for grain seeded at the heavier rates to lodge. Within the limits of these trials the optimum rate of seeding appeared to be independent of environment although the barley yields varied materially from season to season, owing to differing environmental conditions.

[1] THAYER, J. W., JR., and H. C. RATHER, The Influence of Rate of Seeding upon Certain Plant Characters in Barley, *Jour. Amer. Soc. Agron.*, Vol. 29, No. 9, 1937.

Seeding Methods.—The proper depth for sowing oats and barley is 1 to 1½ in. on a well-prepared, moist seedbed. In the drier climates, 2 to 2½ in. is considered preferable. The seed may be broadcast or drilled, most grain drills sowing the seed in rows 7 in. apart. Drilling is more economical of seed and effects a better distribution and coverage; broadcasting, as with an endgate seeder, takes less time and labor. On the heavier soils, there is little difference in respect to yield between the two methods; on the lighter and drier soils, drilling is definitely the better practice.

Fig. 78.—The grain drill is generally preferred to broadcasting for sowing oats or barley. (*Courtesy of E. E. Patton.*)

Oat-Barley Mixtures.—About the only grain mixture grown to any extent in the spring-grain region is that secured by mixing oat- and barley seed in equal proportions and sowing the mixture at 2 bu. an acre. The practice is largely confined to the northern dairy states. It is not advisable if a surplus of grain is produced on the farm, for the mixture does not sell nearly so well as either grain alone. In the production of feed the mixture has a moderate yield advantage, and the oat-barley mixture appears to be better than any other grain combination.

In Michigan trials[1] the oat-barley mixture outyielded the two crops grown separately on equal acreage by an average of about 200 lb. an acre. Varieties of oats and barley that mature at the same time are essential to the success of the practice.

[1] MORRISH, R. H., Crop Mixture Trials in Michigan, *Mich. Agr. Expt. Sta. Spec. Bul.* 256, 1934.

Diseases.—Some of the more noteworthy diseases affecting oats and barley and their causal organisms are:

Oats:

Covered smut—*Ustilago levis.*
Loose smut—*U. avenae.*
Crown rust—*Puccinia coronata.*
Stem rust—*P. graminis.*

Barley:

Covered smut—*U. hordei.*
Loose smut—*U. nuda, U. medians.*
Stripe—*Helminthosporium gramineum.*
Scab—*Gibberella saubinettii.*

In the ordinary loose smut of barley caused by *U. nuda* the head of barley is replaced by a black mass of smut spores about the time the

Fig. 79.—Testing oat and barley mixtures. Varieties used in mixtures should mature together. Left, Wisconsin Barbless barley and Wolverine oats; right, Spartan barley and Iogold oats. (*Michigan Agricultural Experiment Station.*)

heads emerge from the uppermost leaf sheath. The fungus is carried from one season to another inside kernels, infected at the flowering stage, that outwardly have a normal appearance. This loose smut, like that of wheat, can be controlled only by a cumbersome hot-water treatment seldom advised except for seed enough to plant a special seed plot.

The loose smut caused by *U. medians*, the covered smut of barley, and the smuts of oats are carried from one season to another in such a manner as to be subject to control by chemical seed treatment. Other seed-borne diseases including barley stripe, scab, and net blotch and spot blotch and the leaf spot and halo blight of oats are also controlled by seed treatment. The organic mercury dust Ceresan has proved to be especially effective if thorough coverage of all the kernels by the dust is achieved in the treating process. The dust is a poison, and therefore treated seed must not be fed in any form.

In the case of barley scab, seed treatment is only partially effective. This disease also infects wheat, corn, rye, and, to a lesser extent, oats. It is carried over in infected cornstalks, straw, and grain stubble. The extent of the disease may be reduced materially by clean fall plowing of all such refuse. In leading corn states, it is seldom possible to have an intervening crop between corn, the most important carrier, and barley. Where an intervening crop such as sugar beets follows corn in the rotation, the succeeding barley crop is seldom seriously infected. Scabby barley is unfit for malting; and if as much as 10 per cent of the grain is infected, it is also dangerous as a hog or horse feed. Usually the hogs will refuse to eat scabby barley; if they do eat it, they become sick. The diseased grain may be safely fed to sheep and cattle.

The Rusts.—A farmer had a beautiful crop of oats just nicely headed and promising 80 bu. an acre. It was attacked by stem rust, and at harvesttime he threshed 24 bu. an acre of grain that scarcely weighed 20 lb. to the bushel. Such is the common story of a bad case of stem rust. The appearance and life cycle of the disease are similar to those for the stem rust of wheat (see page 271). Crown rust may also be serious. It is found chiefly on the leaves, but it may also occur on the stems and heads. In the North the alternate hosts for the spring stage of this disease organism are species of buckthorn; but in southern states it goes through the winter in the summer stage, and some infection in the North may result from wind-blown spores working northward with the season.

Disease Resistance.—One of the most effective means of combating the rusts and smuts and some of the other grain diseases is the development of inherently resistant varieties. In the South, Red Rustproof is a late-rusting variety of oats that escapes severe damage. The Richland and Iogold oat strains selected in Iowa and lines bred from crosses in which these strains are involved are resistant to stem rust. The Markton strain, developed by the U.S. Department of Agriculture, is essentially immune to the oat smuts and is exceedingly useful in the breeding of new disease-resisting lines. Already several plant breeders have material, resulting from crossing work, that carries resistance to both rust and smut, some new varieties of this kind being Vicland, Boone, Marion, and Tama. Wisconsin Barbless barley is resistant to stripe; and the Spartan variety, bred in Michigan, has shown some resistance to scab.

No one of these varieties is universally adapted; but their valuable germ plasm and that of other worthy lines are being used constantly

Fig. 80.—Harvesting Huron oats, a smut-resistant heavy oat developed cooperatively by the Michigan Agricultural Experiment Station and the United States Department of Agriculture. (*Courtesy of E. B. Swingle.*)

throughout the country for the development of superior disease-resistant varieties adapted to each area.

Review Problems

1. Make a list of the five leading oat states and the five leading barley states based on data from the most recent issue of U.S. Agricultural Statistics.

Oats	Barley
1. _____	1. _____
2. _____	2. _____
3. _____	3. _____
4. _____	4. _____
5. _____	5. _____

2. Of the following characteristics, check the ones preferred for malting barley:

_____Mellow kernels.	_____High test weight.
_____Steely kernels.	_____High germination.
_____High protein content.	_____Closely threshed grain.
_____Large kernels.	_____Medium-sized kernels.

3. After which of the following crops can an Ohio farmer expect best oat yields?

    a. Corn.
    b. Oats.
    c. Sugar beets.

4. If alfalfa is to be seeded with a spring grain, conditions for the seeding should be most favorable if it is made with

    a. An early oat.
    b. A midseason oat.
    c. A late barley.

5. A six-row barley is seeded at (*a*) 1½ and (*b*) 3½ bu. an acre. Indicate to which rate of seeding (*a*) or (*b*) each of the following statements probably would apply?

_____More plants to the acre.   _____More tillering.
_____Longer heads.   _____Stronger straw.
_____Higher weight per 1,000 kernels.   _____Longer straw.
_____Greater yield.

6. Scabby barley may cause illness of the animals if fed to

    a. Cattle.
    b. Sheep.
    c. Hogs.

7. Why are early-maturing varieties of oats preferred in the corn belt whereas midseason varieties are often more productive farther north?

8. Give three reasons why the oat crop is so widely grown in the United States.

9. If 0-20-0 fertilizer retails at $25 a ton, how much of an increase in oat yield must a farmer get, at current farm prices for oats, to pay for an application of 200 lb. an acre of this grade of fertilizer?

10. Do the results of fertilizer tests in your state indicate that the application of commercial fertilizer to oats is warranted on the basis of this year's prices?

11. What influence does the seeding of alfalfa with small grain have on the practice of using fertilizer?

12. Indicate whether each of the following statements is true (T) or false (F):

    a. _____The best winter-barley varieties are as winter hardy as the hardiest varieties of winter wheat.

    b. _____In general, winter-oat varieties are less hardy than varieties of winter barley.

    c. _____Most smooth-awned-barley varieties in use in this country were bred from crosses involving Lion barley, a black variety.

    d. _____The standard test weight of a bushel of barley is 46 lb.

    e. _____As a rule, barley grows better than oats on sandy soils.

    f. _____Small grain should be sown deeper under dry than under moist conditions.

    g. _____A mixture of oats and barley usually yields more than the two crops grown separately.

h. _____Loose smut of barley caused by *Ustilago nuda* may be controlled by treatment with Ceresan.

i. _____Crown rust of oats is a seed-borne disease.

j. _____The Markton oat is essentially immune to the oat smuts.

References

BURNETT, L. C., and C. S. REDDY: Barley in Iowa, *Iowa Agr. Expt. Sta. Bul.* 367, 1937.

CARLETON, M. A.: "The Small Grains," The Macmillan Company, New York, 1924.

HARLAN, H. V.: Growing Barley for Malt and Feed, *U.S. Dept. Agr. Farmers' Bul.* 1732, 1934.

KLAGES, K. H.: Barley Production in South Dakota, *S. Dak. Agr. Expt. Sta. Bul.* 256, 1930.

LEITH, B. D., H. L. SHANDS, and R. A. MOORE: Quality Barley—How to Grow—How to Handle, *Wis. Ext. Cir.* 278, 1936.

MORRISON, F. B.: "Feeds and Feeding," 20th ed., The Morrison Publishing Co., Ithaca, N.Y., 1936.

MUNCIE, J. H.: Common Diseases of Cereals in Michigan, *Mich. Agr. Expt. Sta. Cir. Bul.* 142, 1932.

STANTON, T. R., and F. A. COFFMAN: Oats in the North-central States, *U.S. Dept. Agr. Farmers' Bul.* 1581, 1929.

——— and ———: Spring-sown Red Oats, *U.S. Dept. Agr. Farmers' Bul.* 1583, 1929.

——— and ———: Oats in the Western Half of the United States, *U.S. Dept. Agr. Farmers' Bul.* 1611, 1929.

——— and ———: Fall-sown Oat Production, *U.S. Dept. Agr. Farmers' Bul.* 1640, 1930.

——— and ———: Oats in the Northeastern States, *U.S. Dept. Agr. Farmers' Bul.* 1659, 1936.

STEVENSON, F. J., R. O. BRIDGFORD, and R. F. CRIM: Barley in Minnesota, *Minn. Ext. Bul.* 135, 1930.

STOA, T. E.: Barley Production in North Dakota, *N. Dak. Agr. Expt. Sta. Bul.* 264, 1933.

CHAPTER XVI

MISCELLANEOUS GRAIN AND SEED CROPS

THE GRAIN SORGHUMS

The grain sorghums might well be called the corn crop of the dry lands. Far more drought resistant than corn these tall seed-bearing grasses which have been known in the arid regions of Asia and Africa for hundreds of years are now grown in the southern Great Plains region of the United States to the extent of about 10 million acres. Of the 1940 grain-sorghum acreage, one-third the crop was used for forage;

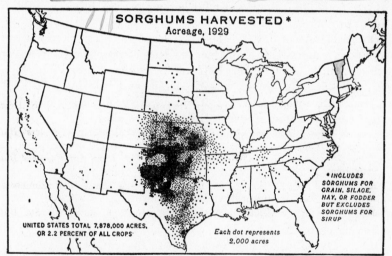

SORGHUMS HARVESTED*
Acreage, 1929

*INCLUDES
SORGHUMS FOR
GRAIN, SILAGE,
HAY, OR FODDER
BUT EXCLUDES
SORGHUMS FOR
SIRUP

UNITED STATES TOTAL 7,878,000 ACRES,
OR 2.2 PERCENT OF ALL CROPS

Each dot represents
2,000 acres

FIG. 81.—The grain sorghums are, perhaps, our most drought-resistant crops. From 1899 to 1909 the acreage of grain sorghums in the United States increased sixfold, and between 1909 and 1919 it more than doubled. The sorghums now have an established place in the farming of the southern Great Plains, where the dry climate is too severe for corn production and the hot winds interfere with pollination and often wither the corn crop. (*U.S. Department of Agriculture.*)

the balance, harvested for grain, yielded 81 million bushels. The 1929–1938 average yields for the states in which the grain sorghums are usually grown without irrigation ranged from 9 to 14 bu. an acre. In Arizona and California where irrigating the crop is the usual procedure 29 bu. was secured. Good yields under favorable conditions in the Great Plains range from 25 to 60 bu.; they are often much higher than this under irrigation. The standard test weight per bushel is 56 lb.

Adaptation.—More than half the United States acreage of grain sorghum is grown in northern Texas, Oklahoma, and Kansas. Eight other states, largely in the Southwest, produce the balance. The advantages of the grain sorghums over corn lie in their greater heat and drought resistance. Production, therefore, is most extensive where average annual rainfall is under 25 in. or where shallow soils reduce the effectiveness of a moderately higher precipitation. Under humid conditions, corn is much more valuable for grain production.

If drought is extreme, even grain sorghums may fail. The tendency is for the plants to remain dormant during very dry weather, and should rains be inadequate only a forage growth is produced. Grain production is also uncertain in the shorter, cooler seasons found in the North or at higher altitudes. J. H. Martin of the U.S. Department of Agriculture states that the most suitable grain-sorghum areas have a frost-free period of 5 months or more and an average July temperature of 75°F. or higher.

Varieties.—According to the U.S. Department of Agriculture,[1] there are now more than 40 distinct varieties of grain sorghums grown in this country. The older, well-known varieties are grouped as kaffir, milo, feterita, durra, hegari, shallu, and kaoliang. In addition, there are several varieties of hybrid origin not easily classified.

Kaffir.—The kaffirs in general have leafy stalks 4 to 7 ft. tall at maturity. The stalks are juicy; but, with the exception of the Sunrise variety, they are not sweet. The heads are long, slender, and cylindrical with small white, pink, or red seeds. Late varieties like Red kaffir are good for forage but require a long season to produce good grain yields. The Blackhull variety has white seeds, which before threshing are partly covered with black chaff. Blackhull kaffir is the leading grain variety in Kansas, Oklahoma, and Texas.

Milo.—Dwarf yellow milo ranks next to Blackhull kaffir among all the grain-sorghum varieties. The milos in general are more drought resistant than the kaffirs. They sucker freely and adjust themselves readily to varying conditions of environment. The heads of most varieties are "goosenecked" rather than straight; the seeds are yellow or white and rather soft. The stalks are slightly juicy.

Double Dwarf, Beaver, and Wheatland milo grow only 1½ to 3 ft. high. The latter two, bred by the U.S. Department of Agriculture, have erect heads and stiff stalks, making them especially suited for machine harvest. The other milos range from 3 to 6 ft. in height.

[1] MARTIN, J. H., J. S. COLE, and A. T. SEMPLE, Growing and Feeding Grain Sorghums, *U.S. Dept. Agr. Farmers' Bul.* 1764, 1936. Varietal descriptions presented here are based on this publication.

Feterita.—The feteritas are earlier in maturity than the kaffirs and milos and are even more drought resistant. The Standard and Spur varieties grow to a height of 5 to 7 ft.; the Dwarf is shorter and has no productive advantages. Feterita stalks are dry and pithy; the seeds, borne on compact oval heads, are large, chalky white, and starchy.

Fig. 82.—Three of the most important grain-sorghum varieties: Blackhull kaffir (top), Dwarf Yellow milo, and Spur feterita. (*Courtesy of R. E. Karper, Texas Agricultural Experiment Station.*)

Durra.—The durra varieties also have dry stalks. The bearded heads are compact, are goosenecked in shape, and carry flat seeds, brown or white in color depending on the variety. Nearly all the durra is produced in California where the seed is preferred over other sorghum grain as feed for poultry.

Hegari.—This sorghum has leafy juicy stalks that make it particularly useful as bundle feed. The seeds are similar to those of kaffir.

Hegari requires favorable growing conditions and may produce only forage in extremely dry seasons. June plantings are considered advisable.

Other Varieties.—In addition to the varieties described above a few others have attained some local significance. Shallu, grown to some extent in the Gulf region of Texas and Louisiana, has little forage value, matures late, and is susceptible to smut. It lodges and shatters excessively. Kaoliang, supposedly suitable in the North because of its early maturity, still does not mature dependably in cool seasons and has little forage value because the stalks are dry and have few leaves. Ajax is a kaffir-feterita hybrid that yields well in the Texas blacklands if soil moisture is ample. Darso appears to resist chinch-bug injury but is not so productive as kaffir and milo in the absence of a severe chinch-bug infestation. The seeds are rather unpalatable.

Rotations.—Like most crops the grain sorghums benefit from a rotation of crops; but they are grown in a region and by means of cul-

Fig. 83.—A field of Early kalo in Nebraska. (*Courtesy of F. D. Keim, Nebraska Agricultural Experiment Station.*)

tural practices that make crop rotations, in the usual sense, impracticable. A substantial acreage of the sorghums is grown in the wheat country where sorghum harvest is too late to permit the planting of winter wheat. Then, too, wheat, the more important of the two crops, yields better in continuous culture than after sorghum. In cotton country the grain sorghums yield well after cotton, but cotton does not yield well after grain sorghum. Spring barley can be grown effectively after grain sorghum in northwestern Kansas, and wheat may then follow the barley. Where grain sorghum and wheat are grown in the same rotation, a desirable procedure is to fallow the land the season following the production of the sorghum in order to conserve moisture for wheat.

Grain Sorghums and the Soil.—Grain sorghums are usually grown on soils fairly well supplied with plant nutrients, and so applications of commercial fertilizers are seldom made. Crops that follow grain sorghums often yield poorly. This may be due to several factors. The sorghums grow until frost and hence often leave the soil depleted in moisture and in readily available plant nutrients. The soil after a sorghum crop is often lumpy and in poor physical condition. It is also likely that the decay of sorghum roots and stubble by the soil microorganisms results in a temporary tie-up of available nitrogen (see page 139). This difficulty may be overcome by applications of barnyard manure or nitrogenous fertilizers or, in the drier regions, by a season of fallow.

Seedbed Preparation and Planting.—In much of the dry country where grain sorghums are most important the cheapest seedbed preparation may be effected by means of the lister. The listing method is rapid and reduces wind erosion. In the eastern portion of the sorghum-growing region, better yields are secured if the land is plowed; but plowing increases production costs and is unpopular in the drier sections where yields are lower.

Subsequent to either listing or plowing, tillage of the land to mellow the soil and control weeds is accomplished with the disk and the usual harrow equipment. Sometimes listed land is merely relisted, the seed being planted during this second operation.

Planting is done with either a lister planter or a corn planter properly equipped with plates to sow sorghum seed. Furrow planting with either type of equipment places the seed in moist soil and reduces soil blowing but may result in reduced germination because of the colder soil or in furrow washing and the burying of the seed if heavy rains follow.

The normal row width is 36 to 44 in. In the drier regions, it is sometimes advantageous to space the rows double the ordinary distance apart to help ensure adequate moisture for the plants. If moisture is ample, the wider rows are at a marked disadvantage, from the standpoint of forage production. Grain yields are also likely to be lower, but this difference is not so marked.

Kaffir, hegari, and durra are usually sown so as to produce a plant every 4 to 6 in. in the row. The seeds must be dropped two or three times more thickly than this because field germination is rather low.

About 3 lb. of seed to the acre is required for 42-in. rows. If forage
production is intended, the rate should be 5 lb. an acre. Milo is
spaced 1 to 2 ft. apart in the row, a stand that can normally be expected
from planting about 2 lb. of seed. If conditions are favorable, milo
will stool out more to thicken the stand. Feterita is seeded at 3 to 4 lb.
an acre, plants every 6 to 12 in. in the row being a desirable stand.

The suitable planting depth for all grain-sorghum seed is 1 to 2 in.

Date of Planting.—Grain sorghums are warm-weather plants and
should not be planted until the soil is warm and the danger of frost is
past. The seeds are quite likely to mold or rot in a cold soil. Hence,

Fig. 84.—A field of Texas Blackhull kaffir ready for harvest. (*Courtesy of R. E. Karper,
Texas Agricultural Experiment Station.*)

sorghum-planting time is a week or two later than corn-planting time
for the same locality. Early-maturing sorghums may be planted
throughout June, but the later varieties must be got under way by May
15 in the northern part of the grain-sorghum territory in order to
mature before frost. The sorghums yield better if the planting date
is such that the grain heads out after rather than during the hottest
part of midsummer.

Seed Treatment.—The grain sorghums are susceptible to seed
rots and to kernel smuts. These can be prevented to a large extent by
treatment of the seed with copper carbonate or Ceresan, the latter an
organic mercury compound. Head smut which destroys the heads
completely is carried in the soil and is not controlled by seed treatment.

Harvest.—The seeds at the tip of grain-sorghum ripen first, and
the ripening process continues progressively down the heads. This

characteristic complicates the harvest by the cheapest method, the combine harvester. To be threshed, whether with a combine or otherwise, the seeds should contain not over 14 per cent moisture. Late heads on suckers further interfere with uniform ripening of a field. Hence, combine harvest is feasible only with uniformly and fully ripe grain of the dwarf, erect-growing varieties. Grain-drying equipment may be used to dry out a threshed or combined crop not fully down to a moisture content of 14 per cent.

FIG. 85.—Harvesting grain sorghum with a row binder. (*Courtesy of R. E. Karper, Texas Agricultural Experiment Station.*)

The most common method of harvest is to cut off the heads by hand, spread them on ricks to dry, and thresh them out with a properly adjusted grain thresher. The grain header is also used to cut off the heads which are gathered in wagons and spread out to dry as in hand heading. Where the fodder is to be saved for feed, the corn binder is used to cut the crop about the time the seeds are fully developed and have begun to harden. Curing is then completed in the shock. At threshing time the heads are cut off with a large knife, and only the heads are run through the thresher. Varieties like Double Dwarf and Wheatland milo may be harvested with a combine.

Grain sorghum may be harvested in immature condition and preserved in the silo, but the forage sorgos are better suited for this.

Use.—The grain sorghums are feed grains and, to a very large extent, are fed on the farms that produce them. Sometimes the sorghum, cut with a corn binder, is fed unthreshed as bundle feed. Thus both the grain and forage are utilized, and threshing expense is saved. The threshed grain of the different kinds of sorghum is all of about the same feeding value. Best results are secured if the grain is ground. Otherwise, much of it passes through the digestive tract of animals without being assimilated. The unground grain is best for poultry. Sheep can also use the whole grain effectively.

Ground sorghum grain is only slightly less valuable, pound for pound, than corn, for all classes of livestock. Moldy grain, however, may be dangerous, especially for horses.

Sorghum Poisoning.—Sorghums used for pasture occasionally develop prussic acid in dangerous quantities. The tendency for this to occur is greater than with Sudan grass, a sorghum relative (see page 138). Environmental conditions that retard the growth of the sorghum, leaving it wilted or stunted, are supposedly conducive to the development of the poisonous constituent, whereas conditions that produce normal, regular growth result in a very low and harmless prussic acid accumulation.

BROOMCORN

Broomcorn belongs to the sorghum group of plants, but its heads have long branches that form a brush. This brush, harvested as soon as it turns green, is cured and used for the making of brooms. The 1929–1938 annual average acreage was 332,000 and the yield 259 lb. of brush to the acre. Most of the crop is grown in Oklahoma and near-by southwestern states, but best yields are reported from the 30,000 to 40,000 acres annually produced in Illinois.

Culture of the crop up to harvest is the same as for corn or grain sorghum; but harvesting, threshing, and baling require special equipment and a great deal of hand labor. Where the crop is harvested at the proper stage for brooms, the seed, as a by-product, has little feed value; but mature broomcorn seed has about the same feeding value as oats.

RICE

To most Americans, rice is something to throw at brides and grooms and to eat, occasionally, as a boiled cereal, in a pudding, or as a base for chop suey. Most of them, even country people, have never seen the crop grown. To millions of Orientals, rice is a major food exceeding wheat in importance, though probably not of such ancient lineage.

India and Burma make up the leading rice-producing regions and grow over 80 million acres annually. Ten other warm-land countries grow 1 to 12 million acres each. The United States usually grows a little less than 1 million acres but the Philippine Islands, prior to 1942, produced 4 to 5 million acres a year.

The relative importance of the crop in different regions is further indicated by the annual per capita consumption which is 6 lb. in continental United States, over 200 lb. in India, China, Java, and the Philippines, and 300 to 400 lb. in Japan proper, Taiwan, and Thailand (Siam).[1]

Adaptation.—Rice is a warm-weather grass that requires an abundance of moisture in order to make its best growth. In fact, irrigating or flooding rice fields is almost the universal practice. In this country, Louisiana produces nearly half the crop. Louisiana, near-by parts of Texas along the Gulf, a low-lying area in eastern Arkansas, and the Sacramento and San Joaquin valleys of California produce essentially all of it. These regions provide warm growing weather, medium to heavy, moisture-retentive soils, and abundant water for flooding. The water may come from wells, the usual source in Arkansas; or it may be diverted or pumped from streams or bayous.

Rice Culture.—The seedbed for rice is prepared by the usual plowing and subsequent harrowing for weed control. Because rice soils must of necessity be rather impervious to moisture, they are subject to puddling if plowed or tilled when wet. The seed may be broadcast but is usually sown with a grain drill at 90 to 100 lb. an acre in southern states and somewhat more heavily in California, depending on the land and the tillering habits of the variety. The time of seeding is Apr. 1 to May 15 in the South, Apr. 15 to June 1 in California.

Irrigation.—When the rice plants are about 6 in. high, the land is flooded to a depth of 1 or 2 in. and the depth of water is gradually increased to about 5 in. Flooding is maintained for the remainder of the growing season, but the water is drained off prior to harvest to permit the use of harvesting machinery. Levees are necessary to control irrigation, but good drainage is also essential in order to get the water off and the land dry for tillage and harvest operations.

Harvest.—Because rice does not mature uniformly, harvesting with combines has been difficult. The customary method is to cut the crop with a binder when the kernels in the lower portion of the head are in the hard-dough stage and the upper kernels are fully ripe. Curing is completed in shocks of 8 to 10 bundles, and the grain is threshed when it is fully dry and hard. Separation of the grain from the straw is difficult when the bundles are damp.

Rough rice as it leaves the thresher is enclosed by the hull. This hull, much of the germ, and some of the starchy endosperm are removed in the milling and polishing of rice for the market. The

[1] JONES, J. W., J. M. JENKINS, R. H. WYCHE, and N. MARTIN, Rice Culture in the Southern States, *U.S. Dept. Agr. Farmers' Bul.* 1808, 1938.

milled rice is used for human consumption in various forms, the hulls for packing and insulating material, poultry bedding, etc., the bran and polish for livestock feed.

Rice Production and Soil Management.—Because of its unusual cultural requirements, rice does not fit well into the ordinary crop rotations. The most feasible procedure, and one widely practiced, is to grow rice on a given area for 1 or 2 years, then pasture the land a season or two before replanting it to rice. In California the trend in rice culture is to grow the crop on fallow or idle land in alternate years. At best, rice culture has a tendency to deplete the soil of its organic matter, a tendency more marked because of the high temperatures under which the crop is grown and the abundant moisture which favors the decomposition of the organic materials that are in the soil.

In California, experiments at the Biggs Rice Field Station[1] have indicated that the most effective fertilization there was an annual application of 150 to 200 lb. an acre of ammonium sulphate. Some of the southern rice fields respond to phosphatic fertilizers as well as to nitrogen, but conditions are so variable that local tests must be conducted to determine what kind of fertilizer should be used.

The 1929–1938 average acre yields for all states was 47.9 bu. an acre, California's crop averaging 68.2 bu. The season farm-price range for this period was 41.8 cents a bushel in 1932 to 83.4 cents in 1936.

BUCKWHEAT

Buckwheat pancakes used to be the favorite part of a winter breakfast for farmers, lumberjacks, woodcutters, and others who worked strenuously in the cold out-of-doors. But woe to the more sedentary urban worker who tried to make a meal of them, in accordance with his boyhood capacity back on the farm. "Buckwheat cakes are a rather heavy food for indoor workers" ranks among the leading understatements.

Apparently people do not work outdoors as much as they used to. This country usually grew over 800,000 acres of buckwheat a year for the 50 or 60 years prior to the First World War and had its record crop of a million acres in 1918. Since then, acreage has declined steadily. In 1939, only 374,000 acres were harvested.

Adaptation.—Buckwheat is a northern crop, New York and Pennsylvania supplying 60 per cent of the commercial acreage and no other state growing more than 5 per cent of the crop. Because of its

---

[1] DAVIS, L. L., and F. W. JONES, Fertilizer Experiments with Rice in California, *U.S. Dept. Agr. Tech. Bul.* **718**, 1940.

ability to utilize relatively unavailable forms of plant food, buckwheat grows on poor and rocky soils better than most other crops. Because it does not have to be planted until the last of June, buckwheat is often put in after other crops have failed. On the average, it yields about 15 bu. an acre; but yields of 25 or 30 bu. are common, and 50 or 60 bu. is occasionally secured when conditions are unusually favorable.

Kinds of Buckwheat.—Buckwheat is not one of the cereal grasses. Its different varieties are species of Fagopyrum. However, it is primarily a seed crop and is often classed with the cereals. Japanese buckwheat is a dark-brown seeded variety, the seeds being nearly triangular in cross section. Silverhull has smaller, silvery-gray seeds. Common buckwheat represents seed intermediate between Japanese and Silverhull as a result of natural cross-pollination between the two. Tartary is of a different species. Its seeds are much smaller than those of Japanese or Silverhull, more round in cross section, and usually pointed. It is inferior for flour making and so is used primarily for poultry feed. It seems to be even more capable of growing on unfavorable land than ordinary varieties.

The common, Japanese, and Silverhull buckwheat varieties are highly self-sterile. Cross-pollination is brought about to a major extent by bees, and these varieties make excellent bee pasture. The Tartary buckwheat, on the other hand, is self-fertile. For this reason, it is a more dependable seed producer when conditions are unfavorable to insect activity.

Buckwheat as a Green Manure.—As has been pointed out, buckwheat can use relatively unavailable plant nutrients. It also decays rapidly. Thus it is very valuable for plowing under to supply organic matter and plant nutrients in available form. Northern potato growers often use buckwheat for this purpose, disking it thoroughly or plowing it under just before the seeds begin to form. It adds nothing to the soil except organic matter, but its use as a green manure does have a stimulating effect on crops that follow it because of its release of the nutrients it has picked up.

When harvested, buckwheat tends to leave the soil less rather than more productive. It grows rapidly, has a great feeding capacity for mineral nutrients, especially phosphorus, and leaves very little to the soil in the way of root and stubble residue.

Other Uses.—Not only are the seeds of buckwheat used for making pancake flour, now usually blended with wheat flour to lighten it, but they are also used in making groats which may be prepared as porridge or used for thickening soups and gravies. The seeds are also used as poultry and livestock feed. The very rapid growth of buckwheat makes it one of the most effective crops for orchard cover and bee pasture or as a smother crop useful in weed control.

Culture.—There is nothing unusual about buckwheat culture. A clean, firm seedbed favors rapid germination and early growth. The crop may be planted as late as early July and should still mature before frost in most localities. The Tartary variety requires a longer growing season and should be planted 2 weeks earlier than other varieties. Three to four pecks of seed per acre is used. The seed crop is ready for harvest when most of the seeds are ripe; and it is usually cut with a binder, cured in the shock for about 2 weeks, and threshed with a grain thresher. Because it is often grown on rough, rocky land, cutting the crop with a cradle is still practiced in some localities. Occasionally, under conditions that favor uniform and complete ripening of the seed the combine harvester is used.

FLAX

Flax as grown in the United States today is primarily a seed crop. A small acreage of fiber flax is grown in Oregon and Michigan, but this acreage amounts to less than one-half of 1 per cent of the more than two million acres grown for seed.

North Dakota leads in flaxseed production, followed by Minnesota, South Dakota, and Montana. There are lesser acreages in several other middle-western and western states. In Montana, rainfall averages about 15 in. annually, whereas in the Dakotas and Minnesota it ranges from 18 in. in the western part of this area to 30 in. in the eastern part. Where annual rainfall is 25 to 30 in., the seed-flax varieties produce a fair quality of fiber suitable for industries that can use tow and waste; but under drier conditions the fiber is coarse, lacks uniformity, and has essentially no commercial value. Hence, seed is the only consideration in production. In California and Arizona, some seed flax is produced under irrigation at about double the yields secured elsewhere.

Uses of Flaxseed.—The chief reason for growing flaxseed is to get the oil, extracted from the seed by a heating and pressure process. Linseed oil is used in the manufacture of paints, varnishes, linoleum, oilcloth, printer's ink, imitation leather, and other industrial products. A bushel of flaxseed weighs 56 lb. and contains 30 to 40 per cent oil, or $2\frac{1}{4}$ to 3 gal. at $7\frac{1}{2}$ lb. per gallon. The U.S. Department of Agriculture uses the conversion factor of 1 gal. of oil from 0.4 bu. of flaxseed.

The residue left after the commercial extraction of the oil is linseed meal, a high-protein livestock feed that still contains 3 to 6 per cent oil. In certain extraction processes, most of this oil could be removed; but livestock feeders prefer linseed meal with the higher oil content because of its mildly laxative effect on the animals.   The protein content of linseed meal is above 30 per cent, the guaranteed analysis being specified for different lots.   It is used as a protein supplement to more carbonaceous feeds such as corn, oats, and barley.

Flaxseed as such is seldom fed directly because of the industrial value of the oil it contains.

Fig. 86.—A flaxseed crop in full bloom.   (*Courtesy of A. C. Arny, Minnesota Agricultural Experiment Station.*)

Culture.—The general culture of flaxseed is the same as for small grain in the same area.   Early seeding is advantageous from the standpoint of effective moisture utilization and getting the crop well advanced during the cooler weather of spring and early summer.   The young flax is not readily injured by late spring frosts.

Although flaxseed yields best if planted early, a wider range in planting dates is permissible than in the case of spring grains.   It can be sown in the Great Plains as late as the first week in June with the likelihood that it will mature a fair yield before frost.   It is most susceptible to frost injury in the green-boll stage when the seeds, with 50 to 75 per cent of moisture, are killed by freezing temperatures.

In California the general practice is to sow flaxseed in the fall.

A thin stand of flax is a poor competitor for weeds.   The control lies first in reducing the weeds by thoroughly tilling the land at intervals of 1 week to 10 days, prior to sowing the flax.   This gives the weed seeds a chance to sprout, then kills the sprouted seedlings.   After a clean, firm seedbed has been prepared, the seed is sown with a grain drill. Farmers in Minnesota and in similar humid areas and those who grow flaxseed under irrigation ordinarily sow at least 3 pk. an acre. In the drier areas, only 2 pk. are sown.

It is harvesttime when the flaxseed is fully ripe. Shattering of the seed is not a serious problem, and so harvest with a combine is generally feasible (see Chap. XVII).

Rotation.—The flaxseed crop yields best after corn; and because the culture of the crop is so nearly like that of the small grains, it follows corn conveniently. The flaxseed crop needs nitrogen; yet it has not yielded so well after legumes, especially after alfalfa or sweet clover, as it has after corn. In the drier localities, this may be attributed to the depletion of soil moisture by the deep-rooted legumes which are extravagant in moisture use. Grass crops like timothy and orchard grass tend to leave the soil too loose for a following flax crop, and they also are likely to have exhausted the quickly available nitrogen. On the other hand, this crop does well after a well-rotted prairie sod; but following small grains or another flaxseed crop it is intermediate in productivity.

Diseases.—Flax wilt once threatened to wipe out the flaxseed industry in the Northwest. Virgin fields grew the crop well; then the soils became flax-sick, and in the course of four or five croppings the flax wilted and, in many cases, produced nothing at all.

Wilt is caused by a fungus that attacks flax plants at all stages. It is carried on the seed and lives in the soil for an indefinite period. As with so many other crop diseases, plant breeding provided the effective remedy. Dr. H. L. Bolley, of the North Dakota Agricultural Experiment Station, developed the Bison variety by selecting for wilt resistance and high seed yield. Since then, Buda, Linota, and Redwing have been added to the list of wilt-resisting varieties. Bison, Buda, and Redwing are also resistant to rust, another flax ailment. Some strains of Argentine flax developed by the U.S. Department of Agriculture and the Minnesota Agricultural Experiment Station have appeared to be immune from rust.

Flax-Wheat Mixtures.—The practice of growing flax in mixture with spring wheat has attained some importance, especially in Minnesota. The mixture is more easily handled in harvesting and threshing, results in better weed control, and gives a slightly greater acre return. The mixture is seeded with 2 or 3 pk. of wheat to 25 to 40 lb. of flaxseed. Light wheat seeding is necessary, or the flaxseed yield will be low. The seeds are separated by screening with an ordinary fanning mill.

Flax Returns.—Flaxseed like wheat is almost entirely a cash crop. In the area of greatest production, it competes favorably with spring wheat in acre returns. Costs of production on an acre basis are not much greater in the case of flaxseed, and the acre income has been consistently a little higher. The average comparisons for the five years 1935–1939 for Minnesota and North Dakota are as follows:

Locality	Average acre income	
	Flaxseed	Spring wheat
Minnesota........................	$14.66	$11.35
North Dakota.....................	7.53	6.38

According to the 1935 agricultural census the average flaxseed grower in Minnesota harvested 19 acres, but operations were on a more extensive scale in North Dakota where the average acreage per grower was 35.

Fiber Flax.—In colonial days, fiber flax was grown in nearly all the northern colonies. Many homes had small looms for weaving the homespun yarns. At one time, several thousand acres of the crop were grown in the Thumb district of eastern Michigan. In 1940, less than 500 acres were harvested. Fiber flax could not compete industrially with cotton after the invention of the cotton gin, and its demand for hand labor caused the drastic curtailment of the younger Michigan industry. At present, the largest acreage is in Oregon. The best grades of flax fiber suitable for fine linens are produced by skilled hand laborers of Europe. The machine methods of production that have been developed thus far have eliminated much of the hand labor and have resulted in good but not the best grades of fiber.

The fiber-flax plant requires a fertile soil, cool weather, abundant moisture, and a fair-weather harvest period. Long-stemmed varieties sparsely branched are necessary, for the usable fiber is found in the stems from the ground to the lowest branches. The best grades of fiber come from hand-pulled crops. Machine pulling is still in the developmental stage, though it has generally replaced hand pulling in this country except for cheaper grades of fiber for which the crop is cut with a special mower.

The entire straw cannot be put through a thresher without spoiling the fiber, and so special equipment to thresh the heads only is necessary. The fiber is separated from the straw after a *retting* process which dissolves the gums in the plant that bind the fiber to the woody tissue. In dew retting, the flax is spread out to be wetted by dew which stimulates the development of bacteria and molds causing the retting action. Water retting of flax is accomplished by immersing the flax straw in water for 6 to 8 days at a temperature of about 80°F. Chemical retting has been tried, but it is not yet used commercially in this country.

After being retted, the flax is put through a breaking process to loosen the woody portions of the straw from the fiber. Scutching machines beat off the woody tissue and separate it from the long, unbroken fiber.

B. B. Robinson gives the yield of fiber flax in its different stages as produced in the United States as follows:

Pulled flax in bundles, unthreshed, as sold by grower, 1 to 3½ tons per acre, average about 1¾ tons.

Threshed flax, before it is retted, after losing 20 to 35 per cent in weight as seeds and chaff, about 1¼ tons.

Retted straw, after it has been dried and has lost about 16 per cent in retting, 1 ton.

Scutched fiber, including tow, after losing about 80 per cent in scutching, 400 lb.

Seed, varying from 5 to 10 bu. per acre, averaging about 7½ bu.[1]

In producing upholstery "tow," the unretted straw is merely crushed to separate the fiber from the wood. This tow is used in upholstered furniture, car seats, and automobile cushions.

EMMER AND SPELT

Emmer and spelt are types of wheat both commonly confused under the name *speltz*. Their kernels are enclosed in a heavy chaff that is not removed in threshing. They are feed grains comparable in value with oats. Because of their hardness, they must be ground before being fed.

In the case of emmer, spring varieties are most useful, the Vernal and Khalpi varieties being highly resistant to stem rust. Although emmer is grown in the Dakotas, Minnesota, and near-by areas, it has not attained the popularity of oats or barley because it is generally lower in productivity. Winter varieties of emmer have not attained any commercial importance in this country.

Interest in the winter varieties of spelt was increased by the wheat-allotment program of the Agricultural Adjustment Administration. Many farmers took up its culture as a feed crop in partial replacement of their reduced wheat acreage. In sections where spring oats and barley often are at a disadvantage because of warm weather, the earlier maturing winter spelt has proved more productive. This advantage

[1] Robinson, B. B., Flax-fiber Production, *U.S. Dept. Agr. Farmers' Bul.* 1728, revised July, 1940.

has been evident in Maryland and Virginia, and it has been noted as far north as southwestern Michigan. In Michigan, however, wheat has produced somewhat more feed to the acre than spelt, and in the event that restrictive measures controlling wheat production are removed the acreage of spelt would be likely to diminish.

Emmer, in the Northwest, is seeded at 6 to 8 pk. an acre whereas spelt, grown in the more humid East, is usually sown at 8 to 12 pk. an acre. Their general culture is the same as that of the more widely grown spring and winter grains of the same localities.

Review Problems

1. The advantages of the grain sorghums over corn for certain areas lies in their

  a. Greater feeding value.
  b. Resistance to frost.
  c. More economical culture and harvest.
  d. Greater resistance to heat and drought.

2. Which one of the following varieties is not classed as a grain sorghum?

  a. Early Amber.
  b. Milo.
  c. Feterita.
  d. Hegari.
  e. Kaffir.

3. Other crops often do poorly immediately after land has grown grain sorghum probably because of all but one of the following reasons:

  a. Sorghums grow until frost and hence leave the soil depleted in moisture and readily available plant nutrients.
  b. The decay of sorghum roots and stubble by soil organisms brings a temporary tie-up of available nitrogen which is being used by these organisms.
  c. The sorghum plant contains a much higher percentage of nitrogen than corn.
  d. The soil after a sorghum crop is often lumpy and in poor physical condition.

4. The chief advantage of starting seed bed preparation for sorghum by listing rather than plowing is

  a. Weeds are controlled more effectively.
  b. Grain yields are usually higher.
  c. Listing is less expensive.

5. The proper time to plant grain sorghum is

  a. As soon as the land can be worked in the spring.
  b. Just before corn-planting time.
  c. The same as for corn.
  d. A week or two after normal corn-planting time.

6. With respect to width of row for grain sorghums, which one of the following statements is false?

    a. The normal row width is 36 to 44 in.
    b. Double this distance is sometimes used.
    c. The wider rows are more likely to produce grain in seasons of extreme drought.
    d. If moisture is ample, grain yields are likely to suffer more from wide spacing than forage yields.

7. Sorghum poisoning may result from the occasional development in wilted or stunted plants of

    a. Coumarin.
    b. Arsenic.
    c. Selenium.
    d. Hydrocyanic acid.

8. Broomcorn is produced most extensively in

    a. Oklahoma.
    b. Illinois.
    c. Texas.
    d. California.

9. All but one of the following estimates of pre-Second World War annual per capita rice consumption are reasonably accurate.

    a. Philippine Islands—200 lb.
    b. China—200 lb.
    c. Japan—350 lb.
    d. Continental United States—100 lb.

10. The harvest of rice with combines is difficult primarily because

    a. The land on which the crop is grown is too rolling.
    b. Riceland at harvesttime is too wet for the use of machinery.
    c. Combines cannot thresh the grain clean.
    d. Rice does not mature uniformly.

11. One of the most effective crop sequences for rice growing is

    a. Continuous rice culture.
    b. Rice 2 years and pasture 2 or 3 years.
    c. Rice, corn, wheat, clover.
    d. Rice, grain sorghum, wheat, alfalfa.

12. The two states leading in buckwheat production are

    a. New York and Pennsylvania.
    b. Michigan and Wisconsin.
    c. North Dakota and South Dakota.
    d. Iowa and Illinois.

13. Which one of the following statements with respect to buckwheat is false?

    a. The flowers of Japanese and Silverhull buckwheat are normally self-sterile whereas flowers of Tartary buckwheat are self-fertile.

    b. Buckwheat is unusually efficient in its use of mineral plant foods, especially phosphorus.

    c. Harvested buckwheat leaves a large proportion of organic growth in the way of roots and stubble in the soil, thus bringing about substantial soil improvement.

    d. Buckwheat, plowed under, is one of the more effective nonleguminous green-manure crops.

14. In the region where most of the United States crop of flaxseed is produced, the climate may be described as

    a. So dry irrigation is usually practiced.

    b. Arid to moderately humid, with hot summers.

    c. Cool, with abundant rainfall.

    d. Warm and humid.

15. A bushel of flaxseed weighs 56 lb. and contains

    a. 5 to 10 per cent oil.

    b. 10 to 20 per cent oil.

    c. 20 to 30 per cent oil.

    d. 30 to 40 per cent oil.

16. Flax is important in the United States chiefly because of

    a. The oil content of its seeds.

    b. It is a high-protein feed for livestock.

    c. The use of its fiber for making fine linens.

    d. Its straw, which is used for upholstery tow.

17. A North Dakota grower of both flaxseed and spring wheat wisely sows his spring wheat first because

    a. Young flax is readily injured by spring frosts.

    b. Flaxseed has a wider range of effective seeding dates than spring wheat.

    c. Flaxseed acre returns are normally less valuable.

    d. Larger flaxseed yields result from the later seedings.

18. Flaxseed is likely to yield best if preceded in the rotation by

    a. Timothy.

    b. Small grain.

    c. Alfalfa or sweet clover.

    d. Corn.

19. Flax wilt which once threatened to wipe out the flaxseed industry in the United States was successfully checked by

    a. Growing the flaxseed only on new land.

    b. The breeding of wilt-resistant varieties.

    c. Growing flaxseed in a crop rotation.

    d. Dusting the crop with suitable chemicals.

References

DILLMAN, A. C., and L. G. GOAR: Flaxseed Production in the Far Western States, *U.S. Dept. Agr. Farmers' Bul.* 1793, 1937.

——— and T. E. STOA: Flaxseed Production in the North Central States, *U.S. Dept. Agr. Farmers' Bul.* 1747, 1935.

JONES, J. W.: How to Grow Rice in the Sacramento Valley, *U.S. Dept. Agr. Farmers' Bul.* 1240, 1924.

———, J. M. JENKINS, R. H. WYCHE, and M. NELSON: Rice Culture in the Southern States, *U.S. Dept. Agr. Farmers' Bul.* 1808, 1938.

MARTIN, J. H., and E. C. LEIGHTY: Emmer and Spelt, *U.S. Dept. Agr. Farmers' Bul.* 1429, 1924.

——— and R. S. WASHBURN: Broomcorn Growing and Handling, *U.S. Dept. Agr. Farmers' Bul.* 1631, 1930.

———, J. S. COLE, and A. T. SEMPLE: Growing and Feeding Grain Sorghums, *U.S. Dept. Agr. Farmers' Bul.* 1764, 1936.

QUISENBERRY, K. S., and J. W. TAYLOR: Growing Buckwheat, *U.S. Dept. Agr. Farmers' Bul.* 1835, 1939.

ROBINSON, B. B.: Flax-fiber Production, *U.S. Dept. Agr. Farmers' Bul.* 1728, revised July, 1940.

WHITE, J. W., F. J. HOLBEN, and A. C. RICHER: Experiments with Buckwheat, *Pa. Agr. Expt. Sta. Bul.* 403, 1941.

CHAPTER XVII

SMALL-GRAIN AND -SEED HARVEST

Ruth was a gleaner. She gathered the scattered wisps of ripened grain left by the reapers. Boaz, whom she married, was a reaper. Reapers cut the grain with sickles and bound it into sheaves with bands of straw. The ancestors of Ruth and Boaz had harvested grain after this fashion for many generations. The years since then have been numbered in thousands, and yet these methods are still the rule in many lands.

The Harvest Revolution.—In an earlier day, three quarters of the American people were farmers. Only by the hardest kind of hand labor were they able to feed and clothe themselves and also provide subsistence for the one quarter who lived in towns and cities. As recently as 1870, one-half of all workers in the United States were engaged in agriculture. By 1930 the proportion of agricultural workers had decreased to one-fifth. During this same period the average agricultural production per capita of all people in the United States increased 22 per cent. Not only have those engaged in agriculture in the United States been supplying food and fiber to more people, but they have actually increased the average amount of agricultural products per capita of total population.[1]

The vast changes in the technology of American agriculture have touched every phase of production. But on none of the practices have they had a more profound influence than on those pertaining to harvest. Not only did Whitney's cotton gin change the agriculture of the South, but it materially influenced its whole economic and social environment. Mechanized haying equipment has changed hay harvest from a hand to a machine job. Mechanical potato diggers have replaced the fork and hoe and have helped make potato growing more of a field rather than a garden enterprise. Corn pickers are replacing many expert hand laborers. The cotton stripper and the sugar-beet topper are currently in the process of development.

[1] KIFER, R. S., B. H. HURT, and A. A. THORNBROUGH, The Influence of Technical Progress on Agricultural Production, "Farmers in a Changing World," *U.S. Dept. Agr. Yearbook of Agriculture*, Superintendent of Documents, Government Printing Office, Washington, D. C., 1940.

Our concern here, however, is with grain and seed harvest which began to change fundamentally when the cradle proved to be a more efficient tool than the hand sickle. At the dedication of Michigan's Agricultural College, established in 1854 as the first of its kind, Governor Bingham, of that state, spoke with pride of "the light and easy cradle, the handsomely turned three-tined pitchfork, the light bright hoe and handy rake" that made possible "four times the labor and four times the production" that could be achieved with the rude implements of an older day.

FIG. 87.—Harvesting fully matured wheat with a combine. (*Courtesy of E. E. Patton.*)

Strange as it may seem, a combine had already been invented in Governor Bingham's own state; in 1837, this Moore-Hascall machine harvested and threshed 20 acres of Michigan grain. But the immediate change in grain harvest was not to be effected by the combine. Six years earlier, McCormick's reaper had been tried in Virginia. Skeptics scorned it as an ill-appearing cross between a windmill and a sailboat. Still its development continued and this machine together with the thresher opened up the vast western prairies and plains to grain growing.

Moore and Hascall's combine, rebuilt in 1844, was shipped around the Horn to California where, in 1854, it harvested 600 acres of wheat.[1] Combines and headers were developed and used in the West; but not

[1] ELWOOD, R. B., L. E. ARNOLD, D. C. SCHMUTZ, and E. G. McKIBBEN, Changes in Technology and Labor Requirements in Crop Production: Wheat and Oats, *WPA Natl. Res. Proj. Rpt.* A10, 1939.

until 1918, when smaller machines mounting internal-combustion auxiliary engines were introduced in Kansas and Oklahoma, did these machines begin to assert a major influence on grain harvest. Rapid acceptance of the smaller combines with less than a 10-ft. cut began in 1930. In 1939, it was estimated that about 110,000 combines were in use and that they harvested something over 50 per cent of the country's wheat crop.

Although the binder and the combine would appear to answer almost every small-grain-harvest requirement in these modern United States, it is of interest to note that the production of 58,000 grain cradles and over 8,000 reapers was reported to the U.S. Bureau of the Census for 1919. In 1920 the domestic sale of these reapers was over 50 per cent of that of either headers or combines, the persistent use in some areas of the older types of equipment being thus indicated.[1]

Significance of Changes.—In the days of the cradle swingers, two good men could cut and bind about 2½ acres of grain a day. They were doubtless long days. A 6-ft. binder, drawn by three horses, will readily cut and bind 10 acres a day. In both instances, shocking, hauling, in some cases mow storage or stacking, and finally threshing are additional operations. The combine, run by a crew of two or three men, cuts, threshes, and often bags the grain in one continuous operation. A combine of the smaller type with its normal crew of 2, harvesting 10 acres a day, does about the work of 28 men in the days of the cradle, hand rake, and flail. The larger combines with their much greater capacity displace the old-time labors of many more men. The fundamental change, of course, is not so great; for in the scene behind the production of the tractor and combine are miners of coal and iron, drillers for oil, the factory workers who make machinery, the salesmen who distribute it, the mechanics who service it, and many others. However, much of the labor saved through the displacement of binders, headers, and stationary threshing machines by combines is net; for these, too, represent the output of industry with similar labor requirements for their manufacture and distribution. Combines reduce the labor of small-grain harvest by an average of about 3.5 man-hours an acre, as compared with binders and threshers, and of 2.5 man-hours where headers rather than binders are displaced. The work of 90,000 combines results in a probable decrease in farm labor of 108 million man-hours.[1]

To the individual farmer the combine has meant a substantial decrease in grain-harvesting costs and a great convenience to his wife who had the threshing-time burden of housing and feeding the hungry

[1] Ibia.

extra crew.   Combine harvest has not been without its disadvantages, many of them agronomic in character, which are discussed later.

Harvesttime.—When grain heads are golden yellow, when the straw has lost its last greenish tinge, when the kernels have passed from the dough stage into a harder condition, it is harvesttime.   At least, it used to be, for a thousand years, when grain was cut with a sickle, a cradle, a reaper, or a binder.   It is not harvesttime, with a combine, until the grain is not only hard but also dry.

The harvest of grain before it has reached full maturity means a sacrifice of yield with no advantage as to quality.   As early as 1882, R. C. Kedzie[1] studied the changes in yield and composition of wheat during the ripening period and found a continual increase in yield from the time the kernels first began to form until they were entirely ripe, but no further increase as the grain advanced to the hard dead-ripe stage.   It has sometimes been contended that wheat cut when slightly green is superior in milling and baking properties, but extensive data secured by T. A. Kiesselbach[2] did not support this contention.   It is easy to lose 2 or 3 bu. an acre of potential grain growth by starting the binder out in a grainfield a few days too soon.

Where combines are used, yield losses may result from delayed harvest.   When grain has attained its full development and growth of the kernels ceases, it probably contains in the neighborhood of 25 per cent moisture.[3]   In Iowa experiments,[4] there was some variation in moisture content when the different varieties attained their peak yields. The general conclusion may be drawn that, at the first date of maximum kernel development, grain is ready to be cut with a binder but still contains far too much moisture to be harvested with a combine.

When grain is down to about 14 per cent moisture, it is ready for threshing whether with a combine or otherwise.   To reach this moisture content in the case of standing grain entails a wait of 4 or 5 days beyond normal binder harvest in regions of very low relative humidity and of 7 to 10 days or even longer in humid regions where rains are frequent during the harvest period.

This delay in starting harvest almost always results in some grain losses due to damage by birds, shattering, and breaking off of heads in

---

[1] KEDZIE, R. C., The Ripening of Wheat, *Mich. State Bd. Agr. Rpt.*, Vol. 1, pp. 233–239, 1882.

[2] KIESSELBACH, T. A., Winter Wheat Investigations, *Nebr. Agr. Expt. Sta. Res. Bul.* 31, 1924.

[3] RATHER, H. C., Influence of Delayed Harvest on Certain Varieties of Oats and Barley in Michigan, *Mich. Agr. Expt. Sta. Quart. Bul.*, Vol. 19, No. 4, 1937.

[4] BURNETT, L. C., and A. L. BAKKE, The Effect of Delayed Harvest upon the Yield of Grain, *Iowa Agr. Expt. Sta. Res. Bul.* 130, 1930.

the case of brittle strawed varieties like Oderbrucker barley. The delay also increases weather risks; and thus severe windstorms, rain, or hail may greatly increase such losses.

Of the major small grains, losses in yield due to delayed harvest are least likely with wheat, the grain most suitable for combine harvest, and are usually greatest with oats. With weather conditions favorable, wheat losses by the time the grain is first down to 14 per cent moisture should be slight. An oat or barley loss of 2 or 3 bu. an acre at this stage would not be unusual. In cases where the delay in harvest has been unduly prolonged, barley losses of 7 bu. and oat losses of over 12 bu. an acre have been reported.[1] Varieties as well as crops differ in their susceptibility to such losses.

Special Combine-harvest Problems.—One problem peculiar to combine harvest is the tendency for combine operators to "beat the gun" and start harvest before the grain is dry enough. It is particularly hard for the custom operator of a combine to wait when the financial success of his enterprise depends on harvesting as many acres of the neighborhood grain crop as possible. Not only is the combine frequently started too soon in a given crop, but often it is run too early of a dewy morning and too late in the evening when the moisture of a humid day condenses on the grain. An excess of either internal or external moisture is potentially damaging to grain quality.

Sometimes excess moisture is neither in nor on the grain itself. It comes from green weed seeds or the green leaves of a vigorous seeding made with the grain. Sweet-clover seedings are most often troublesome in this respect.

Losses in Test Weight.—A prolonged delay in the harvest of small grain also is accompanied by a decrease in test weight. This is most marked during rainy periods. The wetted grain expands and, on drying, fails to shrink back to its original size. Losses in test weight of as much as 5 or 6 lb. per bushel have been suffered during a prolonged delay in harvest as the result of wet weather. But usually this loss is not nearly so severe; and, with favorable weather, it should be possible to combine the grain before test-weight changes become significant.

The mere loss in test weight of wheat, due to delayed harvest, does not necessarily impair flour quality although it does reduce the flour yield per bushel and may lower the market grade of the wheat. In Michigan trials,[2] delayed harvest did not result in changes in the protein content of wheat but the later harvested wheat produced slightly

[1] RATHER, *op. cit.*

[2] BROWN, G. C., Some Effects of Time of Harvest on the Yield and Quality of Wheat, *Mich. Agr. Expt. Sta. Quart. Bul.*, Vol. 18, No. 2, 1935.

larger loaves of bread owing, apparently, to a strengthening of the gluten.

Windrowing Grain.—Although it is usually feasible to combine wheat directly from the standing crop, especially in the drier regions, it is often advantageous to windrow crops like oats, barley, clover and alfalfa seed, buckwheat, and field beans and later thresh them with a combine having an attachment that will pick the crop up out of the windrow. The windrowing of grain may be done with a special windrowing machine or with an old binder with the knotter, or tying

FIG. 88.—Windrowed oats cured on the long stubble, then combined. This procedure saves yield and quality as compared with combining the standing grain. (*Courtesy of E. E. Patton.*)

mechanism removed. Grass- and legume-seed crops are windrowed with special mower attachments or sometimes with a side-delivery rake. Grain windrowed on a high stubble dries rapidly, green weed seeds and green leaves shrivel and are cleaned out during threshing, and grain of uneven maturity tends toward a safe, uniform moisture content. Windrowing adds an extra harvest operation, but at the moderate cost of $0.50 to $1 an acre it is a practice well warranted in the case of crops having a short period during which they can safely be combined. With crops normally of uneven maturity, prewindrowing provides about the only means by which the laborsaving combine can be used.

Saving the Straw.—Livestock farmers in northern states or wherever animals are stabled use straw for bedding. To them, straw provides one of the important reasons for growing grain. It has feeding value, too. There is not much milk or many pounds of gain in a ton of straw. It is low in protein, starch, and fat, low in minerals, low in vitamins, and high in indigestible fiber. Still, straw is valuable for idle work animals and for overwintering breeding beef cows. Animals with free access to a strawstack eat from it freely, especially in cold weather, and they also consume such grain as may have gone through the thresher with the straw. Oat straw is more highly regarded as a feed than that from other grains.

Straw also is used industrially for paper pulp and other cellulose products. Because straw is generally low-priced and somewhat

FIG. 89.—Gathering straw with a pick-up baler following the combining of wheat.

difficult to dispose of, some farmers burn their strawstacks. This is wasteful of organic matter that should be returned to the soil. Straw decomposes slowly; but upon its return to the land, if it is supplemented with nitrogen, decomposition can be hastened and beneficial results secured sooner.

Combine users can spread the straw thinly over the field or leave it in windrows to be picked up later for use as feed or bedding. One of the combine harvester's disadvantages is the necessity for gathering the straw afterward if it is needed. Even with this added job, combine harvest where feasible is still cheaper than binder harvest.

Shocking Bound Grain.—Where grain is cut with a binder, further drying out is necessary before it is ready for threshing. Long shocks consisting of two rows of sheaves set together dry out most rapidly and are desirable for material of uneven maturity or anything containing considerable moisture. Round shocks capped with spread-out sheaves, however, are better at shedding rain. These usually contain 8 to 12 sheaves, 2 more being used to cap the shock.

Lodging in Small Grains.—When the straw of small grains lodges, harvest difficulties are increased. Combines can handle lodged grain to somewhat better advantage than can binders. Nevertheless, lodging entails losses, some of which are primarily harvest losses but others of which may affect yield and quality without respect to harvest practice.

Lodging is primarily a rich-soil problem. Lands that have been so managed as to maintain a high state of productivity for such crops as

Fig. 90.—Harvesting a field of dwarf grain sorghum with a two-row combine harvester. (*Courtesy of R. E. Karper, Texas Agricultural Experiment Station.*)

corn, potatoes, sugar beets, soybeans, and field beans tend to produce small grains with excessive straw growth and weaker straw. This is particularly true if an abundance of nitrogen is available and the weather is wet. If lodging takes place when the grain is in an early stage of development, shriveled, shrunken kernels of light test weight are produced. The losses are largely mechanical in grain that has fully matured before it goes down owing to the difficulty of picking up lodged grain with machinery.

If storms are unusually severe, no grain can withstand their impact. Some storms blow down trees and houses. However, there is opportunity for the practice of measures that will reduce lodging due to factors other than such mechanical forces as violent winds, rain, and hail.

According to work by Welton and Morris[1] in Ohio, small grain is more susceptible to lodging if there is a low content of dry matter per

[1] WELTON, F. A., and V. H. MORRIS, Lodging in Oats and Wheat, *Ohio Agr. Expt. Sta. Bul.* 471, 1931.

unit length of culm. Slender, weak stems are produced where the stand is too thick or through a setting up within the plant of a low carbohydrate-nitrogen relationship such as may result from shading or from an excess of available nitrogen in the soil. Environmental conditions that tend to produce a large proportion of straw in relation to grain have proved particularly conducive to lodging.

Very often, farmers having a fertile soil believe that they should sow more grain seed to the acre because their land will support more plants. These heavier rates of seeding, however, tend to produce dense stands of weaker stemmed plants more likely to lodge. Clipping or pasturing young grain plants reduces straw growth and lodging; but, more often than otherwise, it also reduces grain yields.

F<small>IG</small>. 91.—The preceding crop influences lodging. Right, oats after field beans; left, oats after sugar beets. (*Courtesy of E. E. Patton.*)

The crop preceding small grain in the rotation has its influence on lodging. Small grains that follow sugar beets or corn are less likely to lodge than if they follow field beans or soybeans. Lodging is very likely when the crop preceding the small grain is a good stand of clover or alfalfa. In some cases, straw is strengthened slightly by applications of phosphorus or potash to balance the excess of available nitrogen in rich soils.

Probably the most practicable remedy for lodging is the growing of stiffer strawed grain. Varieties differ greatly in their susceptibility to lodging, and stiff-strawed varieties should be grown where lodging is a problem. Early maturity may help, too, for early maturing varieties escape some of the weather hazards that might cause the crop to lodge.

Storage of Threshed Grain.—If small grain contains too much moisture when it is threshed, the heat generated by its excessive respiration or by mold growth will cause it to spoil in storage. To be safe for storage, it ought to contain not more than about 14 per cent moisture. Market grain containing a little in excess of 13.5 to 14.5 per cent moisture, the amount depending on the kind of grain, is designated as *tough* according to the official grain standards.[1]

If the small grain in a storage bin is dry, respiration is slight and very little heat is developed. However, when excessive heat is generated by mold growth and the active respiration of wet grain, such heat can be dissipated only with much difficulty because the grain itself is effective as insulation. According to work done by C. F. Kelly of the U.S. Department of Agriculture,[2] at the center of bins of 1,000 bu. capacity and 14 ft. in diameter, wheat temperature may lag 1 or 2 months behind air temperature. Even in the metal bins studied, the daily fluctuation of temperature was very slight at a distance 1 ft. from the wall; and, at a mere 6 in. from the south wall, fluctuation amounted to only about 5°F. for each 20° change in bin-wall temperature.

Insulated bins reduce the influence of outside temperatures; but, should the grain generate heat of its own accord, insulation will slow down dissipation of this excess heat. Large storage bins require some kind of bin ventilation to dissipate effectively such heat as may be spontaneously generated. In small bins or shallow bins, additional ventilating facilities are less essential. However, even relatively small high-moisture spots in a large bin are potential centers for the development of heat damage despite a comparatively low average moisture content for the whole bin of grain. Once wet grain starts to heat in the bin, it must be removed, cooled, and dried to prevent serious losses. In larger granaries, it is a decided convenience to have mechanical facilities for moving the grain from one bin to another.

Storage Insects.—Not only do insects that attack stored grain cause direct damage, but their activity on a large scale also results in a rise in temperature of the grain. Several kinds of weevils and moths are capable of living on whole grain. Important examples are the granary weevil, which confines its attacks to stored grain, and the Angoumois grain moth, which is destructive of grain in storage but may also attack grain in the field.

[1] See *Handbook of Official Grain Standards of the United States* for exact moisture tolerances.

[2] KELLY, C. F., Temperature of Wheat in Experimental Farm-type Storages, *U.S. Dept. Agr. Cir.* 587, 1941.

Prolonged high temperatures (130°F. for 6 to 12 hours) or extreme cold may destroy stored-grain insects, but the practicable procedure for farm storage is fumigation. Carbon disulphide, once widely used for this purpose, is dangerous because of its ready inflammability. Very effective fumigants that do not carry this fire hazard have been devised. A very high percentage of farm bins are not sufficiently airtight for any fumigant to be fully effective. Fumigants work best at temperatures above 70°F., and treatment must be repeated to kill such larvae as may hatch out after the first treatment. Hydrocyanic acid gas is a very effective fumigant. This gas is extremely poisonous and should be applied only by professionals.

Review Problems

1. From the following, which statement is true of the quantity of agricultural production per capita of total population during the period 1870–1930?

    a. It fell off 15 per cent.
    b. It increased 22 per cent.
    c. It did not change materially.
    d. It more than doubled.

2. The first harvest of grain in the United States with a combined harvester thresher took place

    a. In Michigan in 1837.
    b. In California in 1854.
    c. In Montana in 1910.
    d. In Kansas in 1918.

3. Which one of these statements with respect to harvest of grain with a combine is false?

    a. The grain must be drier than is necessary for the beginning of binder harvest.
    b. Saving of the straw is more difficult.
    c. Larger yields are harvested.
    d. A material saving of labor is effected.

4. Grain is not dry enough for safe storage until its moisture content is down to

    a. 40 per cent.
    b. 33 per cent.
    c. 25 per cent.
    d. 18 per cent.
    e. 14 per cent.

5. Oats would be most likely to lodge if immediately preceded by which of the following crops?

    a. Alfalfa.
    b. Corn.

c. Timothy.
d. Sugar beets.
e. Oats.

6. A cultural practice that tends to reduce the lodging of small grains is

a. Plowing rather than just disking the seedbed.
b. Sowing more seed to the acre.
c. Sowing less seed to the acre.
d. Sowing the seed earlier.
e. Application of a nitrogenous fertilizer.

7. Indicate the false one of the following statements concerning grain in storage:

a. The temperature of the grain in the bin fluctuates rapidly with changes in outside-air temperature.
b. Small wet spots of grain are potential centers of damage even though the average moisture content of the bin of grain is low.
c. The activity of grain weevils tends to cause an increase in the temperature of stored grain.
d. Some respiration continues even in cool, dry grain.

8. The proper time to start binder harvest of small grain is

a. A few days before the grain is fully mature.
b. When the grain is in the soft-dough stage.
c. When the grain is fully developed and somewhat beyond the hard-dough stage.
d. When the grain is dead ripe, dry, and hard.

9. For a grainfield containing many green weeds and of uneven maturity,

a. Binder harvest only is feasible.
b. No loss is entailed by delaying harvest until all grain and weeds are ripe and then combining the uncut crop.
c. The grain may be combined safely when three-quarters of the crop is dry.
d. The use of the combine is practical if preceded by a windrower and the grain is allowed to dry out in the windrow.

References

BURNETT, L. C., and A. L. BAKKE: The Effect of Delayed Harvest upon Yield of Grain, *Iowa Expt. Sta. Res. Bull.* 130, 1930.

CARLETON, M. A.: "The Small Grains," The Macmillan Company, New York, 1924.

ELWOOD, R. B., L. E. ARNOLD, D. C. SCHMUTZ, and E. G. McKIBBEN: Changes in Technology and Labor Requirements in Crop Production: Wheat and Oats, *WPA Natl. Res. Proj. Rpt.* A10, 1939.

KELLY, C. F.: Temperature of Wheat in Experimental Farm-type Storages, *U.S. Dept. Cir.* 587, 1941.

WELTON, F. A., and V. H. MORRIS: Lodging in Oats and Wheat, *Ohio Agr. Expt. Sta. Bul.* 471, 1931.

CHAPTER XVIII

LARGE-SEEDED LEGUMES

The culture of certain large-seeded legumes for their seed is of importance in the United States. The soybean crop, ancient in oriental agriculture but new in importance in this country, has taken the lead among these crops; field beans, peanuts, and cowpeas occupy fairly comparable acreages each year, and field peas are grown to a much more limited extent, their production being confined to cooler areas. In recent years another large-seeded legume, the velvet bean, has increased in importance in the southeastern states.

Of these crops, all but field beans are of some importance as forage crops, this use having already been discussed in Chap. VIII. These legumes are also utilized for soil improvement, an effective procedure if the whole plant is plowed under. On the other hand, their mere inclusion in a crop rotation may not improve or even maintain soil productivity if the crop is harvested. They are often grown as row crops, the better to control weeds. Such interrow tillage stimulates the decomposition of organic matter and the consequent loss of nitrogen through leaching. The proportion of tops to roots is large, and they leave little residue in the field. In the case of field beans a substantial portion of root growth is removed with the tops at harvesttime. Land growing row crops is also more subject to erosion.

As a cash crop the field bean is most remunerative, but its production is necessarily limited to the restricted areas to which the different varieties are adapted. The soybean is useful for food, as livestock feed, and industrially. The peanut and the cowpea have helped diversify the source of income in the cotton country. The cowpea has been especially useful in the South for soil-improvement purposes.

SOYBEANS

The increase of soybean acreage in the United States during the 1930's was phenomenal. In oriental countries, notably China and Japan, this legume has been important as a food crop since long before the time of recorded history. In the United States, soybeans first attained some importance about 1880. Their first culture here was

333

largely for forage; as late as 1920, when nearly 1 million acres were grown, but 20 per cent of the crop was harvested for seed. By 1930, 3 million acres were grown for all purposes, 30 per cent of the acreage being harvested for seed. In 1940, Illinois alone grew over 3 million acres, the United States grew over 11 million acres, and nearly 5 million acres were harvested for seed.

Adaptation.—The soybean has come to be a corn-belt crop, production in the cotton belt being next in importance. Illinois, Indiana, and Iowa produce about half the United States acreage. Soybeans are

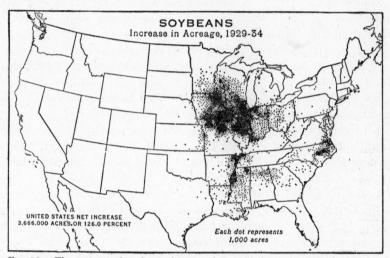

SOYBEANS
Increase in Acreage, 1929-34

UNITED STATES NET INCREASE
3,666,000 ACRES, OR 126.0 PERCENT

Each dot represents
1,000 acres

Fig. 92.—The acreage of soybeans harvested in 1934 was more than double that of 1929. The greatest increase took place in Illinois, Wisconsin, Iowa, and northern Missouri. The trend of the crop was northwestward. The climate of Manchuria, the great center of world production, resembles that in the area bounded by lines from Omaha to St. Paul, Winnepeg, Canada, and Williston, North Dakota, thence back to Omaha. By 1941 the total soybean acreage in the United States was in excess of 10 million and still going up. (*U.S. Department of Agriculture.*)

grown from the Great Lakes to the Gulf of Mexico and eastward to the Atlantic seaboard, but to the west only to where the dry lands begin, for this crop does not set seed well where the climate is hot and dry.

Fertile soils high in organic matter, phosphoric acid, and potash produce the best yields; but the crop grows better than many on fairly sandy soils, and it is reasonably tolerant of soil acidity. Soybeans will not make as good growth in poor soil as cowpeas.

Effect of Soybeans on the Soil.—Because well-inoculated soybeans make possible the fixation of liberal quantities of atmospheric nitrogen, the crop has the reputation of being decidedly beneficial to the soil. With respect to nitrogen, however, unless part of the tops of the soybean plant is returned in some form to the soil, this element will be depleted. This is true even though well-nodulated plants may obtain about two-thirds of their nitrogen from the air.[1]

Soybeans can be and sometimes are used as a green-manure crop; in this case a good crop, plowed under, supplies organic matter containing 60 to 100 lb. of nitrogen to the acre. Under most conditions, however, it is possible to keep up the organic-matter content of the soil in a less expensive way with such legumes as alfalfa and the clovers.

The minerals that are removed from the soil by soybeans must eventually be replaced by the application of fertilizers. Sears[2] points out that a 20-bu. crop of soybeans sold as seed, the straw being returned to the soil, removes slightly more phosphorus than a 40-bu. crop of corn, of which only the grain leaves the field, and the soybeans remove more than three times as much potassium. A 2½-ton soybean hay crop takes twice as much phosphorus and five times as much potassium from the soil as does 40 bu. of corn. Hence, like alfalfa, soybeans draw heavily on minerals.

It is important that these minerals should quickly be replaced in the soil. Experiments have shown that small grains that immediately follow soybeans in the rotation are very responsive to mineral fertilization.

Soybean land erodes easily. The erosion is due partly to the type of tillage and cultivation that goes with soybean growing and even more to the loosened condition of the soil that the soybean-root growth develops. If soybeans are to be grown on sloping land, such erosion-control practices as strip cropping and contour tillage can be employed effectively to reduce soil losses. E. S. Dyas of the Iowa Agricultural Experiment Station states, "No data are available on soybeans in rows up and down the slope in comparison with rows on the contour, but at the Soil Conservation Experiment Station at Clarinda, Iowa, corn listed up and down a slope lost 13.27 tons of soil per acre per year, whereas corn listed on the contour lost practically no soil. It seems reasonable to expect similar results with soybeans."[3]

As a means of reducing erosion on rolling land the Iowa Agricultural Experiment Station recommends that the crop be drilled solid on the contour and followed immediately after harvest with a cover crop such as winter rye or winter wheat. This makes necessary the use of a

[1] SEARS, O. H., Soybeans: Their Effect on Soil Productivity, *Ill. Agr. Expt. Sta. Bul.* 456, 1939.

[2] *Ibid.*

[3] DYAS, E. S., Soybean Production in Iowa, *Iowa Agr. Expt. Sta. Bul.* P30 (new series), 1941.

variety early enough in maturity to permit harvest in time for sowing the fall grain.

Soybean Culture.—Most land is plowed in preparation for soybeans; and if this is followed by thorough surface tillage, over a reasonable period of time, weeds will be far less troublesome. Because so much of the soybean acreage is drilled solid, precluding interrow

FIG. 93.—A fine field of soybeans in Indiana. Somewhat better yields are usually secured by drilling the seed in rows suitable for interrow cultivation than by drilling it in solid. (*Courtesy of J. C. Allen and Son.*)

cultivation, weed control before the seed is planted becomes unusually important.

Better yields are secured by drilling soybeans in 24-in. rows than by drilling the seed in solid (8-in. rows), according to results secured in Illinois.[1] The more effective seeding rates were 90 to 130 lb. an acre

[1] BURLISON, W. L., C. A. VAN DOREN, and J. C. HACKLEMAN, Eleven Years of Soybean Investigations, *Ill. Agr. Expt. Sta. Bul.* 462, 1940.

for solid drilling and 50 to 70 lb. of seed for drilling in 24-in. rows. At these rates the rowed soybeans outyielded the beans drilled solid by 4.7 bu. an acre. In addition to this yield increase, there is the saving of 40 to 60 lb. of seed to compensate for the necessary interrow cultivation. In the absence of serious weed trouble, row plantings may still be at an economic disadvantage despite their superior yield. If weeds cannot be effectively controlled by preplanting tillage and two or three workings with the rotary hoe or weeder while the plants are young, then row plantings that permit interrow cultivation are advisable.

In Illinois, soybean seedings made from May 1 to May 20 were not markedly different in yield; they averaged about 2 bu. an acre higher over a 6 year period than seedings of June 1 or June 10 and 6 bu. higher than those of June 20.[1] These results appear to be generally applicable throughout the corn belt. In fact, farmers in general may regard corn-planting time as the desirable time to plant soybeans with the reservation that a moderate delay in the case of soybeans is usually not so objectionable as it is with corn.

Inoculation of the seed with the proper nitrogen-fixing bacteria ensures the presence of these organisms which make for a more vigorous growth of the plants and the development of a higher protein content.

Varieties.—In *Illinois Agricultural Experiment Station Bulletin* 462 there is presented a tabular description of 66 soybean varieties. There are more than 2,000 varieties, but the ones tested at Urbana, Ill., serve to illustrate some of the characteristic differences. There are yellow, green, brown and black varieties. In many of the yellow varieties the hilum is brown. The Black Eyebrow is brown with a black saddle. The Laredo, a black variety grown for forage, has such small seeds that it takes more than 7,000 to make a pound. With some Manchu selections, only 2,500 are required. The Minsoy matured at Urbana, Ill., in 95 days; varieties popular in central Illinois, like Illini and Dunfield, matured in 110 days; the Laredo took 135.

Early-maturing varieties are sometimes used in the corn belt so that the crop can be combined in time to sow winter wheat. In general, they are outyielded by the longer growing kinds, each region having its favorites of proved adaptation. Yellow-seeded varieties are demanded by the oil industries. The so-called *hay* varieties, usually of late maturity, have in fact shown no advantages for forage production in the corn belt over such grain-type varieties as Manchu, Dunfield, Mukden, and Illini if the latter are harvested just before the leaves begin to turn yellow and drop but after the beans in the pods are well developed.

[1] *Ibid.*

Edible Soybeans.—The edible, or vegetable-type, soybeans have been introduced into the United States as a horticultural crop, can be widely grown, and provide a rich source of protein and fat, as well as vitamins A, B, and G. They are harvested when green, shelled, and prepared in different ways comparable with methods used for green Lima beans and green peas. However, they remain much firmer than green peas. Green vegetable soybeans are harvested as soon as the seeds have attained full size but before they start to dry out. The pods at this stage are still green in color. The green beans shell much more easily if boiling water is poured over the pods and they are left standing in the hot water for about 5 minutes. Strangely enough, these vegetable varieties, which shell with difficulty when they are green,

Fig. 94.—An important factor in the great increase of soybean production in the United States is that the crop can be conveniently harvested with the combine. (*Courtesy of W. L. Burlison, Illinois Agricultural Experiment Station.*)

shatter too readily when ripe. To harvest them for seed, they may be cut with a grain binder and tied in small bundles before the seed is fully dry. Curing is completed in the shock, and threshing is done with a properly adjusted grain separator.

Harvest.—One of the major factors in the great increase in soybean acreage in the United States is the use of the combine to harvest the crop. This is not merely a matter of cost, although the harvest of soybeans with the combine costs only about one-half as much as by the binder-and-thresher method; it is also a matter of timeliness and convenience. The combine harvest of soybeans extends over a long, late-fall period. In general, the beans stand well and shatter but little. Combines have been designed to cut close to the ground, and losses incurred with this method of harvest have become relatively insignificant. Probably the first consideration is to delay the start of harvest until the beans are down to 14 per cent moisture to ensure their safety from heating and spoilage.

Soybean Uses.—As has already been stated, more than one-half the United States soybean acreage is grown for forage, including a moderate acreage for pasture and green manure. The 4,961,000 acres harvested for beans in 1940 produced a crop of nearly 80 million bushels, and over 100 million bushels were estimated for the 1941 grain crop.

About 56 per cent of the threshed crop of the late 1930's and early 1940's went to the oil mills. The balance was used on the farm for feed and seed. Whole soybeans contain too much oil for fattening animals, especially hogs, which produce soft pork if fed too heavily on soybeans. The oil content of the seed often exceeds 20 per cent, but a normal average extraction is between 15 and 16 per cent.

Extracting the Oil.—Three general methods are used to extract the oil from the soybean seed. In the "old," or hydraulic, process the beans are ground, cooked at a temperature of about 200°F., and subjected to hydraulic pressure. If well cooked the meal has a nutlike, pleasing taste; but "raw" meal is none too palatable.

In the expeller process the seed is dried to about 2 per cent moisture, ground, and passed through screw-type friction presses at temperatures somewhat above the boiling point. This meal, still containing about 5 per cent oil, is very palatable.

In the solvent process the cleaned soybeans are cracked, tempered with moisture, and rolled into thin flakes. The oil is removed from the flakes with a solvent from which it is separated by distillation. The solvent must be thoroughly removed from the meal by a process that cooks the meal to give it a suitable taste.

Soybean meal usually contains 41 to 45 per cent protein and is equal to cottonseed meal or gluten meal and somewhat superior to linseed meal in feeding value.

Soybean-oil Products.—Over one-half the soybean oil is used in vegetable shortening, about 20 per cent in margarines, and around 10 per cent for salad dressings and similar culinary usage. The balance goes to industry where soybean oil, like linseed oil, is used in paints, varnishes, enamels, linoleum, oilcloth, and waterproofing; large quantities are used in the soapmaking industry.

Soybean Meal.—Much of the soybean meal with its highly digestible proteins goes back to agriculture to supplement carbonaceous rations. But the meal, too, has its industrial uses. Treated with organic solvents, it can be made into almost transparent plastics that are light, durable, waterproof, fireproof, and rotproof. The automobile industry, in particular, has made use of these plastics for various parts. In 1941, the Ford Motor Company at Dearborn, Mich., made an experimental car in which much of the fender and body construction was made from plastics composed of soybeans and several other agricultural products. Fabrics made from a woollike material derived from soybean protein have also been used in automobile upholstery.

Despite the versatile usage to which soybeans have been put industrially, such technological uses at present account for the disposal of only 2 or 3 per cent of recent crops.

Soybeans for Food.—The use of vegetable soybeans and of soybean oil for human consumption has already been mentioned. In oriental countries, soybeans have contributed to the food supply in many other ways. Over 400 ways of preparing soybean products for food have been in use in these lands, though such usage in the United States has developed slowly. The various food preparations include flour, sprouts, roasted beans as a coffee substitute, shoyu sauce, milk, curds, and a vegetable cheese.

Soybean Trends.—The leading small grain in the corn belt is oats. In the 4-year rotation corn, oats, wheat, clover, the soybean crop can be substituted for oats. It may also be substituted for the oat crop in other ways. From 1930 to 1939, there was a drop in United States oat production of over six million acres and an increase in soybean production of six million acres. It should not be implied that soybeans have primarily supplanted oats; for the corn and wheat acreage has also declined somewhat, and the soybean acreage has continued to expand since 1939. Its final place in the American farm plan has not yet fully been established.

Soybean-yield trends as well as acreage trends have been upward. The 5-year average acre yield for the United States for the years 1925–1929 was 12.4 bu.; for 1935–1939, it was 17.9 bu. The best average yield for the 1925–1929 period was 13.6 bu. an acre, the poorest for the 1935–1939 period was 14.1 bushels. Better varieties, better cultural practices, and the growing of soybeans on more suitable land help account for this definitely upward yield trend.

As for prices, the unweighted average farm price for a bushel of soybeans for the 1930–1939 period was $0.88. The highest was $1.32 in 1930, the lowest $0.48 the next year. Under the influence of a wartime demand the price exceeded $1.50 a bushel for a substantial period of time in 1941. During the 1930–1939 period the average gross acre return from soybeans in the United States ranged from a low of $7.30

in 1931 up to $18.05 in 1936. The returns were consistently higher than from any of the common small grains, the difference being more than enough to cover such additional costs as may be involved in soybean culture.

FIELD BEANS

Farmers in Michigan Territory supplied beans to Commodore Perry on Lake Erie in 1812. Whether or not that is why white pea beans are often called *navy beans* is questionable; but dry beans have long been an important military food, because they are easily transported, keep well, can be readily prepared in a number of ways, and are highly nutritious. White dry beans of the pea-bean, Great Northern, and small-white classes made up one of the major food items supplied by the United States to Great Britain during the Second World War.

Beans are important as a food during peacetime as well, the annual production for the 1929–1938 period for the United States being over 13 million bags of 100 lb. each. Michigan and California lead in production.

TABLE 16.—DRY EDIBLE BEANS, AVERAGE PRODUCTION BY CLASSES, 100-LB. BAGS, UNITED STATES, 1929–1938; WITH LEADING PRODUCING STATES

Class	1,000 bags	Leading states
Pea (navy)	4,127	Michigan, New York
Pinto	1,798	Colorado, New Mexico, California
Great Northern	1,602	Idaho, Montana, Wyoming
Lima	1,103	California
Baby Lima	692	California
Red kidney, light and dark	609	New York, Michigan, California
Blackeye	596	California
Pink	566	California
Small white	480	California
Small red	325	Idaho, California
Cranberry, light and dark	200	Michigan, California
White marrow	144	New York
Yelloweye	123	Michigan, New York
White kidney	80	New York
Other beans and seed	649	
Total	13,094	

Kinds of Beans.—Varieties of beans are numbered by the score. They come in almost every color of the rainbow, including various mottlings, and range in size from the tiny mung bean, not much bigger than a grain of wheat, to the giant horse bean, longer and almost as broad as the diameter of a 25-cent piece.   Incidentally, the horse bean (*Vicia faba*) is in reality one of the vetches rather than a true bean (*Phaseolus spp.*).   Some beans are grown primarily for forage, a great many varieties are horticultural crops harvested for food in an immature condition, but the dry beans with which this discussion deals are one of the important field crops in several regions.

The major field-bean types and the chief areas of production are given in Table 16.

Bean-growing Areas.—In days gone by to say that land was so poor "it wouldn't grow beans" was to classify it at the bottom of the scale in productivity and to imply that the bean crop was suited for growing on poor land.   Experienced bean growers know better.   The Thumb district and Saginaw Valley of Michigan and the areas of western New York that together produce nearly all the white-pea-bean (navy-bean) crop are characterized by rather heavy fertile soils.   Michigan's best bean crops are produced on Brookston soils.   These are loams and clay loams with a dark-colored plow soil underlaid by wet, mottled, gritty clay to a depth of several feet.   They are not acid and are high in organic matter and retentive of moisture.   Climatically these areas tend to provide a cool and humid growing season.   When hot, dry winds occur at blossom time, a poor set of beans results.   Northward expansion of bean culture on suitable land is limited by the earlier occurrence of frosts which are very damaging to an immature crop.

About 85 per cent of the pea-bean crop is grown in Michigan. One-half of these beans are normally canned in the well-known pork-and-bean combination and for soup making.   The balance is marketed to the consumer as dry beans for home cooking.

Both Michigan and New York grow red kidney beans, as does California.   The dark-colored type usually is somewhat higher priced because of its excellent appearance in the can.   Large shipments are made to the West Indies, as well as to eastern states.   Michigan, along with California, produces the cranberry-bean crop which is marketed in eastern mining districts.   The yelloweye produced in Michigan and the Northeast goes primarily to a New England trade.   New York, besides growing pea beans and red kidney beans, grows a number of miscellaneous varieties including white marrows, white kidney beans, and yelloweye beans.

The pinto bean, a dark mottled variety, is grown under irrigation in Colorado and New Mexico and to a lesser extent in California.   It is sold almost entirely as a dry bean and is a favorite in Texas, to which more pinto beans are shipped than any other state.   However,

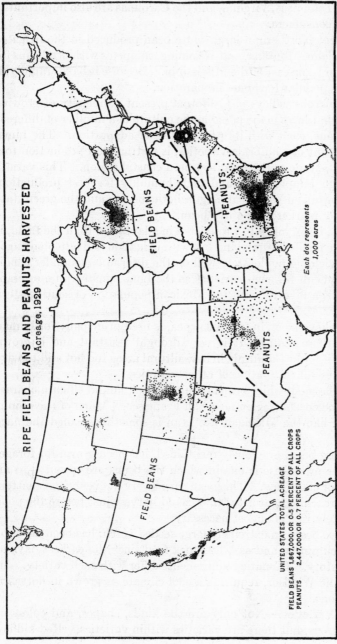

RIPE FIELD BEANS AND PEANUTS HARVESTED
Acreage, 1929

FIELD BEANS

FIELD BEANS

PEANUTS

PEANUTS

FIELD BEANS

Each dot represents
1,000 acres

UNITED STATES TOTAL ACREAGE

FIELD BEANS 1,867,000, OR 0.5 PERCENT OF ALL CROPS
PEANUTS   2,447,000, OR 0.7 PERCENT OF ALL CROPS

Fig. 95.—In western New York and central Michigan the leading types of field beans are white pea and red kidney; on the high plains of eastern New Mexico and Colorado, mostly the native Mexican or pinto bean is grown. California produces practically the entire commercial crop of limas and part of the crop of white beans (small whites) and blackeye beans. Idaho, Montana, and Wyoming grow the Great Northern, a white variety. Peanuts for human consumption are grown mostly in the Virginia–North Carolina district between Richmond and Raleigh. Those grown in Georgia, Alabama, and Florida, in Texas, and Oklahoma, are the smaller Spanish variety and are mostly fed to hogs or made into peanut butter or oil. (*U.S. Department of Agriculture.*)

Kentucky, Tennessee, Virginia, and the Carolinas are also important as pinto-bean consumers.

The Great Northern, a large white bean produced in the irrigated valleys of Idaho, Montana, and Wyoming, competes with pea beans for the dry-bean trade east of the Mississippi. Because it bakes rapidly, it has become popular for home preparation.

The numerous valleys of California present a diversity of growing conditions that have made possible the culture of a number of different kinds of beans, each with its peculiarities of adaptation. The Lima, most important of California varieties, is restricted in production to a narrow fog belt along the most southern coastal region. This variety requires high temperatures and high humidity for best production. The Lima bean is used for canning in both the dry and the green state and is widely marketed as a dry bean.

The pink bean, much less restricted in adaptation than the Lima, is at its best on fertile bottom land but with irrigation and late planting is capable of yielding moderately well on the drier uplands under conditions too difficult for such varieties as the Lima, small white, or cranberry.[1] It is a favorite with the Mexican population of southwestern states.

The blackeye bean, in fact a cowpea, is used principally for human food in southern states. It is very drought resistant and is grown throughout interior California in agricultural areas too hot and too dry for the successful cultivation of other varieties.

California small white beans require a cool, humid climate characteristic of the coastal region near San Francisco. Much of the crop is canned and like the Michigan pea bean is sometimes called the navy bean.

The mung bean, previously mentioned, has been grown for forage, but a higher priced use is one in which the beans are sprouted as an ingredient for chop suey. This bean ripens very unevenly and shatters quickly on reaching maturity; thus, hand harvest just before the pods are completely ripe is almost necessary.

The horse bean, an extremely large seeded vetch, has been used for human consumption and as a livestock feed since the earliest days of recorded history. Climatic requirements differ with each variety. In California the Windsor, requiring a cool climate, is grown in northern coastal regions.

Special Varieties.—Not only are the kinds, shapes, and colors of beans numerous, but there are varieties within varieties. Red kidney

[1] HENDRY, G. W., Bean Culture in California, *Calif. Agr. Expt. Sta. Bul.* 294, 1921.

beans are normally very susceptible to bean blight, a serious bacterial bean disease in humid regions. The Wells red kidney bean, of the light-red class, has found favor in New York because of its resistance to this disease.

Mosaic, a disease that in virulent form causes crinkling of the leaves and failure of the plants to produce pods, attacks many varieties and was formerly very damaging to the pea-bean crop of Michigan and New York. This disease was successfully forestalled by the develop-

Fig. 96.—A Michigan field of white pea (navy) beans of the Michelite variety. This variety is highly resistant to mosaic and blight and is of superior quality. (*Courtesy of E. E. Patton.*)

ment at the Michigan Agricultural Experiment Station of the Robust bean. The Robust variety, strictly a white pea bean, also proved resistant to blight and anthracnose. E. E. Down of this station later crossed the Robust bean with the Early Prolific variety and from the progeny selected the Michelite bean, whiter, more vigorous, and more even in size and shape than its Robust parent but still carrying its remarkable disease resistance. The Michelite bean, introduced in 1938, is now the leading pea-bean variety in Michigan.

Bean Prices.—From the foregoing discussion of the many kinds of beans may be deduced something of the whims and fancies of the great American consuming public. There probably is not a great deal of practical difference in the nutritive value of all the different kinds of beans—still, "some like them hot, some like them cold." Dark-colored red kidney beans bring a higher price than light-colored ones. Light cranberry beans are more popular than dark ones. The Mexicans prefer one color, the eastern miners another, and Boston wants them white.

Let the rather limited market for red kidney beans become a bit surfeited, and the price may fall to $2 a hundred as in 1931. But should these beans be somewhat scarce, the demand is so insistent that the farm price may exceed $10 a hundred, as in 1941, though beans of other colors be abundantly available at one-third the price. In the long run, the prices tend to even out, with more moderate price differences among varieties, in line with the production costs and hazards for each.

Price relationships among several leading types are given in Table 17.

TABLE 17.—SEASON AVERAGE PRICES FOR PRINCIPAL COMMERCIAL CLASSES OF DRY EDIBLE BEANS, 1934–1938*

Kind	Price per 100 lb.	Remarks
Pea................	$3.56	Choice hand-picked in bags, f.o.b. Michigan
Great Northern........	3.61	U.S. No. 1 in bags, f.o.b. southern Idaho
Pinto................	4.70	Choice recleaned in bags, f.o.b. Colorado
Light red kidney.......	4.14	Price to Michigan farmers
Standard Lima.........	5.66	Choice recleaned in bags, f.o.b. rail California

* ROND, R. K., Economic Data for Dry Edible Beans 1924–1940 (revised), *U.S. Dept. Agr. Surplus Market. Admin. Mimeographed Pub.*, April, 1941.

No data are available to show the average yields of the different kinds of beans each in its own favored territory. The 1929–1938 average yield in leading states without regard for kind was as follows:

State	Yield, Pounds
Michigan...	725
California...	1,187
Idaho...	1,282
Colorado..	336
New York..	755

Bean Culture.—The field bean is a row crop, the more common row width being 28 in. Wider rows are used for large-growing Lima and blackeye beans. The usual cultural practices for row crops are followed, with emphasis on seedbed preparation and subsequent between-the-row tillage to control weeds. Almost the entire plant, tops and roots, is removed from the field at harvest; thus, beans can be hard on the soil unless a good program of soil management is practiced. The beans themselves respond much better to a long-time soil-improvement program involving the growing of green manures, fertilized leguminous forages, and similar fertility-enhancing measures than they do to direct applications of commercial fertilizer. In fact, the germinating bean seed is very likely to be injured by excess fertilizer which may contact it in the row; row applications, therefore, should not exceed 40 lb. of fertilizer an acre. Much larger quantities may be used in bands near but not in contact with the seed.

FIG. 97.—A modern bean drill with a fertilizer attachment. This kind of drill is also used for planting sugar beets. (*Courtesy of E. E. Patton.*)

Bean seed germinates poorly in cold, damp soil, and slow-growing seedlings are subject to maggot injury. Therefore, bean planting is a late-spring job, coming in the month of June in Michigan, New York, and areas of comparable temperature. In California the climatic conditions and kinds of beans are so diverse that beans are planted as early as Mar. 15 and as late as Aug. 15. In general, the common kinds of beans yield best if planted after June 1 in the interior districts and before May 10 along the coast.

The rate depends on the size of seed of each variety and the character of the top growth. For small bush beans like the red kidney, a seed every 4 in. in the row is desirable. In California on good soil, large-topped varieties may be spaced as far apart in the row as 12 to 18 in. The desired spacing for white pea beans is secured with 30 to 45 lb. of seed an acre in 28-in. rows.

The bean plant is indeterminate in development, and blossoms are produced over a period of several days or even weeks. For the most part the flowers are self-pollinated, but natural cross-pollination is not at all uncommon. Hot, dry weather is often responsible for failure of the flowers to become fertilized. The 1941 Michigan crop was delayed a full 3 weeks in maturity because the first flowers blasted in an extremely dry heat wave in July. New flowers continued to develop farther out on the vines, and these set pods in mid-August. If the first flowers do set pods, the later blooming is curtailed and the plants reach maturity more rapidly. Not infrequently some early and some late pods develop on the same plant, such unevenness in maturity handicapping timely harvest operations.

Fig. 98.—Pulled beans raked into windrows and threshed with a small combine. This harvest procedure is economical on clean land in good weather.

Harvest.—Most kinds of beans can be held for harvest until the entire set of pods is ripe, though the blackeye and tepary beans of California shatter easily. Any kind of bean may shatter, in fact, if handled too much when fully dry. Bean harvest machinery is designed to avoid much movement or shaking of the vines. The cutter, or puller, consists of two broad blades set in a wheeled frame at a 60-deg. angle to cut under two adjacent rows about 2 in. below the ground. Prongs pull the rows together into one windrow.

The simplest harvest procedure then, if weather conditions permit, is to rake two of the windrows together with a side-delivery rake and thresh the beans from the windrow with a combine. Where wet weather at harvesttime is common, however, a far safer procedure is to fork the pulled beans into field stacks about 4 ft. in diameter and 7 ft. high. These are built on a straw base and supported by a center stake (a steel fence post is satisfactory), driven firmly into the ground. The stacks, similar to the ones used for curing peanuts in the South, dry out rapidly, and weather losses are thus prevented.

Cleaning, Picking, and Grading.—Threshed beans are cleaned and graded at local and terminal bean elevators. Colored varieties are screened, cleaned, and polished with special machine equipment. White beans, especially those produced in humid areas where diseases

Fig. 99.—A terminal bean elevator where beans are dried when necessary, hand picked, and made ready for the canner or the dry-bean market.

and wet harvest more often affect quality, may be hand-picked to essential purity in preparation for the consumer. The standard grade of pea beans in Michigan is *choice hand-picked*. The customary price deduction for cull beans includes deduction of the weight of the culls plus the cost of picking them out. Beans carrying in excess of 18 per cent moisture are also discounted on the market.

The "hand picking" of white beans is being done at certain terminal elevators by the "electric-eye" method according to which each bean is picked up by vacuum holders and passed before a photoelectric cell. Beans that show any discoloration are "picked" off at this point and separated from white, undamaged stock.

The Bean Weevil.—The chief insect enemy of field beans is one that appears in storage, the bean weevil. The adult bean weevil is a tiny beetle. Its eggs may be deposited on bean pods in the field or on dry beans in storage. Eggs, laid on or among beans, hatch into practically invisible grubs which penetrate the beans through tiny holes and grow to maturity there. A new generation may arise every 30 days under favorable conditions of temperature and moisture. When the adults emerge from the beans, the seed is left perforated with holes as big around as the lead in a pencil. Control is effected in storage by the sort of fumigation used for small grains. A propylene dichloride mixture has been found to be very effective. The plowing under or other complete disposal of all bean straw, cull beans, and unfumigated granary refuse by May 15 is a sanitary measure designed to eliminate both field and storage infestation.

PEANUTS

The roasted peanut, salted or direct from the shell, is a tasty, crunchy tidbit enjoyed by most of our 130 million Americans. Peanut butter is a wholesome, nutritious sandwich spread, and peanut oil has many industrial uses. The peanut plant may be used for forage—it is especially popular for "hogging off" and for cattle feed—and above all the peanut is a cash crop for thousands of southeastern farmers, about one-third of them in Georgia.

There were 1,907,000 acres of peanuts picked and threshed in 1940, producing 1,611,635,000 lb. of peanuts. Another 1,920,000 acres were harvested for hay, with a production of a little over $\frac{1}{2}$ ton to the acre.[1] On about one-third of this acreage the peanuts were interplanted in corn (occasionally in cotton); therefore, the actual peanut acreage for 1940 as reported by the U.S. Department of Agriculture was about 2,950,000.

Type of Growth.—The peanut is of tropical origin, probably from Brazil, though now it is widely grown in temperate regions. It has angular, hairy stems and bright yellow flowers. The peduncles bearing the female flowers bend after pollination and push the pointed ovaries into the ground where they develop seed-bearing pods to maturity. The plant has a small taproot with strong lateral branches. Nodule-development is usually abundant. Some kinds of peanuts make a bunchy type of growth in which the pods are formed in a cluster about the base of the plant. Runner varieties spread out.

Varieties.—The North Carolina Runner is typical of the spreading varieties with large pods. It produces large yields of both hay and nuts, is a preferred type for hogging off, but brings a somewhat lower price at the shelling plants than the Spanish variety. The Virginia Bunch and Jumbo are large podded varieties with the bunch type of growth.

[1] Forage uses of peanuts are discussed in Chap. VIII.

The Spanish peanut is the most widely grown of the small, bunch varieties. It is considerably less productive of forage than the North Carolina Runner or Virginia Bunch, but it has a higher shelling percentage and is favored for confectionery purposes. It is ready for hog pasture a month earlier than the North Carolina Runner variety but is not so suitable for late grazing because the ripened nuts are prone to sprout. Valencia, Tennessee White, Tennessee Red, and Georgia Red are other small bunch varieties.

Fertilizers and Rotations.—Peanuts make their best growth after such heavily fertilized crops as cotton, tobacco, and truck crops. The crop itself responds well to applications of complete fertilizer. U. R. Gore[1] of the Georgia Experiment Station suggests the following rotation for the southern part of that state:

1. First-year cotton—fertilized.
2. Second-year Spanish peanuts (300 lb. of a 3-8-8 fertilizer and side-dressed with nitrogen) and hay put back on land. Sow Austrian winter peas or oats after peanuts are harvested.
3. Third-year corn interplanted with Runner peanuts hogged off, or oats followed with cowpeas.

This 3-year rotation may be changed to a 4-year rotation by the addition of a small-grain crop before going back to cotton. To maintain organic matter, Gore suggests following the small grain with crotalaria or cowpeas for green manure.

A soil reaction of pH5.6 to 6.5 is considered most favorable for the peanut crop.

Culture.—The weed problem is an important one in peanut growing, necessitating thorough tillage of the seedbed. To accomplish this, plowing should be done at least 2 weeks before the peanuts are planted. In the planting of small-podded varieties in 30-in. rows, 30 to 40 lb. of hand-shelled seed should provide approximately a 6-in. spacing of plants in the row. If planted in the shell, 60 to 70 lb. would be required. The large runner varieties are spaced at least 12 in. apart in the row, the rows being 36 in. apart or more. To plant an acre of North Carolina Runners in 36-in. rows would require approximately 40 lb. of seed in the hull.

A large proportion of the Runner peanut crop is interplanted with corn, one or two rows of peanuts being planted down the middle of the wider corn rows.

The planting dates range from Apr. 10 in the Gulf states to May 10 in the Virginia-Carolina district. This is usually a little after corn-

[1] GORE, U. R., Culture and Fertilizer Studies with Peanuts, *Ga. Expt. Sta. Bul.* 209, 1941.

planting time and as soon as possible after the danger of frost is past.

Peanuts must be free from weeds when cultivation is completed. Early working with a weeder run diagonally to the rows, followed by shallow interrow cultivation and some hand hoeing, is usually necessary.

Harvest.—Peanuts are ready for digging when the foliage has yellowed and the leaves begin to shed. At this stage the nuts should be well formed, the inside of the shells turned brown, and the veins darkened. Immature peanuts, if harvested, will shrivel; ripe ones, more

Fig. 100.—Stacking peanuts in North Carolina. Drying of the peanut crop is carried on in small field stacks. (*Courtesy of E. R. Collins, North Carolina Agricultural Experiment Station.*)

especially in the Spanish varieties, if left unharvested too long may sprout, or the pegs may rot off, leaving many of them in the ground.

One simple method of loosening the plants is to take an ordinary plow, moldboard removed, and run the share under the peanut row, the taproots thus being severed. Standard potato diggers can also be used; they tend to leave the nuts cleaner.

Final curing is done in small field stacks built around a stake driven firmly into the ground, with crosspieces 2 to 3 ft. long nailed at right angles to the stake 1 ft. above the ground. In the best stacks the nuts are kept toward the center so that they may be sheltered from the rain. An umbrella of grass, weeds, or kraft paper placed on top of these stacks affords additional protection.

Picking is a late-fall job that is done after the pods are thoroughly cured and the vines are dry and brittle. Picking machinery has taken over this work, once done by hand; it is designed to remove the nuts from the vines, clean them free from soil and trash, and shell just as few as possible. The leftover straw makes good cattle feed.

Cash Returns.—For the average grower, during the 1930–1939 period, the peanut crop has yielded 713.7 lb. an acre. Prices to farmers hit a low of 1.54 cents a pound in the depression year of 1932, averaged 3.02 cents for the 1930 decade, and were, in general, lower during this period than at any time during the preceding 20 years. The acreage trend has been upward.

COWPEAS

The cowpea is essentially a southern legume though it is of some importance in the warmer part of the corn belt and is produced to a

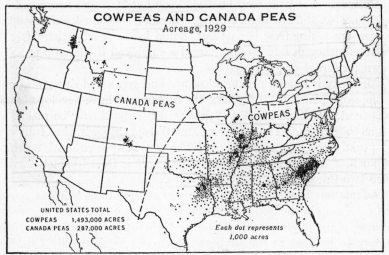

FIG. 101.—Cowpeas are the principal annual legume in the cotton belt as soybeans are in the corn belt. Both crops are grown in the intervening corn and winter-wheat belt. Field peas (Canada peas in the map) are locally important along the lake shores of northern Michigan and Wisconsin, in the San Luis Valley of Colorado, the Snake River Valley of Idaho, and the Columbia Plateau—all areas of cool summer climate. (*U.S. Department of Agriculture.*)

limited extent even in southwestern Michigan. Its hay, pasture, and green-manure usage (see Chap. VIII) accounts for more than 2½ times the acreage threshed for peas; yet South Carolina, Georgia, Alabama, Mississippi, and Texas each grow in excess of 100,000 acres to be threshed. No important acreage is grown in the far west except for the blackeye bean of California, a cowpea marketed as a dry edible bean.

For the cowpea-growing districts as a whole, a yield of between 6 and 7 bu. an acre is average, but yields of 10 to 15 bu. are not at all uncommon. The farm prices during the 1930's ranged from $0.81 to $1.96 a bushel. In the 1920's they were generally above $2 and sometimes exceeded $3 a bushel.

Varieties and Seed Uses.—Cowpea seeds are used in various ways as a human food. They may be prepared as green peas in the pod, shelled green, and shelled dried. An important channel of seed disposal is to other farmers who plant it to produce forage or green manure. Varieties may be prostrate in habit of growth; low, half bushy; tall, half bushy; and erect. Some varieties are uniform in color; others are spotted, marbled, or speckled. The Whippoorwill sets the standard of values, with most of the others bringing somewhat higher prices, according to J. E. Barr.[1] Other varieties of importance are Brabham, New Era, Iron, Groit, and Clay.

Culture.—Cowpeas may be drilled solid at 90 lb. an acre or in 24- to 40-in. rows at 30 to 40 lb. an acre. Seeding time must wait until the danger of a killing frost is past but should follow as soon thereafter as possible, although late seeding may be employed if the crop is to be grown for forage or green manure.

Maturity is indeterminate; blossoms and green and ripe pods hang on the same plants from the time the first flowers have developed pods until frost. If hand harvest is practiced, the pods may be picked as fast as they ripen. The seed is separated from the pods when fully dry by special small cowpea hullers. If the crop is to be cut with machinery such as a mower or a self-rake reaper, it is time to start harvest when two-thirds of the pods are mature.

Adaptation as a Seed Crop.—Acreage returns from cowpeas grown as a cash crop in the South approximate those secured from soybeans. Because of its indeterminate flowering habits the cowpea is not nearly so easy to harvest as the soybean which can be so readily threshed with a combine. Though no more drought resistant than the soybean, according to Arkansas investigators,[2] the cowpea is better suited for growing on the lighter, sandier soils. On the richer bottom lands the vegetative growth is excellent and large yields of hay may be produced, but seed setting is likely to be poor on such soil unless very dry weather prevails at the time of fruiting.

The general effect on the land of growing cowpeas is beneficial. The greatest soil improvement follows where the cowpeas are left on the land over winter to be turned under the next spring, an expensive

[1] BARR, J. E., Marketing the Cowpea Seed Crop, *U.S. Dept. Agr. Farmers' Bul.* 1308, 1923.

[2] NELSON, M., and C. K. McCLELLAND, Varieties of Cowpeas for Seed and Hay Production, *Ark. Agr. Expt. Sta. Bul.* 212, 1926.

practice because of loss of the use of the land for a full season. Following several years of investigation, C. A. Mooers of the Tennessee Agricultural Experiment Station concluded:

It is unprofitable to turn under a cowpea or soybean crop for the sake of increasing the productivity of the soil as measured by the corn crop of the following year. It is evident, however, that a much better than average condition can be expected where the legumes are pastured off or are fed as hay and the manure returned. Even where the summer legume is removed as hay a larger corn crop may be expected than where corn follows corn, but the effect is small in comparison with the aftereffects of such legumes as clover and alfalfa.[1]

FIELD PEAS

Field peas and garden peas differ only in variety and the purposes for which they are grown. Garden peas are harvested in an immature condition to be cooked and served as green peas or to be canned for subsequent use. Field peas are grown for forage, soil improvement, or mature seed. The mature seed may be split and prepared in various ways for human consumption, a favorite dish being pea soup, or the seed may be used for stock feed. One market for peas of some consequence is to pigeon fanciers. The pea crop is sometimes allowed to mature and, in this condition, is used for sheep pasture, a practice not uncommon in the Rocky Mountain states. In the North, field peas are often grown for hay in mixture with oats (see Chap. VIII). The crop may be ensiled while in green enough condition to be cut for hay. In the eastern part of the cotton belt the Austrian Winter pea makes a very satisfactory winter cover and green-manure crop.

Adaptation.—At present the 250,000 to 300,000 acres harvested as dry field peas are grown in the western states of Washington, Oregon, Montana, Idaho, and Colorado and in Wisconsin and Michigan of the Middle West. The yield average is about 16 bu. an acre, a bushel weighing 60 lb.; yields of 20 to 30 bu. an acre are considered very good.

Effective seed production is confined to regions with a cool growing season. The crop will withstand moderate frosts but not high temperatures. If planted in April in the northern states that grow dry peas the crop is usually subjected to several spring frosts without injury; but if planted in May, it fails to mature before hot weather sets in and yields are greatly curtailed. It is not a poor-land crop in any sense but requires a fairly rich soil, preferably calcareous.

[1] MOOERS, C. A., Influence of Cowpea Crop on Yield of Corn, *Tenn. Agr. Expt. Sta. Bul.* 137, 1927.

Culture and Harvest.—The culture of field peas is not unlike that for small grains; in fact, the oat-pea mixture is sometimes cut and threshed as well as being used for forage. A bushel of oats and a bushel of peas constitute an appropriate seeding rate for the mixture, whereas 1½ bu. of peas alone may be seeded in humid areas, with lesser quantities used under drier conditions. When grown with grain the crop may be cut with a binder. When grown alone, as is usually the case with the seed crop, harvest is with a mower with a windrowing attachment on the back of the cutter bar to roll the peas to one side so that they will not be trampled when the next round is made. Harvest should start at maturity but before the vines are thoroughly dry. Dry peas are easily shattered. A properly adjusted grain separator can be used to thresh the crop.

Enemies.—Field peas are subject to several diseases of leaf, stem, and root for which no practicable control measures are known. The growing of the pea crop on different fields that are rotated helps moderately in the case of bacterial blight, leaf blotch, downy mildew, anthracnose, and root rot.

Insects have proved even more troublesome than diseases. The pea weevil drove the pea crop from Michigan's Thumb district into the more northern parts of the state, and the pea moth has seriously threatened the whole dry-pea industry of the Great Lakes region. In some years the pea aphid has been exceedingly destructive; and though this insect is subject to control by dusting, the expense of such control measures has not been warranted except for the more valuable canning peas.

The pea weevil, a small grayish beetle with lighter spots, lays its eggs on young pea pods, and these produce larvae that bore their way into the immature seed where they feed and later pupate. The insect emerges from the seed any time from soon after harvest until planting time the next year. Damage to harvested seed may be prevented by fumigation.

The pea moth also produces larvae that feed on the seed. These insects overwinter in the soil and are difficult to control although the early planting of early-maturing varieties and the full destruction of pea rubbish is at least a partial remedy.

VELVET BEANS

The velvet bean (*Stizolobium spp.*) is an annual legume that has become sufficiently popular in the Gulf states and South Carolina for about 2½ million acres to be grown annually. Over half the crop is produced in Georgia.

The vines of this bean sometimes attain a length of 30 to 40 ft., and so the crop cannot readily be handled for hay. It is usually interplanted with corn; following corn harvest, it is pastured off with cattle and hogs. However, the pods may be picked by hand when mature. The ground velvet-bean feed consists of both pods and beans and is roughly comparable with wheat bran in feeding value. The feed is satisfactory for cattle and sheep as a minor part in the concentrate mixture but causes digestive disorders in hogs unless it comprises only a very limited proportion of the ration.

The crop must be grown on warm, well-drained soils, and its climatic requirements are best met in the southeastern United States. It does not have a high lime requirement and is not particularly restricted as regards soil type. It is therefore decidedly useful for soil-improvement purposes.

Review Problems

1. Which of the following large-seeded legumes is seldom grown as a forage crop?

    a. Soybeans.
    b. Field beans.
    c. Cowpeas.
    d. Field peas.

2. In the United States the most extensive use of soybeans is for

    a. Human food.
    b. Feed for livestock.
    c. Oil production.
    d. The manufacture of plastics.

3. The largest acreage of soybeans is grown in

    a. The corn belt.
    b. The cotton belt.
    c. The spring-wheat country.
    d. The Pacific coast area.

4. The growing of a soybean seed crop tends to

    a. Increase the nitrogen content of the soil.
    b. Leave the soil packed and hard.
    c. Make the soil more susceptible to erosion.
    d. Draw very lightly on mineral nutrients.

5. A production factor that had a very pronounced influence on the increase in soybean acreage in the 1930's was

    a. The wide use of the combine harvester throughout the corn belt.
    b. The development of better methods for ensiling legumes.
    c. The improved methods for controlling weeds in soybeans drilled solid.
    d. The beneficial influence of soybeans on the soil.

6. Which of the following dry-bean varieties is really a cowpea?

    a. White pea bean.
    b. Great Northern bean.
    c. Cranberry bean.
    d. Pinto bean.
    e. Blackeye bean.

7. All but which one of these states normally grow more than 100,000 acres of dry edible beans each year?

    a. Idaho.
    b. Oregon.
    c. Michigan.
    d. California.
    e. New York.

8. Which one of the following kinds of dry beans is not of major commercial importance?

    a. Pinto.
    b. White kidney.
    c. Great Northern.
    d. White pea.
    e. Lima.

9. The peanut-growing industry is most important in

    a. Texas.
    b. Pennsylvania.
    c. North Carolina.
    d. Virginia.
    e. Georgia.

10. Rich bottom lands often fail to produce good cowpea-seed yields because

    a. The plants grow poorly in the presence of abundant soil nitrogen.
    b. The plants make too vigorous a vegetative growth.
    c. Lowlands are too warm and humid for cowpeas.
    d. Seed will not mature under bottom-land conditions.

11. Which of the following statements concerning field peas is false?

    a. Field peas are markedly resistant to spring frosts.
    b. The crop is more susceptible to high-temperature injury at podding time.
    c. An annual rainfall of 20 in. is more likely to prove adequate for peas in Nebraska than in North Dakota.
    d. When grown for hay or green manure, field peas are more tolerant of high temperatures than when grown for seed.

12. Why are soybeans important in the corn and cotton belts and not in the spring-wheat country, the southern plains region, or the Pacific coast area?

13. Why have soybeans apparently taken the place of oats to a considerable extent in corn-belt rotations?

14. What is one of the chief objections to growing winter wheat after soybeans?

15. What is the major advantage of growing winter wheat after soybeans?

16. Explain the relationship between soybean culture and the erosibility of the soil.

17. At what stage of development is hot, dry weather likely to prove unusually damaging to the dry-bean crop? Why?

18. How were losses due to mosaic in white pea beans greatly reduced?

19. How has the photoelectric cell been used in the bean industry?

20. Why is the Spanish peanut less suitable for late grazing than the North Carolina Runner variety?

21. At what stage of development are peanuts ready for harvest?

22. A southern farmer has a sandy field that has grown a poor crop of corn. Which is likely to give the better results as the next crop on this field, cowpeas or soybeans?

23. In general, which crop is the easier to harvest for its seed, cowpeas or soybeans? Why?

24. Is fumigation of threshed peas in storage a complete control for pea weevils? Explain.

References

BARR, J. E.: Marketing the Cowpea Seed Crop, *U.S. Dept. Agr. Farmers' Bul.* 1308, 1923.

BEATTIE, W. R.: Peanut Growing for Profit, *U.S. Dept. Agr. Farmers' Bul.* 1127, 1924.

BURLISON, W. L., C. A. VAN DOREN, and J. C. HACKELMAN: Eleven Years of Soybean Investigations, *Ill. Agr. Expt. Sta. Bul.* 462, 1940.

DIBBLE, C. B.: The Bean Weevil, *Mich. Ext. Bul.* 138, 1934.

DOWN, E. E., and J. W. THAYER, JR.: The Michelite Bean, *Mich. Agr. Expt. Sta. Bul.* 295, 1938.

DYAS, E. S.: Soybean Production in Iowa, *Ia. Agr. Expt. Sta. Bul.* P30 (new series), 1941.

GORE, U. R.: Culture and Fertilizer Studies with Peanuts, *Ga. Expt. Sta. Bul.* 209, 1941.

HARDENBURG, E. V.: "Bean Culture," The Macmillan Company, New York, 1927.

HENDRY, G. W.: Bean Culture in California, *Calif. Agr. Expt. Sta. Bul.* 294, 1921.

HUTCHESON, T. B., T. K. WOLFE, and M. S. KIPPS: "The Production of Field Crops," McGraw-Hill Book Company, Inc., New York, 1936.

LLOYD, J. W., and W. L. BURLISON: Eighteen Varieties of Edible Soybeans, *Ill. Agr. Expt. Sta. Bul.* 453, 1939.

MCKEE, ROLAND: Culture and Pests of Field Peas, *U.S. Dept. Agr. Farmers' Bul.* 1803, 1938.

PARK, J. B., and J. A. SLIPHER: The Soybean: Its Place in a Farming System, *Ohio Ext. Bul.* 199, 1939.

PETTIGROVE, H. R., and C. R. OVIATT: Producing Beans in Michigan, *Mich. Ext. Bul.* 116, 1931.

PIPER, C. V., and W. J. MORSE: "The Soybean," McGraw-Hill Book Company, Inc., New York, 1923.

SEARS, O. H.: Soybeans: Their Effect on Soil Productivity, *Ill. Agr. Exp. Sta. Bul.* 456, 1939.

CHAPTER XIX

POTATOES AND SWEET POTATOES

The potato of commerce is a tuber, the enlarged portion of an underground stem. The portion of the sweet potato that is edible is an enlarged root. Though the one is a member of the nightshade family and the other a morning-glory, they have much in common. Both are apparently of South American origin; both are propagated vegetatively; both are grown in rows and harvested for their underground growth. They are roughly similar in composition, being high in carbohydrates, and they are prepared in comparable ways for the dinner table. There the comparison stops; for potatoes occupy about four times the United States acreage that is planted to sweet potatoes, and their total production in bushels is five times as great.

POTATOES

When Sir Francis Drake took potatoes from the West Indies and gave some to his friend Sir Walter Raleigh for planting in county Cork, Ireland, he started the production of one of the Old World's most important crops. After some misgivings the Irish adopted the crop so completely that they gave it a name as Irish as Murphy and used it to defeat starvation in a period of famine. France, in area comparable with Texas, eventually came to grow as many acres as, and many more bushels than, the entire United States. Germany and Poland of pre-Second World War days each more than doubled the production of France. Vast Russia with its 16 million acres (1938 crop) grew nearly one-third as large an acreage as that of all the world. Truly this South American tuber attained astounding heights as the world's most important vegetable when its 1938 production reached close to 8 billion bushels.

Adaptation.—Although Drake reputedly found his first potatoes in the West Indies, the crop is at its best in a cool, moist climate. To be sure, potatoes are grown in Texas, Florida, Alabama, Louisiana, and other southern states, but there the crop is grown in the cooler part of the season and often has a special price advantage through supplying the off-season market. Even so, southern potato acreage is small compared with that in the highly intensified area of Aroostook County,

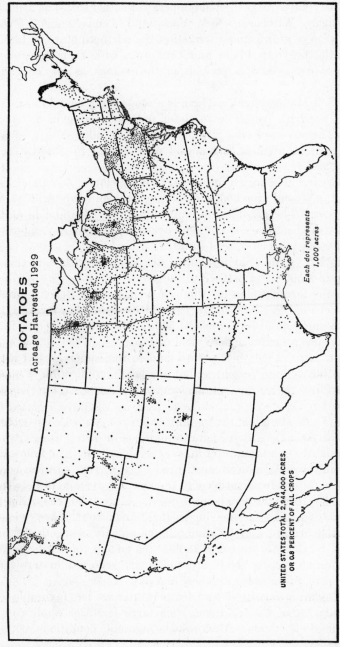

POTATOES

Acreage Harvested, 1929

Each dot represents 1,000 acres

UNITED STATES TOTAL 2,944,000 ACRES, OR 0.8 PERCENT OF ALL CROPS

FIG. 102.—The districts of heaviest production of potatoes lie in latitudes north of the corn belt. These areas have a cool climate and many of the potato-producing centers are in districts of sandy or loamy soil—Aroostook County, Maine, Long Island, N. Y., New Jersey, eastern Virginia, western Michigan, central Wisconsin, and eastern Minnesota. In recent years potato production has become more important in the South during the cooler part of the growing season. (*U.S. Department of Agriculture.*)

Maine, or the total acreage in such temperate-weather states as Minnesota, Michigan, Wisconsin, New York, and Pennsylvania. Even where the crop is grown under irrigation the northern state of Idaho leads all others. Only Idaho and California with their controlled irrigation produce as large acre yields, on the average, as does cool and humid Maine.

Potato Soil Management.—There is a moderately acid 40 acres in Michigan's northern peninsula used for potato growing in a 4-year rotation. The sequence on a given 10 acres is as follows:

First year. A planting is made of oats, seeded to timothy, red clover, and alsike.

Second year. The mixed hay is cut in early clover bloom and left on the land; a second crop comes up through the clover mulch.

Third year. The grass-legume mixture is plowed under in early June, and buckwheat is seeded. The buckwheat is disked to a powder when in blossom but before seed forms.

Fourth year. The field is planted to potatoes with a fertilizer application of 1,500 lb. of 3-12-12 to the acre.

Such is the farming plan of Alphonse Verschure, a Belgian immigrant, who cleared this land in the early 1920's and who, for over 10 years, has secured an average yield of 500 bu. of potatoes an acre in a locality that has an average acre yield of 125.

Very few farmers get their potato land so well supercharged with organic matter as does Verschure, but the heavy application of commercial fertilizer is not at all uncommon among northern potato growers.

Schrumpf[1] in studying the potato enterprise on 165 Aroostook County farms found less than 5 per cent of the potato crop being grown after a straight green-manure crop, practically all the rest following hay of which the clovers have constituted a major part. In this cool, moist region, heavy fertilization was the rule, an average of between 1,800 and 2,000 lb. to the acre being applied. Since 1930 the fertilizers of high analysis have become increasingly important. Acre yields reported by Schrumpf were 292 and 321 bu. an acre, respectively, for two groups of table-stock growers and 351 bu. an acre for certified-seed growers. Maine potato yields are commonly reported in terms of barrels, a barrel of potatoes weighing 165 lb.

Where moisture conditions and temperatures are less favorable for potatoes than in northern Maine, such large fertilizer applications cannot be used effectively. Under fairly favorable conditions, 600 to

[1] SCHRUMPF, W. E., Costs and Returns in Producing Potatoes in Aroostook County, Maine, *Maine Agr. Expt. Sta. Bul.* 390, 1937.

1,000 lb. of such analyses as 3-9-18, 3-12-12, and 4-16-8 may be used, whereas on the sandier soils inclined to droughtiness not over 500 lb. an acre is considered safe. The most effective placement appears to be in bands 2 in. on either side and level with the bottom of the seed pieces. Fertilizer in direct contact with the seed piece may injure the sprouts.

Stable manure is best applied during the summer or fall previous to planting potatoes. If lime must be applied in order to grow alfalfa or the clovers in a potato rotation, light applications are usually recommended; if heavier amounts are used, they are preferably applied 4 or 5 years in advance of the growing of the potato crop. Fresh stable

Fig. 103.—Well-fertilized potatoes in Aroostook County, Maine, grown on terraced soil to prevent erosion. (*Courtesy of U.S. Department of Agriculture Soil Conservation Service.*)

manure and excessive lime both are conducive to the development of the organisms that cause scabby potatoes. On the other hand, potatoes can be grown effectively in acid soil, and many growers supply organic matter with green manure crops that do not require so much lime as do alfalfa and sweet clover. Rye, rye and vetch, and buckwheat are among the organic-matter-producing crops that can be used effectively on acid soils.

Potato Culture.—Because sod-forming or green-manure crops practically always precede potatoes in the rotation, the plowing of the land is the first essential in seedbed preparation. Deep soils may be plowed deeply; a 10-in. plowing depth is not uncommon for soils having a deep, dark-colored surface. Soils that have not been deeply tilled and have only a 6-in. layer of the darker surface material are best plowed no deeper than 6 to 7 in. Plowing is followed by thorough tillage to kill weeds, to prevent crust formation, and eventually to leave a deep, mellow seedbed at planting time.

Planting Time and Depth.—The early-maturing varieties of potatoes intended for early harvest are planted as soon as the danger from severe spring frosts is past. The planting date for the late crop in northern states is governed by seasonal conditions in the different localities. Late varieties require 120 to 130 days to mature a crop. If planted too early the development of tubers may occur in the hottest, driest part of the summer; if planted too late, full maturity of the tubers may not be attained before fall frost. The planting of late-crop potatoes from May 20 to June 1 is considered desirable in most parts of western New York, Michigan, Wisconsin, Ohio, and regions of similar climate.

Potato planters are designed to plant the seed pieces $3\frac{1}{2}$ to $4\frac{1}{2}$ in. deep in moist soil but to cover them with only about $1\frac{1}{2}$ in. of soil. Thus the sprouts will penetrate the surface more quickly, and rots from black-scurf injuries are less likely. When the sprouts are aboveground, the seed furrow is gradually filled by early cultivation.

Rate of Planting.—Certified-seed growers who do not want the tubers to get too large and who provide their potatoes with a highly productive environment sometimes use as much as 30 bu. of seed an acre. A more normal rate of planting on good soils is 20 bu. an acre; even on the soils of lower productivity, at least 15 bu. of seed should be used. This amount of seed is used in rows 30 to 36 in. apart, with seed pieces every 8 to 10 in. on the fertile soils, up to an 18-in. spacing on those less fertile. Wide spacings and hill plantings often result in the production of hollow heart, growth cracks, and rough, oversized potatoes.

Size of Seed Pieces.—For planting purposes, potato tubers are usually cut in pieces $1\frac{1}{2}$ to 2 oz. in size. Small whole tubers from selected, disease-free stock are satisfactory for seed, but unselected small potatoes are more likely to carry diseases than large, clean tubers. Potatoes 6 to 10 oz. in weight, free from flesh discolorations and true to varietal type in shape, are most desirable.

Green Sprouting.—Any seed treatment of potatoes with chemical disinfectants must be done before the seed is cut and made ready for planting. Some of the most successful growers green-sprout their seed as soon as it has been treated. In this process the potatoes are spread out in a 6-in. layer on a dry floor and exposed to sunlight, preferably at temperatures of 60 to 70°F. for a period of 10 days to 2 weeks. This results in the development of short, green sprouts. Tubers with weak sprouts are discarded, for these may be the result of chilling injury or certain diseases. Green-sprouted seed starts growth quickly when planted and is less subject to rotting than unsprouted seed.

Cultivation.—Early, shallow cultivation is most effective in weed control. The weeder is very effective from the time the potatoes are planted until they are 4 in. high. Row cultivations follow, the first fairly deep but the later ones shallow to avoid root injury. All row cultivation must be completed when the plants begin to blossom. In general, level tillage is considered best; but, in the case of varieties that set their tubers near the surface, the tubers are better protected from sunburn and frost injury if 2 in. of soil is thrown over the row at the last cultivation.

Fig. 104.—Spraying potatoes with a modern tractor-drawn, trailer-type, row-crop sprayer. (*Courtesy of John Bean Manufacturing Company, Lansing, Mich.*)

The Control of Potato Diseases and Insects.—No crop is more plagued by diseases and insects than potatoes. To consider each pest in any detail is beyond the scope of this discussion. The work of both the plant pathologist and the entomologist has been vital to the continuance of successful potato culture. The control measures that researches in these sciences have developed have become a part of everyday potato culture. Their application as a part of the potato-growing enterprise commands our attention.

Spraying and Dusting.—The spraying of commercial fields of potatoes with Bordeaux mixture is standard procedure in the United States. The making of Bordeaux mixture is described by H. C. Moore of Michigan[1] as follows:

[1] Moore, H. C., Better Potatoes for Michigan, *Mich. Ext. Bul.* 49, 1939.

Bordeaux mixture ↑

1. Dissolve 50 lb. of copper sulphate in 50 gal. of water. Suspend the copper sulphate crystals in a burlap bag just under the surface of the water. It will require several hours for the chemical to dissolve.

2. In a separate vessel, dissolve 75 lb. of chemical hydrated lime in 50 gal. of water.

3. These are stock solutions and will keep in good condition for several days if kept covered to prevent evaporation of water. They will be sufficient to make 625 gal. of Bordeaux mixture.

4. When ready to spray, stir each of the stock solutions vigorously. Fill the spray tank (100-gal. tank) half full of water. Pour into the spray tank 8 gal. of the copper sulphate solution, and stir thoroughly. Then add 8 gal. of the lime solution. Stir thoroughly, and add enough water to fill the tank. Do not pour together the strong stock solutions.

Bordeaux mixture controls leafhoppers, flea beetles, early blight, and late blight. The addition of 4 or 5 lb. of calcium arsenate to every 100 gal. of Bordeaux mixture is used to make control of flea beetles more effective and to control the Colorado potato beetle, the "potato bug" so familiar to every grower.

The first spray application is made when the plants are about 4 in. high; it should be repeated at intervals of 10 days to 2 weeks throughout the season. A sprayer with three nozzles per row delivering a pressure of 300 lb. is designed to give thorough coverage to both upper and lower leaf surfaces. The requirement for each application is 100 to 125 gal. of Bordeaux mixture an acre.

When conditions favor the development of late blight, a thorough spraying program involving five or more applications may mean the difference between a good crop of potatoes and no crop at all. Late blight is caused by the downy-mildew fungus (*Phytophthora infestans*). The fungus is usually present not only in the soil but in at least a few tubers in practically all lots of ordinary seed potatoes each year. It develops and spreads rapidly in humid seasons when mean daily summer temperatures are 70 to 74°F. Thorough and timely spraying with Bordeaux mixture is very effective as a field control measure, and spread of the disease in storage bins is controlled by putting externally dry tubers in the storage bins and preventing excessive humidity with proper storage temperatures at 40°F. or a little cooler.

If the acreage is small or the problem of getting water for spraying too difficult, potatoes may be dusted to control late and early blight, leaf hoppers, and, with the addition of 15 lb. of calcium arsenate to 100 lb. of dust mixture, flea beetles and potato bugs as well. The copper-lime dust used for this purpose is made by mixing 20 lb. of monohydrated copper sulphate dust with 80 lb. of chemical hydrated lime. Thirty to forty pounds of dust per acre is used at each application, and the same schedule of dust application is necessary as in the case of the somewhat more effective spray treatment.

Seed Treatment.—The treatment of seed potatoes with disinfectants is designed to destroy surface-borne disease organisms such as cause scab and rhizoctonia disease, or black scurf, and to reduce as much as possible tuber infection with blackleg, silver scurf, early blight, and late blight. Materials commonly used for this purpose are corrosive sublimate, calomel, formaldehyde, and specially prepared organic mercury compounds, notably Improved Semesan Bel. The mercurial treatments have been particularly advantageous in the control of black scurf.

In the case of both black scurf and scab, the chief targets of seed treatment, the organisms may be so prevalent in the soil that the treatment of the seed by no means effects full control. Both diseases are very destructive to potato quality. The scab organism *Actinomyces scabies* is usually inhibited in growth at soil acidities of pH5 to 5.2, a degree of soil acidity that is not at all unfavorable for potato culture.

Rotation of crops is desirable as a supplement to seed treatment to reduce the build-up of scab and black-scurf organisms. The development of scab-resistant varieties is a promising approach to the control of this disease.

Seed Certification.—Since 1920, a system of potato seed certification has been established in a large number of states, with the major objective of providing seed that is essentially free from the serious seed-borne diseases. In 1939, nearly 14 million bushels of certified seed potatoes were produced, the highest point in a continuous increase up to that time. Seed was certified that year in 26 states, the largest production being in Maine, North Dakota, and Minnesota. In general, the northern states, even more specifically the northern parts of northern states, are in the best position to produce disease-free certified seed because their climatic conditions are less conducive to the development and spread of seed-borne diseases. The real merit of certified seed, however, is vitally dependent on the establishment of high certification requirements and their rigid enforcement by the seed-certifying agency. By an intense spraying program, by the maintenance of disease-free seed plots, and by thorough roguing of diseased plants from their seed fields, certified-seed growers are able to produce seed of exceptional value with respect to freedom from disease. To make sure that the seed does maintain high standards of value, official seed-certifying agencies conduct field and bin inspections and issue certification tags only for seed that meets rigid requirements with respect to type, quality, size, varietal purity, and freedom from seed-borne diseases.

Further to check the disease freedom of certified-seed stocks, some of the seed-certifying agencies plant samples of each seed lot in the South in the winter and make disease readings on each lot before the bulk of seed is planted in the North for commercial potato production.

Fig. 105.—Roguing diseased plants from potatoes being grown for certified seed. (*Courtesy of H. C. Moore, Michigan Crop Improvement Association.*)

Some of the more important seed-borne diseases held under control by the rigid roguing and culling requirements of seed certification are as follows:

1. Virus or degenerative diseases carried in the seed and spread from plant to plant in the field by means of the sap of diseased plants. Certain potato insects such as aphids and leaf hoppers are often responsible for the field spread of virus diseases. Notable examples are

Mosaic:
  Mild.
  Leaf-rolling.
  Rugose.
  Crinkle.
Leaf roll—one of the most prevalent.
Curly dwarf.
Spindle tuber.

Yellow dwarf.
Spindling sprout.

2. Diseases caused by fungi or bacteria.

Rhizoctonia disease.
Scab.
Blackleg.
Fusarium wilt.
Verticillium wilt.
Bacterial ring rot.

Other Disorders.—There are several other disorders of potatoes sometimes confused with fungus, bacterial, or virus diseases that are in fact caused by insects, abnormal environmental conditions, and mechanical injury. Among these are hopperburn, a yellowing at the tips of the leaflets followed by blackening and drying out of the affected tissue and caused by the feeding of the potato leaf hopper on the foliage; blackheart, a breakdown of internal tissues in storage as a result of insufficient oxygen in a poorly ventilated storage space; internal brown spot, an aggravated form of heat and drought necrosis that develops in potatoes grown on light, gravelly soil during seasons of drought and high temperature; and hollow heart, the development of hollow-centered tubers when growth is too rapid, usually due to an oversupply of moisture following periods of drought. Varieties differ in susceptibility to the latter, and the ailment is greatly checked by close spacing and timely applications of water, if irrigation is practiced.

Potato Harvest and Storage.—The season for the harvest of potatoes in the United States begins in December in the early-crop sections of the South and continues throughout the year, winding up about Nov. 1 in the late-crop area of the North. Harvest begins in southern Florida, the December crop coming from early fall plantings of the current season, and proceeds to southeastern Texas and then to northern Florida followed by Louisiana, Alabama, South Carolina, and Georgia. This covers the winter and spring season up to June.

North Carolina, Arkansas, and Oklahoma potatoes are harvested in late May, June, and early July; the bulk of the Eastern Shore crop of Virginia and Maryland is harvested in July, followed by the crops of the Kaw Valley in Kansas and the Orrick section of Missouri, and then by Kentucky, New Jersey, and Long Island (New York) crops, in order.

Early potatoes of the northern late-crop area are harvested in August, and the late crop is harvested in September and October. California, classed with the late-crop surplus states, harvests potatoes continuously from the beginning of the early-crop season to the end of the late-crop.[1] Thus, somewhere in the United States, potatoes are being harvested and marketed almost continuously, and their distribution to every section of the country is fairly constant.

Practically all of the commercial crop is harvested with the elevator type of digger, horse- or tractor-drawn, which brings the potatoes out of the ground, shakes them relatively free from dirt and vines, and

Fig. 106.—A tractor-powered, elevator-type, two-row potato digger. (*Courtesy of John Deere, Moline, Ill.*)

deposits them in rows from which they are picked by hand into suitable containers and taken to storage or the market.

The important consideration in harvest is to avoid bruising or injuring the potatoes in any way, for injured tubers are discriminated against on the market and are far more susceptible to spoilage in storage.

A potato storage must be insulated to maintain even temperatures of 38 to 40°F. and ventilated to prevent excess humidity on the one hand or a lack of oxygen on the other, and it must be dark to prevent the greening and spoilage of tubers that occurs if they are exposed to light. It is not advisable to store potatoes in bins at a greater depth

[1] Strowbridge, J. W., Origin and Distribution of the Commercial Potato Crop, *U.S. Dept. Agr. Tech. Bul.* 7 (revised), 1939.

than 5 or 6 ft., nor should bins be larger than 12 by 12 ft. in floor dimensions.

Potato Varieties.—In days gone by, potato varieties, like Topsy, "just grow'd." Some excellent lines came into being in this haphazard fashion. But a multitude of "just potatoes" were also named, and there was much confusion in the way of different names for the same variety and the same names for different varieties. So long as names were cheap, there were names for varieties that did not deserve such distinction. Seed-potato certification and varietal standardization have tended to focus consideration on a relatively few varieties of real merit. In recent years the potato-breeding program of the U.S. Department of Agriculture, conducted in cooperation with the several interested state agricultural experiment stations, has made available new varieties of great promise. The aim of this breeding work has been to develop varieties of superior culinary and market quality, to maintain in the new lines a high standard of productivity, to develop in them inherent resistance to some of the more troublesome diseases, and to find lines adapted to various conditions of environment.

Some of the more widely grown late varieties of long standing are the Green Mountain, Russet Rural, Russet Burbank (Netted Gem), and White Rural (Rural New Yorker). The Green Mountain is a favorite on the market because of good culinary qualities. It requires cool, moist growing conditions and is widely grown in Maine, on Long Island, in northern Michigan, and elsewhere. The Rural group includes varieties that are less restricted in adaptation than the Green Mountain. They stand heat and dry weather better, and the Russet Rurals are less susceptible to scab than most white varieties. They are widely grown in Pennsylvania, western New York, southern Michigan, Wisconsin, and other middle-western areas.

The Russet Burbank is popular as a baking potato. It is an elongated, russet-skinned, late potato at its best under favorable growing conditions such as are provided in the irrigated potato-growing districts of Idaho.

The Irish Cobbler, a white-skinned, deep-eyed potato, is the most widely grown of early varieties, followed in popularity by the Triumph, a round, red-skinned early potato.

Of the new varieties resulting from organized plant-breeding work the Chippewa and Katahdin varieties have thus far been most widely accepted. Both are white-skinned, shallow-eyed potatoes of excellent quality and good productivity if grown under conditions that are unfavorable for the development of scab. The Chippewa, about 10 days earlier than Katahdin and 3 weeks earlier than Russet Rural, is sometimes planted early and harvested shortly after the Irish Cobbler as an early potato.

Some other new varieties currently of considerable promise are:

Pontiac—a late red potato that has yielded well on muck.

Sebago—selected from a Katahdin × Chippewa cross and showing evidence of some late-blight resistance.

Earlaine—an early variety from a cross between Irish Cobbler and an unnamed variety, highly resistant to mild mosaic, promising in Maine and parts of New York and Colorado.

Potato Grading and Marketing.—The U.S. Department of Agriculture has established grades for the classification of potatoes on the market. These grades are based on size, trueness to type, freedom from disease or blemish, and other attributes of quality.

Grading machines are used to separate the potatoes of different sizes. If these are equipped with a roller-type picking table, the removal of scabby, off-type, cut, and otherwise undesirable potatoes is greatly facilitated.

The packaging of high-quality potatoes in small (usually 15-lb.) sacks has proved attractive to consumers who appreciate the convenience of the smaller package and associate the branded sacks with quality if a good job of sorting and grading has been done.

Every surplus-potato-producing state produces a certain percentage of cull potatoes regardless of how good the general crop may be. The low-grade potatoes if marketed as table stock are low-priced, do not warrant high transportation costs, and hence clutter the markets of the locality in which they are produced to the detriment of the price and good repute of all potatoes grown in that area. Their conversion into industrial channels, for starch or alcohol manufacture, or their retention on the producing farms as stock feed would unquestionably benefit the potato market in general and improve consumer satisfaction.

If potatoes are shipped for long distances, only the best repay transportation cost. Often on potato markets the potatoes that are shipped in from the greatest distance bring the best prices, though the growers obliged to ship such long distances net relatively low prices because of marketing and transportation expenses.

Potato markets fluctuate widely or even wildly from year to year. The crop is perishable, with no carry-overs from one season to burden the next crop. Hence, the potato market is a weather market highly sensitive to current crop conditions and prospects for immediate supplies.

Potato Growing as a Farm Enterprise.—The potato needs no processing except that which it gets in the kitchen. There are hundreds of thousands of farms on which but a few rows are grown for the home table. Even in many of the great surplus-crop states like Michigan, Wisconsin, Minnesota, New York, and Pennsylvania the average acreage of farms reporting potatoes in the 1935 agricultural census was only 1.5 to 2.0 per farm.

Many growers who sell potatoes produce the crop at a disadvantage as regards such equipment as mechanical planters, power sprayers, diggers, graders, and suitable storage facilities. To some extent the cost of such equipment is spread over more acres by cooperative ownership and custom work. To an even larger extent the smaller acreages are put in by hand, inadequately sprayed, poorly graded and packaged, and marketed with too little regard for the attributes of quality that appeal to the consumer.

Some growers in almost every state operate on a much larger than average basis, and certain localities have made potato growing a major enterprise. Some of these specialized potato-growing areas and the extent of the potato enterprise in each are given in the following table.

Locality	Number of potato-growing farms	Average acreage per farm	Average yield per acre, bushels
Aroostook County, Maine..............	6,014	22.2	348
Twin Falls County, Idaho..............	1,343	14.0	245
San Joaquin County, California........	165	83.2	281
Suffolk County, New York (Long Island)	1,229	26.9	205
Monmouth County, New Jersey........	1,007	14.3	171
St. Lucie County, Florida..............	204	34.5	161

The figures are from the 1935 Census of Agriculture.

Growers with large acreages can utilize mechanical equipment effectively. The special potato areas have been producing good acre yields, one of the major considerations in efficiency. However, investments and expenses are also high. In the Schrumpf study in Aroostook County, previously referred to (page 362), the farm capital averaged $40,184 on certified-seed farms, $31,100 on Presque Isle farms, and $17,896 on Holton farms, the latter two groups being table-stock growers. Yearly expenses for these groups averaged $10,977, $7,571, and $4,917, respectively; and the labor income per farm was $2,134, $689, and $702. These farms were larger and grew a much greater acreage of potatoes than the average for Aroostook County. More than 85 per cent of the receipts were from potatoes.

In some years the specialized potato farm thrives, especially in those rare seasons when high yields and high prices coincide. However, the grower who depends almost exclusively on potatoes hazards his whole year's income against the uncertainties of weather, the destructive influence of diseases and insects, and the fluctuations of a capricious market.

SWEET POTATOES

Botanically, *Ipomoea batatus* is a perennial vine like some of its bindweed relatives. However, this species develops an enlarged,

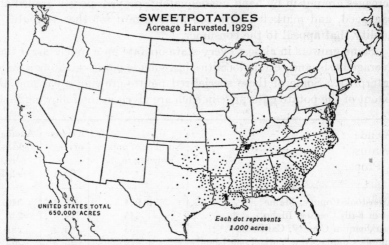

FIG. 107.—Sweet potatoes are a southern crop but are grown in sandy soils as far north as Muscatine County, Iowa, and southern New Jersey. In general, New Jersey sweet potatoes are drier than those of the South (some of the latter are called yams) and are highly esteemed for their quality. In the eastern and central cotton belt, sweet potatoes largely replace potatoes as a staple food of the people. It will be noted that there are four intensive areas of sweet potato production. (*U.S. Department of Agriculture.*)

fleshy root growth that people throughout most of the United States, but more particularly in the South, have found desirable as a food. Because the edible roots of the sweet potato develop during the first season of growth, this perennial is managed agriculturally as an annual.

Production and Prices.—As a home-garden crop, sweet potatoes may be grown as far north as southern Michigan and southern New York. Profitable commercial production is restricted largely to the cotton belt although a small acreage is grown in southern Indiana, Illinois, and Iowa. Georgia had the largest 1929–1938 average acreage, 115,000; and Georgia and North Carolina each produced an average annual crop of over 8 million bushels. The data for all states,

22 of which reported substantial commercial production, were 72,436,-
000 bu. grown on 860,000 acres. The New Jersey–Delaware–Maryland–Virginia region produced the highest average acre yields, 112 to
138 bu. to the acre, compared with 85 for all states. The United
States farm price in the 1930–1939 decade ranged from a low of 54.2
cents a bushel in 1932 to 108.2 cents a bushel in 1930 and maintained
an unweighted average of 77.9 cents a bushel for that 10-year period.[1]

Soil Requirements.—Sweet potatoes are grown on a wide range of
soils; but their requirements are best met on light, well-drained sandy
loams with a heavier subsoil. Organic matter such as is provided by
leguminous crop residues or green manures is essential for the production of good yields; but, on highly fertile soils, vine growth is excessive,
and the roots are apt to be reduced in quantity of growth and rough and
irregular in appearance.

Fertilization is much the same in principle as for Irish potatoes. A
complete fertilizer is generally recommended, with applications of not
more than 600 lb. an acre on light, poor soil, 600 to 1,000 lb. for the late
crop, and 1,500 to 2,000 lb. for the early crop.[2] The specific analysis
depends on the soil. Stable manure at the rate of 2 to 5 tons an acre is
often used advantageously.

Propagation.—Sweet potatoes are propagated vegetatively by
means of slips and vine cuttings. The slips are grown directly from
sweet-potato roots, usually planted in hotbeds. The bed consists of
about a 6-in. layer of horse manure covered with a 3-in. layer of soil on
which the sweet potatoes are planted. The potatoes are first covered
with 1½ in. of sand or light loam, and this layer of dirt is built up as the
plants show through until there is 6 in. of soil over the original potatoes
when the vines are ready to be cut into slips. The temperature of the
bed should be 80 to 85°F. when the plants are bedded, and it should
gradually fall to 70 to 75°F. and remain there until the time for field
planting.

It takes about 8,000 slips to plant an acre of sweet potatoes in
4-foot rows, with the plants spaced at 15 in. in the row. Eight to
twelve bushels of seed potatoes should produce enough slips for the
direct planting of 1 acre, the practice followed for the early-planted
crop.

In most of the cotton belt the main crop of sweet potatoes is grown
from vine cuttings. In this case, only enough roots need be bedded to
produce slips for about one-eighth the area to be planted. The slips
are set out in the usual manner, and cuttings are made from their vines,

---

[1] *U.S. Dept. Agr. Crops and Markets*, Vol. 17, No. 12, 1940.
[2] SPENCER, A. P., Sweet Potatoes, *Fla. Ext. Bul.* 61 (revised), 1931.

as they develop, and are used to plant the balance of the acreage. Growth from cuttings is generally more vigorous and better able to withstand adverse conditions but, of course, can be used practicably for only the later plantings.

It is customary to grow the sweet-potato crop on ridges made with a plow before planting and maintained throughout cultivation. However, where poor drainage is not a factor, level plantings seem to be fully as satisfactory as those made on ridges. The transplanting of slips and cuttings to the field was formerly a hand job accomplished with the aid of various hand trowels, dibbles, tongs, etc. Transplanting machines are now used for the larger acreages. These remove much of the stoop labor from sweet-potato growing and make the time of setting less dependent on favorably moist weather, for the transplanting machines themselves are usually equipped to give each plant a squirt of water as it is being set. Frequent shallow cultivation is desirable until the vines cover the ground.

Harvest.—Early-crop sweet potatoes may be harvested any time after they reach marketable size. They are moved to the market for immediate consumption. The main crop is intended for storage, curing, and shipment to distant points. In this case the roots are allowed to mature as much as possible. Light frosting of the leaves is not damaging, but a severe frost spoils the keeping quality of the potatoes and must be avoided.

Harvesting implements vary, but the ordinary turn plow equipped with two rolling colters to cut the vines is entirely effective if run deep enough to avoid bruising the potatoes. The dug potatoes are scratched out of the dirt and left to dry for a short time, but not overnight. Prolonged exposure to sunlight causes sunburning. Windrowing or piling the roots is to be avoided because of their susceptibility to bruising and mechanical injury.

Preliminary sorting of the crop is done in the field on the basis of size, color, freedom from blemish, and general quality. Regrading of a stored crop is usually necessary before it is finally marketed. The storage of small crops is accomplished in small straw-covered piles or banks. Crops of 1,500 to 2,000 bu. or more, regularly grown on a farm, warrant the expense of a storage house in which the crated or binned potatoes are dried with ample ventilation at temperatures of 80 to 85°F. for about 10 days or until the roots begin to sprout and the outside is soft and velvety. The temperature is then reduced to 50 to 60°F. Heating facilities are usually necessary to prevent lower temperatures and to dry the house out if moisture starts to collect on windows or the ceiling.

Varieties.—Northern markets prefer the drier mealy varieties, one of the most popular being Big-Stem Jersey. Others of this group are Yellow Jersey, smaller and smoother than Big-Stem; Red Jersey, with a red skin; and Triumph.

The Nancy Hall is very sweet, with a soft texture, and is grown in the South for both southern and northern markets. The Porto Rico has the rich color, moist, soft flesh, and sweet flavor preferred in the South. It keeps well in storage if harvested without being bruised. In all, about a dozen varieties have attained some importance, some of them in localized areas; but the ones named above are the most widely grown.

Review Problems

1. That portion of the plant used for food is

    a. Stem tissue in the case of potatoes; root in sweet potatoes.
    b. Enlarged root growth with both crops.
    c. Enlarged portion of underground stem with both crops.
    d. Stem growth in sweet potatoes; root growth in potatoes.

2. The potato is a native of

    a. Ireland.
    b. France.
    c. Russia.
    d. United States.
    e. South America.

3. The potato grows best where the climate is

    a. Warm and humid.
    b. Cool and moist.
    c. Temperate and dry.
    d. Cool and dry.

4. The soil requirements of potatoes are best satisfied on

    a. Sandy loam to loam soils moderately acid.
    b. Rich clay loam to clay soils high in lime.
    c. Light, acid sands.
    d. Gravelly limestone soils.

5. The thorough spraying of potatoes with Bordeaux mixture properly supplemented with calcium arsenate is a control measure for all but which one of the following pests?

    a. Early blight.
    b. Rhizoctonia disease.
    c. Late blight.
    d. Potato bugs.
    e. Leaf hoppers.

6. Which of the following is not a virus disease?

    a. Mosaic.
    b. Yellow dwarf.
    c. Leaf roll.
    d. Fusarium wilt.

7. When potatoes in storage get insufficient oxygen they are apt to develop which of the following conditions?

    a. Internal brown spot.
    b. Blackheart.
    c. Hollow heart.
    d. Spindling sprout.

8. Highest average acre yields of sweet potatoes are secured in

    a. The southern Indiana–Illinois–Iowa region.
    b. Florida, Georgia, and the Carolinas.
    c. The Gulf coast region of Louisiana and Texas.
    d. The New Jersey–Delaware–Maryland–Virginia region.

9. The main crop of sweet potatoes is propagated from

    a. Seed.
    b. Root cuttings.
    c. Tubers.
    d. Vine cuttings.

10. After sweet potatoes have been cured the proper storage temperatures are

    a. 80 to 85°F.
    b. 70 to 80°F.
    c. 50 to 60°F.
    d. 38 to 40°F.

11. Under what conditions can 1,500 to 2,000 lb. of fertilizer be used to best advantage for potatoes? Why?

12. Why have potato growers been shifting to the use of higher analysis fertilizers?

13. What planting practice aids in the control of potato hollow heart? Why?

14. What are the advantages of green-sprouting seed potatoes?

15. Why is seed treatment only partly effective in the control of scab and black scurf?

16. Look up current machinery prices, and make an estimate of the cost of the special planting, spraying, and harvesting machinery a farmer would require for the annual growing of 20 acres of potatoes.

17. What variety of potatoes is most widely grown in your state? Why?

18. Describe the soil and climatic conditions best suited for sweet-potato production.

19. What soil-management practices are followed to improve the acre yield of sweet potatoes?

20. What difficulties are likely to be encountered in trying to grow sweet potatoes on dark-colored, very fertile soils?

21. Why is the elevator type of Irish potato digger not used for the harvest of sweet potatoes?

22. What factors determine the time to harvest sweet potatoes?

References

BUSHNELL, JOHN: Experiments with Potatoes on Muck Soil, *Ohio Agr. Expt. Sta. Bul.* 570, 1936.

CUMINGS, G. A., and G. V. C. GOUGHLAND: Fertilizer Placement for Potatoes, *U.S. Dept. Agr. Tech. Bul.* 669, 1939.

GILBERT, A. W.: "The Potato," The Macmillan Company, New York, 1917.

HUTCHESON, T. B., T. K. WOLFE, and M. S. KIPPS: "The Production of Field Crops," McGraw-Hill Book Company, Inc., New York, 1936.

MUNCIE, J. H.: Michigan Potato Diseases and Their Control, *Mich. Ext. Bul.* 162 (revised), 1936.

SCHILLETTER, A. E., and G. E. PRINCE: The Sweet Potato Industry, *Clemson Agr. Col. S.C. Ext. Serv. Bul.* 84, 1927.

SPENCER, A. P.: Sweet Potatoes, *Fla. Ext. Bul.* 61, 1931.

STROWBRIDGE, J. W.: Origin and Distribution of the Commercial Potato Crop, *U.S. Dept. Agr. Tech. Bul.* 7 (revised), 1939.

STUART, WM.: Production of Late or Main-crop Potatoes, *U.S. Dept. Agr. Farmers' Bul.* 1064 (revised), 1933.

WERNER, H. O.: The Cause and Prevention of Mechanical Injuries to Potatoes, *Nebr. Agr. Expt. Sta. Bul.* 260, 1931.

CHAPTER XX

SUGAR CROPS

The average American has a sweet tooth.   Just prior to the entry of the United States into the Second World War he annually consumed about 105 lb. of sucrose, the sugar that comes from the cane and the beet, besides the sugar in other forms that he got in sweet fruits, maple sirup, honey, and many other foods.   In other countries the next highest per capita consumption was about 75 lb.   The United States sugar budget for 1941 planned for the consumption of over 8,000,000 tons of refined sugar.   That amount allowed for much more sweetening than that derived from the extra lump of sugar that goes in the coffee cup.   It covered the sugar in cakes, pastries, icings, and scores of dessert recipes; it included the sugar for the thousands of bushels of fruits canned at home and in commercial canneries and the sugar used in myriads of candied confections that are eaten nowhere to such an extent as in the United States.   And, in 1941 it covered considerable sugar hoarding in anticipation of a wartime shortage, for normal United States consumption had been about 6,500,000 tons. This amount can readily be produced in the United States and near-by cane-growing islands.

It is a commonplace to refer to the sugar spread so liberally over our breakfast cereal, that added to the natural sugars of strawberries or to the bananas that we eat with the cereal, or the heaping spoonfuls used as sweetening for the tart citrus fruits and their juices.   It is less of a commonplace to remember that the pure sucrose which is cane or beet sugar is one of the most concentrated sources of human energy and that most of us practically never eat a meal without it; yet our not too remote ancestors scarcely knew of sugar—considered it a medicine rather than a food—and depended on wild sweets that today merely supplement the sucrose we use so directly.

Sources of United States Sugar.—Continental United States produces only about 25 per cent of its sugar requirements; yet so great is the potential production of its insular areas and near-by Cuba that the management of sugar production to keep it in line with effective demand has long been an important problem.   Legislation designed to bring about this control (the Sugar Act of 1937) provided for the budgeting of the United States sugar market to the following areas:

Continental United States:
  Beet sugar.
  Louisiana and Florida cane sugar.
Offshore areas:
  Hawaii.
  Puerto Rico.
  Virgin Islands.
  Philippine Islands.
  Cuba.
  Other countries (a minor share).

Under this act, provision was made for the revision of quotas in line with changes in market conditions and requirements. For the most part, the measure was restrictive on production up to the 1942 crop when wartime shipping difficulties made expansion of continental production advisable. Restriction was brought about through sales allotments to processors and production allotments to growers. Under this legislation, growers received not only returns from the sale of cane or beets to the processors but also an additional payment from the Federal government based on the amount of sugar produced and contingent on compliance with specified labor provisions and soil-conservation practices.

The Cane-producing Areas.—The offshore sugar-producing areas that contribute in a major way to United States sugar supplies are tropical islands with climatic conditions suited for the growing of sugar cane. Cuba leads this group. Its average production for 1925–1929 was over five million tons of raw cane sugar annually, the largest of any country in the world. For the 1930–1934 period, Cuba's average was under three million tons and for 1936–1940 slightly over that amount, and India became the leading producer. Production in India, however, is of a low-grade sugar called *gur*, which is consumed almost entirely within that country.

Hawaii and Puerto Rico are each capable of producing well over a million tons of sugar annually but have tended to produce just under this amount because of the restrictive provisions of sugar legislation. Philippine production is somewhat greater than that of either Hawaii or Puerto Rico, and production in the Virgin Islands is usually only about 6,000 to 8,000 tons.

Largest acre yields of cane are secured in Hawaii where the average is often in excess of 60 tons an acre as compared with 14 to 18 in the Philippines and 25 to 28 in Puerto Rico. In Hawaii, however, only a portion of the total acreage in cane is harvested each year, the harvested crop consisting of 18 to 24 months' growth. The length of the growing season for cane in the Philippines is about 11 months; in Puerto

Rico about one-third the crop is of 18 months' growth and two-thirds is 12 months' growth. The length of the cane-growing season in Cuba is normally 18 months, but the acre yields are more nearly comparable with those secured in the Philippine Islands.

In continental United States, cane sugar is grown in Louisiana and Florida. Louisiana has the larger acreage, 238,000 in 1939, with an estimated production of 21.4 tons of cane to the acre grown in a 9-month season. The Florida season is of 12 months' duration; the 1939 acreage was about 20,000, and the average yield 35.5 tons an acre.

Beet-sugar Areas in the United States.—The chief source of home-grown sugar in continental United States is the sugar beet. Incidentally, both the cane and the beet produce sucrose; and the sugar from these two plants, when pure, is chemically identical and likewise identical in its culinary performance. There are two major sugar-beet-growing areas in the United States—the western area in which the crop is grown under irrigation, with Colorado and California leading in production; and the eastern, or humid, area, with the largest acreage in Michigan and Ohio. Largest yields are secured in the western area, the 1928–1937 average ranging from about 11 tons an acre in Idaho to 13 tons in California. During the same years, Ohio averaged 7.7 tons an acre and Michigan 8.6 tons. In the humid area, 14 to 16 tons an acre is considered a very good crop, and anything over 20 tons is exceptional. Under the most favorable conditions in California, yields of well over 40 tons an acre have been secured. Normally, 250 to a little over 300 lb. of sugar is secured from a ton of beets.

THE SUGAR-BEET CROP

The sugar-beet plant is a biennial; but for sugar production it is managed as an annual, with commercial interest centering in the large fleshy taproots in which the sugar is stored.

Although sugar beets in the West are grown under irrigation and the crop in the East is not, the cultural systems of the two regions have much in common.

Climatic and Soil Requirements.—R. H. Tucker and T. G. Stewart of Colorado state:

[Sugar beets] do best where there is a moderately long growing season or frost-free period, and also where temperatures are not excessively high in this growing period. Either the young or the mature sugar-beet plant is not generally injured by light spring or fall frosts. This makes it possible to plant early and to prolong harvest over a rather long period. . . .

Probably fine sandy loam or clay loam soils are preferred [for sugar-beet culture], but a good deep soil properly drained, whatever its texture, may be ʇsed if it contains a plentiful supply of available plant food. All soils and particularly sandy or very heavy soils will be improved by applications of organic matter in the form of barnyard or green manure and crop residues. Beets do not grow well where the water table is too close to the surface.[1]

Similarly we find in a Michigan publication,

Michigan's best beet soils are well drained, frequently by means of tile. They are high in organic matter and contain sufficient lime to test neutral or

Fig. 108.—Many of the better sugar-beet soils are drained by means of tile. (*Courtesy of E. E. Patton.*)

essentially neutral in reaction. Their clay and silt content is high—high enough so they are classified as loams, silt loams, clay loams, or clays. Popularly, this whole group is called clay soil. It is good, dark, "heavy" soil with a deserved reputation for fertility.[2]

An exceptionally high tonnage of sugar beets can be grown on muck. But ordinary varieties, when grown on muck, have normally been lower in percentage of sugar and sometimes also in sugar purity.

[1] TUCKER, R. H., and T. G. STEWART, Sugar-beet Growing in Colorado, *Colo. Agr. Col. Ext. Bul.* 363A, 1941.

[2] RATHER, H. C., *et al.*, Sugar Beets in Michigan, *Mich. Agr. Expt. Sta. Circ. Bul.* 175, 1940.

Acid soils are unsatisfactory for growing sugar beets. If they are otherwise satisfactory, they will produce sugar beets well if the acidity is corrected with suitable applications of lime. Sugar beets tolerate as high alkalinity in soil as nearly any crop; but excess alkali salts, sometimes found in the West, should be removed by drainage and heavy irrigation if beets are to be grown effectively.

Crop Sequence.—The fundamentals of a good crop rotation for sugar beets are the same as for good crop rotations in general. In both the western and eastern areas, alfalfa is often the basic legume. It is considered difficult but it certainly is by no means impossible to grow a good crop of beets immediately following alfalfa. Some of the difficulties are mechanical, and these can be overcome by fall plowing of the alfalfa so as to cover the crowns deeply in moist soil in order that they may be well decomposed by beet seeding time. Fall plowing of alfalfa may not result in the complete destruction of the plants which, if they survive, become a serious weed the following season. In this respect, alfalfa is similar to sweet clover though the latter is more likely to recover. The destruction of alfalfa that is to be plowed under is aided by previous frequent and early cutting for hay or by close grazing during the early fall period when root reserves are being stored. Other difficulties have been associated with the fungi that cause damping off of beet seedlings, fungi that live on alfalfa and beets but not on corn. Damping off, or black root, is supposedly less prevalent in sugar beets when beets follow corn than when they follow alfalfa. The management of alfalfa in a beet rotation is being studied intensively; in the absence of serious black-root infection, much better beet yields are secured immediately after alfalfa than if an intervening crop of corn is grown.

Sugar beets leave the soil in desirable condition for most following crops. In both Ohio and Michigan trials, spring grains have produced better yields after beets than after corn when fertilization of the beets and corn was the same. Usually, much higher applications of fertilizer are made on sugar beets, a very responsive crop, than on corn, and the residual effect of the fertilizers is beneficial to subsequent crops.

A common rotation is as follows:

1. Sugar beets.
2. Oats or barley seeded to alfalfa.
3. Alfalfa.
4. Alfalfa.
5. Corn or field beans.

In the West, two beet crops are often grown in succession. This is not considered objectionable for 2 years, except in areas infested with the sugar-beet nematode.

Fertilizer for Beets.—Because the sugar-beet crop has a high acre value, a moderate increase in yield due to fertilization pays for liberal applications. As a matter of fact, beets respond very well to the application of such nutrients as are deficient in the soil. The natural supply of phosphorus is inadequate in most beet soils; and although potassium may be present in abundant quantities, it often is in unavailable form. Hence, complete fertilizers are most commonly used. The effectiveness of the fertilizer for sugar beets is improved if it is placed in a single band $1\frac{1}{2}$ to 2 in. below the seed level and either directly under or $\frac{1}{2}$ to 1 in. to the side of the row. In this manner, 300 or 400 lb. an acre of a fertilizer such as a 4-16-8 can be used without danger of injury to the seed and young seedlings.

Some sugar-beet soils are deficient in boron. In such cases the small heart leaves of the sugar beet may die at an early age or, if they survive, may appear stunted and ill-shaped; and crown rots frequently develop. The soil's deficiency can be corrected by a row application of 7 or 8 lb. or a broadcast application of 20 lb. an acre of borax. Materially larger applications may be injurious. The borax, where needed, is most conveniently applied in a mixture with commercial fertilizer.

Preparation of Land.—Sugar beets require a firm, granular seedbed well supplied with moisture. This condition is most readily obtained on fall-plowed fields. Much of the land on which sugar beets are grown is fairly level, and erosion is not a serious problem. On sloping land covered with vegetation, really early spring plowing is usually the better practice. Regardless of time the direction of plowing should be across rather than up and down the slopes. Thorough use of the disk harrow and Cultipacker brings desirable granulation and firmness, and tillage prior to planting can greatly reduce the amount of weed-control effort required after the beets are up.

Planting.—Sugar-beet planting time follows that for spring grain as closely as is possible, with due allowance for thorough seedbed preparation. In order to avoid labor congestion at the time the beets are thinned, growers with large acreages often plant at a succession of two or three dates. There is usually a period of around 3 weeks during which differences in time of planting do not materially influence yield.

Sugar-beet drills plant the seed in rows; the newer types place the fertilizer in bands below but near the seed. The drills used in districts practicing irrigation are equipped with ditchers to furrow out the land. The seed is planted 1 to $1\frac{1}{2}$ in. deep.

The amount of seed recommended for ordinary planting is 18 to 20 lb. an acre. Single-seed planting plates have been used in an effort to reduce labor at thinning time. With these plates, only 6 to 10 lb. of seed an acre is required; but the lesser amount of seed must have ideal conditions and the absence of any crust formation, or a poor stand may result.

Width of Rows.—Most of the experiments dealing with width of rows for sugar beets, especially those under favorable conditions, have indicated that the narrower rows of 18, 20, or 22 in. produced greater acre yields and generally somewhat smaller beets of higher sugar content. In actual practice, many beet growers who also produce beans grow sugar beets in 28-in. rows, the standard width for beans, in

Fig. 109.—Repeated shallow cultivation and one or two hoeings in addition to that accomplished by blocking the beets are usually necessary to bring about effective weed control. (*Courtesy of E. E. Patton.*)

order that the two crops may be cultivated with the same equipment without change. The 24-in. row is also widely used. Beets planted at 24 in. result in a 16.5 per cent increase in row length per acre as compared with 28-in. rows; a 22-in. row results in a 27.3 per cent increase. The labor of drilling, blocking, thinning, hoeing, cultivating, and lifting is increased roughly in proportion to the use of narrower rows, but this additional labor would be more than paid for by an increased yield in the narrower rows of a ton of beets to the acre, a conservative expectation.

Blocking and Thinning.—Sugar-beet seed as it is planted is in reality a seed ball made up of one to several seeds with their dry, adhering floral parts. Each medium-sized seed ball usually contains two or three seeds capable of growth. Thus, even in single-seed planting the seedlings grow in clusters, and in normal planting there is produced a more or less continuous row of seedling clusters. When the seedlings reach the six- to eight-leaf stage the stand is reduced to one beet plant in 10 to 12 in. of row. One hundred beets to 100 ft. of row is considered a perfect stand. Minor differences in the distance between beets are less important than uniformity of spacing.

Blocking (cutting out excess beets between clusters with a hoe) and thinning (reducing each cluster to a single seedling) are two of the hand jobs in sugar-beet culture. Various machines have been invented to do this job, but none of them does it so well as a good beet laborer. Mechanical blocking by cross cultivation of perfect stands is effective and economical and encourages a more vigorous early growth.

Cultivation.—Experiments in both Colorado and Michigan have shown that in the case of sugar beets, as with other row crops, the function of cultivation is to control weeds and that cultivation beyond the needs of weed control is unnecessary. However, young beet seedlings are not good weed competitors, and poor weed control on good sugar-beet soil can readily cost $20 to $40 an acre in reduced yields. Repeated shallow cultivation and one or two hoeings in addition to that accomplished in blocking the beets are usually necessary to bring about effective weed control.

Irrigation Methods.—Where beets are grown under irrigation, the water requirement is greatest during the last half of the growing season. It is best met by frequent moderate applications which keep the beets growing and in good condition rather than by heavy irrigation at longer intervals. A light irrigation is 1 to 2 acre-in. of water. Six inches is heavy, excessive, and wasteful of water.

Harvest.—Beets store most of their sugar in the autumn, with bright days and cool nights favoring development of a high sugar content. In order to secure maximum tonnage of roots and a high sugar content, harvest is deferred as long as it is safe to do so without danger of part of the crop being frozen in the ground. It usually extends over a period of at least 2 months to permit orderly delivery of the crop to the factory.

The beets are first loosened in the ground with a lifter, then pulled by hand, knocked together to remove adhering soil, and thrown into piles or windrows. Topping consists of cutting off the crown and leaves, another hand job. Machines invented to do this work have shown some promise where the soil at harvesttime is not too wet and where the leaves are strong and free from disease so that they do not break to pieces under machine handling. Some machines top the unpulled beets which are dug mechanically after the tops are removed.

The topped beets are piled and covered with leaves to reduce shrinkage until they can be delivered to the factory or weighing station.

Fig. 110.—Beets store most of their sugar in the fall with bright days and cool nights favoring development of a high sugar content. (*Courtesy of E. E. Patton.*)

Sugar-beet Diseases.—The chief diseases of sugar beets in both eastern and western areas are leaf spot or blight, caused by the fungus *Cercospora beticola*, and black root of three different types, each caused by a separate fungus and primarily affecting the seedling root on wet, poorly aerated soils. No very satisfactory control methods have been devised for black root. Leaf spot may be controlled by spraying or dusting with copper fungicides where the incidence of the disease is great enough to warrant the expense. Varieties significantly resistant to leaf spot have been developed and are in commercial use.

Curly top, a virus disease of the sugar beet found in certain parts of the western area, is spread by a leaf hopper commonly called the *white fly*. The disease is very destructive and at one time seriously threatened the existence of the beet industry of infested areas. The control was eventually accomplished by the development of curly-top-resistant varieties now used generally throughout areas where this disease is likely to occur.

Root-knot Nematodes.—Root-knot nematodes when present in the soil make it almost impossible to grow sugar beets. They spread rapidly throughout a field and may be transferred from one location to another in the soil that falls from the beets as they are hauled from the field.

Nematodes are usually controlled by crop rotations that always avoid beets after beets and that provide for the culture of nonsusceptible alfalfa, corn, beans, or small grain for a 5-year or longer period between beet crops. In cases of extremely severe infection, abandonment of sugar-beet culture may be necessary.

By-products.—The by-products of sugar-beet culture are the beet tops on the farm and the beet pulp and molasses at the factory. Beet tops are fed to livestock or returned to the land. They can be fed most economically by turning livestock, usually cattle or sheep, into the beet field after the roots have been removed. Sometimes they are brought to the feed lot and fed from small piles. Occasionally they are ensiled. Because they usually contain well over 80 per cent water, they must be ensiled with drier material such as straw or cornstalks to bring the average moisture content of the silage down to about 70 per cent. A ton of green beet tops contains digestible nutrients equivalent in amount to the digestible nutrients in about 2.4 bu. of shelled corn. The production of 4 to 8 tons of tops an acre can be expected from beets yielding 8 to 16 tons of marketable roots.

Wet beet pulp is sometimes fed on farms near western sugar factories, but most of the pulp is dried and sold as stock feed. The molasses is also sold for stock feed. Approximately 90 to 95 lb. of dried beet pulp and 35 lb. of molasses are secured from a ton of beets in addition to the sugar.

Grower-Processor Relationships.—The sugar-beet industry of the eastern area provides an interesting illustration of grower-processor cooperative relationships. At one time, beets were contracted at established prices that gave no recognition to grower interest in anything but tons of beets. Sometimes this arrangement worked to the advantage of processors, sometimes to the advantage of growers. In 1933, with economic depression threatening to close many factories, a participating contract was adopted which provided that growers and processors share essentially on a 50-50 basis the net sales price of sugar and the by-products, beet pulp and molasses. The new type of contract increased the interest of both growers and processors in agronomic and management practices that resulted in greater productivity and better quality in beets. Under this arrangement, there is mutual concern in all problems of sugar-beet growing, processing, sugar marketing, and distributing; and jointly the growers and processors have sponsored research and educational work for the advancement of the industry.

FIG. 111.—Mechanical loaders make the hauling job easier. (*Courtesy of E. E. Patton.*)

Sugar-beet Labor.—It has been difficult to mechanize the culture of sugar beets. Some of the work is intricate, and judgment is demanded for almost every detail. No blocking machine has been devised that can do a good job in an uneven stand; thinning requires minute care if but one strong seedling is to be left from each cluster; in best topping work the cut of the knife for a large beet is quite different from that for a small one. The problem is further complicated in that an entirely different sort of equipment is needed for blocking and thinning from that which might prove effective in harvest. Unless both kinds of equipment are developed simultaneously, hand labor will still be essential for an important part of beet culture.

The hand labor required for growing sugar beets sometimes is furnished entirely by the farmer and his family. Much more frequently, however, the blocking, thinning, hoeing, pulling, and topping are done by contract labor, to a large extent migratory and of foreign extraction. Agricultural workers of Mexican descent have shown a particular aptitude for this work. The relationship among the contract laborer, the farmer, and the factory has agronomic implications, for the yield of beets depends in no small measure on the skill and thoroughness with which the laborer does his job. An effective inducement to good work is an arrangement whereby the laborer's wage is increased with increases above a certain standard in the acre yields of the sugar beets he cares for.

Sugar-beet-seed Production.—Sugar-beet-seed growing is a special enterprise. At one time the industry in the United States depended on Europe for beet seed. Usually, minimum germination require-

Fig. 112.—Sugar beets are also unloaded mechanically. (*Courtesy of E. E. Patton.*)

ments for imported seed were 70 per cent. It is remarkable how seldom any lot of seed materially exceeded 70 per cent in germination.

The old method of producing seed involved the digging up of first-year roots, overwintering them in storage, and transplanting these stecklings, or mother plants, to the seed-growing field the next spring. The labor and costs involved in this method of seed production made the enterprise unattractive to American producers.

As a result of experiments carried on cooperatively by the New Mexico Agricultural Experiment Station and the U.S. Department of Agriculture, a new method of seed growing was devised. By this method the sugar beets are seeded in late summer or in September in New Mexico; they are not blocked and thinned but are given just enough irrigation to carry them through the winter. The next spring, irrigation is applied as necessary; and the beets, still unthinned, go on to produce seed. Most of the cultural operations, except hoeing, are mechanical, harvest being carried on with mowers, reapers, specially designed equipment, and, to some extent, by hand.

In 1938, there were 8,376 acres harvested in the states of New Mexico, Utah, Nevada, Arizona, and California, with a total production of 13,661,900 lb. The average seed yield of curly-top-resistant varieties has been consistently above 2,000 lb. an acre.

Domestic seed production has implications far beyond the mere establishment of a sugar-beet-seed industry. The widespread use of curly-top-resistant varieties would have been extremely difficult if not impossible oɪ attainment without a domestic seed industry. Further improvement and better adaptation of varieties are greatly

Fig. 113.—A Michigan factory in the midst of a beet-sugar campaign. (*Courtesy of E. E. Patton.*)

enhanced by this development. It seems unlikely that the United States sugar-beet industry will ever again be dependent, even in part, on foreign sources of seed.

SUGAR CANE

The sugar-cane plant is a tall perennial grass that often grows to a height of more than 15 ft. It is of tropical origin, and wild types are found in New Guinea. It is our oldest source of crystalline sugar, having been introduced into Africa from the East Indies; and it supposedly was carried from Africa to southern Europe, thence to the West Indies, and eventually to Florida and Louisiana.

Propagation and Planting.—Sugar cane is propagated vegetatively from stem cuttings. The usual varieties set seed only after a long, warm growing period, and only a small proportion of the seed is viable. It is used in breeding work but not for commercial propagation even where plants produce seed.

After a clean seedbed has been prepared, stripped stalks of cane are laid out end to end in furrows 4 to 7 ft. apart and covered with 3 to 4 in. of soil. A soil high in organic matter and well watered naturally or by irrigation is essential.

The stalks grow in clusters, for the main stem produces additional stems from underground nodes.

Culture.—Sugar-cane growing is usually a large-scale enterprise. In describing sugar-cane growing in the Everglades of Florida, H. A. Bestor[1] tells of the clearing of large tracts of rank weeds, some of them 10 to 14 ft. high, heavy grasses, such as Pará, Napier, and crab-grass, and scattered brush.

After being cleared the land is plotted into 80-acre planting fields with provision for headlands, roadways, and ditches, the latter spaced at quarter-mile intervals.

Carefully selected stalks are cut into three- or four-eye lengths and planted, usually in August and September, in 4- to 8-in. furrows 4 ft. apart. Tractor-drawn implements are used that distribute a band of fertilizer in the furrow with the "seed" cane, cover it at any desired depth, and pack the soil on top of the "seed," all in one operation. A complete planting crew for these extensive operations consists of 180 men, using nine tractors, one of which is the covering unit, and twenty-four 5-ton crawler-type cane wagons to distribute the seed cane.

The cane is first ready for harvest after 13 to 14 months. It may be harvested for several years although apparently it is profitable to replant about every fifth year.

Soon after harvest, 200 to 250 lb. an acre of fertilizer is distributed in bands along the cane rows to supply additional nutrients for the next crop.

Harvest.—When the cane is ready for harvest, the leaves are stripped off, the tops are cut off, and the stalks are then cut close to the ground, loaded into wagons, and taken to the mill or to the railroad for shipment to the mill.

From 1930 to 1938, the amount of raw sugar made per ton of sugar cane in Louisiana ranged from 143 to 168 lb. and in Florida from 146 to 207 lb. In the insular areas the quantity was higher, being 213 to 240 lb. for Hawaii, usually about 230 lb. for the Philippines, and 228 to 245 lb. for Puerto Rico. Various factors are used to determine the refined-sugar equivalent of raw sugar; that used for the Florida-Louisiana crop is 0.9346, indicating that, on the average, 100 lb. of raw sugar is required to produce 93.46 lb. of refined sugar.

[1] BESTOR, H. A., Sugar Cane Growing in the Everglades, *Facts About Sugar*, Vol. 36, No. 1, 1941.

By-products.—Molasses is the chief by-product of the sugar-cane industry. However, another important by-product is building material processed from the sugar-cane stalks after the sugar-containing juices have been extracted.

Review Problems

1. Among the islands that have normally supplied sugar to the United States, greatest total sugar production is secured in

    a. Hawaii.
    b. Cuba.
    c. The Philippines.
    d. Puerto Rico.

2. The largest acre yields of cane are secured in

    a. Hawaii.
    b. Cuba.
    c. The Philippines.
    d. Puerto Rico.

3. The proportion of sugar consumed in continental United States supplied by the domestic sugar-beet industry is approximately

    a. 25 per cent.
    b. 45 per cent.
    c. 60 per cent.
    d. 75 per cent.

4. The measure that proved most practical in the control of the curly-top disease of sugar beets was

    a. Crop rotation.
    b. Seed treatment.
    c. Spraying and dusting with copper-containing fungicides.
    d. The breeding of resistant varieties.

5. Contract sugar-beet labor usually takes care of all but which one of the following operations?

    a. Planting.
    b. Blocking and thinning.
    c. Hoeing.
    d. Pulling.
    e. Topping.

6. One hundred pounds of raw sugar when refined will produce approximately

    a. 45 lb.
    b. 62 lb.
    c. 86 lb.
    d. 93 lb.

7. Compare the qualities of beet and cane sugar.

8. The growers for a certain factory produce beets under a contract calling for a 50-50 division of the net sales price of sugar, pulp, and molasses. The factory report is as follows:

Amount Secured per Ton of Beets Delivered	Net Sales Price
295.3 lb. of sugar	4.8 cents per pound
93.7 lb. of dried pulp	$32 per ton
33.7 lb. of molasses	$17 per ton

What would the returns be to the grower, per ton of beets delivered?

9. Describe the soil and climatic conditions considered favorable for sugar-beet growing. ˙

10. What are the advantages and disadvantages of following alfalfa with corn in a rotation that includes sugar beets rather than growing sugar beets immediately following the alfalfa?

11. Discuss the difficulties encountered in the attempt to mechanize the sugar-beet industry.

12. Describe the methods used to produce sugar-beet seed in southwestern United States. What are the implications of this work as regards sugar-beet improvement?

13. Why is sugar cane normally propagated vegetatively?

14. How is sugar cane harvested?

References

COONS, G. H.: "Improvement of the Sugar Beet," *U.S. Dept. Agr. Yearbook of Agriculture*, pp. 625–656, 1936.

LILL, J. G.: Sugar Beet Culture in the Humid Area of the United States, *U.S. Dept. Agr. Farmers' Bul.* 1637 (revised), 1939.

NUCKOLS, S. B.: Sugar Beet Growing under Irrigation in the Utah-Idaho Area, *U.S. Dept. Agr. Farmers' Bul.* 1645, 1931.

RATHER, H. C., *et al.*: Sugar Beets in Michigan, *Mich. Agr. Expt. Sta. Cir. Bul.* 175, 1940.

TUCKER, R. H., and T. G. STEWART: Sugar Beet Growing in Colorado, *Colo. Agr. Col. Ext. Bul.* 363A, 1941.

WRIGHT, K. T.: Sugar Beet Costs and Returns, *Mich. Agr. Expt. Sta. Spec. Bul.* 305, 1940.

CHAPTER XXI

COTTON

Cotton culture in this country was started very shortly after the first English settlements in the southern colonies. As a result of the labor saved by Eli Whitney's cotton gin, invented in 1793, the culture of the crop received a tremendous stimulus and cotton became America's greatest export crop. In 1892 the boll weevil crossed the border from Mexico into Texas, and in the years that followed this devastating insect spread rapidly throughout the eastern Gulf states. Nevertheless, in spite of the damage caused by boll-weevil infestation, cotton production continued to increase until the acreage in cultivation in both 1925 and 1926 exceeded 45 million.

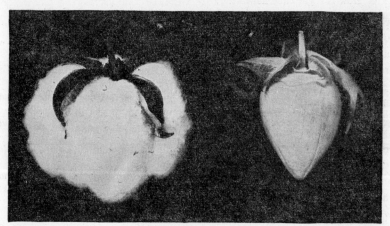

Fig. 114.—A close view of an individual open cotton boll and a green boll. (*Courtesy of Anderson, Clayton and Company, Houston, Tex.*)

Economic Problems.—Then came economic difficulties. The season average farm price per pound in 1931 was 5.66 cents,[1] the lowest in 37 years. Beginning with the crop of 1934 the acreage was sharply restricted under government control measures, some of them compulsory. There were nearly 20 million less acres in cotton in 1939 than in 1929. Government loans were used to bolster prices for the

[1] *U.S. Dept. Agr. Agricultural Statistics*, Superintendent of Documents, Government Printing Office, Washington, D. C., 1940.

cotton produced on the remaining acres, and intensive efforts were made to diversify the agriculture of this vast southern region.

The full impact of cotton adjustment measures cannot be measured. Temporarily, at least, restriction of acreage was associated with a marked increase in average acre yield. The crop of 1937 set an all-time high by yielding 269.9 lb. an acre. Acre yields in 1938, 1939, and 1940 were not much less and were higher than those in any of the preceding 75 years. The extent to which these higher yields mark a definite trend, due possibly to better culture and better choice of land, can be determined only after a much longer period of time.

Nor can the future possibilities for export of American cotton be estimated accurately when politico-geographical adjustments world-wide in scope are taking place. In the years 1925–1929 the United States produced more than half the world's cotton. The 1939 American production amounted to 41 per cent of the world crop on 32 per cent of the world acreage. But reduced production in the United States that year was more than made up for by increases in Brazil, Russia, South Africa, and elsewhere. American cotton exports in 1925–1929 averaged 8,805,000 bales, over 57 per cent of the crop. Exports in 1938 were 4,577,000 bales, just over 38 per cent of production. Any return to the production of more than 40 million acres of cotton in the United States seems destined to depend upon a revival of effective export trade.

Cotton Districts.—H. B. Brown[1] describes the cotton belt as being made up of five distinct districts. The first of these is the old sea-island region composed of parts of South Carolina, Georgia, and Florida and near-by coastal islands. The characteristic high humidity of the region is considered favorable to sea-island cotton, but production has been shifting to upland varieties because of the boll weevil.

A second area includes North Carolina, western South Carolina, and portions of Georgia, Alabama, Mississippi, Louisiana, and eastern Arkansas. Much of the soil is infertile, red clay subject to severe erosion. Big-boll, short-staple varieties are grown.

The delta district is made up of rich alluvial land along the Mississippi River and its southern tributaries. Rainfall is high, about 50 in. a year, and the environment is suitable for the production of long-staple upland cotton varieties.

Texas, Oklahoma, southeastern New Mexico, and western Arkansas make up a hot, dry-weather district growing big-boll, medium-length-staple varieties. Still farther west, in the Salt River Valley

[1] BROWN, HARRY B., "Cotton," McGraw-Hill Book Company, Inc., New York, 1938.

of Arizona and the Imperial Valley of California, Egyptian cotton and certain upland varieties are grown under irrigation.

Fig. 115.—Cotton-picking time in Mississippi. (*Courtesy of P. W. Gull, Delta Experiment Station, Stoneville, Miss.*)

The 10-year (1928–1937) average acre yield for selected states from each of these areas was as follows:

State	Yield, Pounds
Georgia	212
North Carolina	281
Missouri	313
Texas	147
California	491

The average for the United States for these same years was 190.8 lb. The influence of the Texas crop on these averages is marked; for Texas produced 38 per cent of the country's 34,984,000 harvested acres, which was average for the period.

Kinds of Cotton.—The major differentiation between kinds of cotton is based on length of staple. Sea-island cotton, which in pre-boll-weevil days was the predominant type in Florida and the coastal areas of Georgia and South Carolina, has the greatest length of staple of any of the commercial American types. The American-Egyptian type grown chiefly in Arizona ranks next. The upland varieties of cotton, however, make up the great bulk of the American crop. With respect to staple length, these may be long staple, 1⅛ in.

and longer; medium-length staple, $1\frac{1}{32}$ to $1\frac{3}{32}$ in.; or short staple, 1 in. or less in length.[1] Production of cotton with a staple length of less than $\frac{7}{8}$ in. is diminishing, but approximately 75 per cent of the upland crop has a staple length of $\frac{7}{8}$ to 1 in.

Besides varying in staple length, cotton varieties range from early to late in maturity. Also, they may be of the big-boll type, requiring fewer than 70 bolls to make a pound of seed cotton, or the small-boll type. These three characteristics and intermediate ones are combined in all sorts of ways. Finally, there are a vast number of characteristics relating to appearance and productivity that serve to differentiate the host of varieties being grown throughout the cotton country.

There are a host of cotton varieties if varietal status is accorded the great number of local strains that have acquired names regardless of whether or not they represent fairly distinct types. In 1930 a committee of cotton breeders and agronomists selected a list of 31 varieties, commercially important at the time, as a step in varietal standardization. Provision for the registration of new varieties that show definite improvement over those already in existence has been made through the cooperative efforts of the American Society of Agronomy and the Southern Agricultural Workers Association.

One reason for the great number of cotton varieties is the common occurrence of natural crossing even though the majority of flowers are self-pollinated. Bees, butterflies, and other insects readily transfer pollen from one cotton flower to another. Some varieties are cross-pollinated more easily than others, but all are sufficiently susceptible so that constant vigilance is necessary to keep a variety true to type. Community varietal standardization offers the most promising solution to this problem. If all the cotton in one community is of one variety, genetic mixtures, due to cross-pollination, and mechanical mixtures of different varieties at the gin are reduced to a minimum. Even then the seed needs special attention to prevent varietal deterioration, for genetic segregations of inferior sorts occur in the more or less hybrid complex that goes to make a cotton variety. These inferior types hybridize with other plants to lower the general value of the seed. Certified and registered seed that conforms to high standards of purity and quality as determined by competent inspection provides a reliable source of seed for the maintenance of the most desirable varieties.

Climatic and Soil Requirements.—Cotton is a warm-weather crop. Very little is grown north of the northern boundary of North Carolina.

[1] *Ibid.*

In eastern North Carolina and southern Mississippi, annual rainfall ranges from 55 to 60 in., in Texas and western Oklahoma the normal is only about 23 in., and in Arizona and southern California the crop is produced under irrigation. These climatic variations are probably responsible for the adaptation of different kinds of cotton to different regions, sea island to the southern Atlantic seaboard, long-staple varieties to the Mississippi delta, short-staple varieties to the dry cotton-growing regions of Texas and Oklahoma, and Egyptian to the hot, necessarily irrigated regions of Arizona and California. Ideal weather provides moisture to germinate the seed at planting time without being so wet that the seed rots, followed by a warm and moderately moist growing period. Too much rain leads to increased boll-weevil damage and excessive vegetative growth. Dry weather is preferred during the ripening period that extends from August to October. Dry weather tends to stop vegetative growth, stimulates boll development, reduces boll rot, and permits picking of the crop with a minimum of lint damage.

Throughout the cotton country, there is a wide range of soil types, and cotton is grown on most of them. The most satisfactory crops are produced on medium loamy soils. The lighter sands produce poor yields except under the most skillful management; the richest of the heavier soils is likely to produce much vegetative growth without proportionate fruiting, and if rainfall is heavy the damage from fungus diseases is more likely to be serious.

Soil Management.—Cotton culture has taxed the productivity of southern soils. Its tillage as a row crop has stimulated the decomposition and loss of organic matter under climatic conditions themselves conducive to such losses. Cotton lands left bare over winter, the rainiest part of the year, have been subject to exceptionally severe erosion which, not uncommonly, has forced abandonment of the land for agricultural purposes.

The influence of forces destructive to soil productivity, most damaging under continuous cotton culture, may be greatly diminished by effective crop rotations—rotations that provide legumes not only as the most economical source of soil nitrogen but also as protective winter cover for the land.

H. B. Brown[1] has suggested the following rotations:

Three-year Rotation for General Farming

First year. Corn, with cowpeas at laying-by time, or soybeans in drill at planting.

[1] *Ibid.*

Second year. Oats, followed by cowpeas after harvesting the oats.
Third year. Cotton, with rye and vetch in middles after first picking.

FOUR-YEAR ROTATION FOR A COTTON FARMER

First year. Cotton, with rye and vetch in middles after first picking.
Second year. Corn, with cowpeas at laying-by time or soybeans in drill at planting.
Third year. Oats, followed by cowpeas after harvesting the oats.
Fourth year. Cotton, with rye and vetch in middles after first picking.

THREE-YEAR ROTATION FOR A COTTON FARMER

First year. Cotton, with rye and vetch in middles after first picking.
Second year. Corn, with cowpeas at laying-by time, or soybeans in drill at planting.
Third year. Cotton, with rye and vetch in middles after first picking. .

The principles illustrated by these rotations may be applied widely with crops suited to the conditions of each locality.

Rotations, of course, do only part of the job. On sloping land the various measures such as contour tillage and strip cropping, practical as erosion deterrents, are necessary to reduce soil losses.

Finally the cotton crop itself has proved remarkably responsive to direct applications of commercial fertilizer in all but the Arizona–New-Mexico–California regions. Despite the variations in soils of the different areas, there is a striking similarity in the cotton-fertilizer recommendations of southern agronomists. Most of these recommendations call for complete fertilizers with the percentage of nitrogen and available potash running about the same and with twice as much available phosphoric acid as of either of the other two constituents. A typical recommended application is 300 to 600 lb. an acre of 4-8-4 fertilizer. Where a soil is known to be well supplied with or markedly deficient in some particular constituent, as determined by trials, analyses, and experience, the fertilizer usage may be modified accordingly. The most economical use of the fertilizer results from its application in a band about 2 in. to one side and slightly below the level of the planted seed.

Culture.—Plowing for cotton ranges from a tractor-powered job in the West to one-horse light turning plow work in the uplands of the eastern part of the cotton belt. A substantial part of the acreage for cotton is not plowed at all in the usual sense but is first fitted in beds with a heavy middlebuster, or lister. Fall plowing is advisable only where erosion is not a serious problem. The final seedbed must be clean, well-pulverized, and firm. If the crop is to be planted on beds or low ridges, these are worked down with a spike-tooth harrow to a height of about 6 in. The beds provide better surface drainage and warmer soil for the tender young cotton plants.

Cotton is ordinarily planted in 3- to 4-ft. rows, the 3½-ft. rows being the most usual. In general, the seed is planted in continuous drills, and as soon as the danger of losing the stand from cold weather or disease is past the plants are thinned to the desired spacing. Where the boll-weevil infestation is heavy, it seems desirable to space the plants as close together as possible and still permit effective hoeing for

FIG. 116.—Preparing the seedbed for cotton with a lister in Texas. (*Courtesy of Anderson, Clayton and Company, Houston, Tex.*)

weed control. In the absence of serious boll-weevil infestation the 12-in. spacing within the row is considered desirable.

Planting must wait until the danger of frost is past in any region. Plantings made late in the planting season permit better preliminary weed control and less subsequent cultivation, but plantings as near to the last spring frost as is possible with safety are considered advisable where the boll weevil is troublesome. In humid regions the seed is barely covered; in the West, deeper plantings are necessary so that the seeds may be in moist soil.

Drilled cotton yields more than checked cotton, and young cotton plants are weak. These two considerations make it necessary to plant the seed in drills, use enough extra seed to ensure a good even stand, and, by hoeing or chopping, thin the plants to the desired stand. Hoeing is also necessary for weed control in the cotton row. Between the rows the weeds are controlled by the same sort of inter-row cultivation as is practiced for other crops—fairly deep early in the season to give the weeds a real setback, and shallow as the cotton plants get larger in order that vital roots may not be pruned.

Harvest.—Cotton harvest starts in early August in southern Texas but not until late September in the northern part of the cotton belt. Cotton picking is a hand job primarily because cotton is indeterminate in maturity and the bolls that mature first must be picked before the later ones are ready lest they be spoiled by adverse weather. The

Fig. 117.—A two-row cotton planter. Planting in any region must wait until the danger of frost is past. (*Courtesy of Anderson, Clayton and Company, Houston, Tex.*)

bolls are scattered up and down the plants, some do not open fully, and the seed cotton must be picked with a minimum of trash and leaves. The picking season is of several weeks' duration.

Despite these difficulties a large number of cotton-picking machines have been invented. Some of these have shown considerable promise.

The picked seed cotton when properly dry is run through a cotton gin to separate the seed from the lint. The lint is then baled for shipment. Although bales vary in size, pressure, and method of making, the standard bale of cotton weighs 500 lb. gross, 478 lb. net.

Cotton Grades.—Cotton is graded according to Universal Standards with a nomenclature all its own. In general, price quotations are based on the *middling* ⅞-in. staple grade. Premiums are paid for staples longer than ⅞-in., whereas middling cotton of shorter staple is discounted.

The middling grade of cotton is white, nearly free from cuts and nips, but containing some particles of cotton seed and leaves. As the cotton is classed as better than middling with respect to color and freedom from nips, gin cuts, and foreign material, it successively becomes *strict middling, good middling, strict good middling,* and *middling fair,* all premium grades. *Middling fair,* the supreme in cotton quality, is attained but rarely on the commercial market. The discounted grades are *strict low middling, low middling, strict good*

Fig. 118.—Cotton harvest starts in early August in southern Texas. (*Courtesy of Anderson, Clayton and Company, Houston, Tex.*)

ordinary, and *good ordinary.* The latter two grades are untenderable in settlement of futures contracts according to Section 5 of the United States Cotton Futures Act. Good ordinary is usually somewhat stained and discolored, may contain up to 1 per cent sand, dust, or dirt, and does contain a considerable quantity of leaf particles plus a sprinkling of motes, seed fragments, and gin cuts.

Cottonseed.—Cottonseed is a very important by-product of cotton growing. In processing the seed the *linters,* or fuzz clinging to the seed hulls, are removed as completely as possible by a process similar to ginning except that five-toothed saws are used. The linters have some commercial value, especially in wartime when they are used for making explosives. They are also used in stuffings, low-grade yarns, felt, rayon, and paper. The average quantity reclaimed from a ton of cottonseed is 65 lb.

The hulls are next separated from the seed meats by a crushing-milling process, and the meats are cooked and put through an oil-extraction process, leaving the crude oil and the cottonseed cake, or meal. The hulls are used as low-grade stock feed somewhat less nutritious in character than cornstalks or grain straw. The cottonseed meal, however, is one of the standard high-protein concentrates competing with linseed meal and soybean meal as a protein supplement in the grain rations of livestock. The refined oil has many of the same uses as other vegetable oils in the making of soaps, butter substitutes, lard substitutes, salad oils, etc.

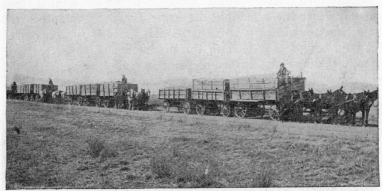

Fig. 119.—The Texas farmer hauls his cotton to town on tandem wagons or by truck and trailer. (*Courtesy of Anderson, Clayton and Company, Houston, Tex.*)

The Boll Weevil.—No insect has attracted public attention, even in regions remote from the cotton belt, more than *Anthonomus grandis*, the Mexican boll weevil. This insect did considerable damage to Texas cotton as early as 1894. By 1909, it had spread to Alabama, and it was soon playing havoc with the cotton crop of the Gulf states. A close relative of the same species is found in the Arizona cotton-growing areas.

The weevil passes the winter in adult form, and the females deposit their eggs in small openings that they make near the base of the flower bud. The young grubs hatch in 3 or 4 days and reach full larval development in 1 to 2 weeks. They feed on the plant tissue around them, go into a pupal stage in which they are inactive, and emerge as adult winged insects in 3 to 4 weeks from the time the eggs were laid. They develop rapidly in warm, humid weather, but their mortality is high if the weather is hot and dry. In both the adult and the larval stages, the boll weevil is destructive to cotton. The damage may be slight or so severe as completely to ruin an entire crop.

Factors that work against the boll weevil are hot, dry weather, cold weather in winter, a number of parasitic enemies, ants that destroy the larvae, and birds.

Artificial control is difficult and expensive. Where the land is productive and if the proper procedure in application is strictly followed, dusting the cotton, preferably at night, with pure calcium arsenate by means of special cotton-dusting machinery has been a fairly effective control measure.

Other control measures might be classed under the general term of *insect sanitation.* These include the plowing under of infested plants or burning them before the first fall frost under the limited circumstances in which this is feasible, the destruction of all volunteer cotton plants, and the cleaning up of trash and rubbish in which weevils hibernate. Steps that lead to the production of an early crop of cotton, including early seedbed preparation and planting, fertilization, and the use of early varieties, tend to reduce boll-weevil damage.

Review Problems

1. From the beginning of cotton-production control measures under the Agricultural Adjustment Administration in 1933 through the 1940 crop the trend in United States cotton production was

    a. Toward higher acre yields with acreage unchanged.
    b. Toward a reduced acreage with acre yields unchanged.
    c. Toward a lower acreage but higher acre yields.
    d. Essentially unchanged.

2. During the period 1925–1929 the United States produced

    a. More than half of the world's cotton.
    b. 40 per cent of the world's cotton.
    c. 25 per cent.
    d. 5 per cent.

3. Which of the following fertilizer analyses is most likely to give best results with cotton on light sandy soils?

    a. 6-8-0.
    b. 4-8-4.
    c. 4-8-8.
    d. 0-16-0.

4. In areas where boll-weevil infestation is serious, cotton should be planted

    a. As late in the season as possible.
    b. As near to the last spring frost as is safe.
    c. At any convenient time, irrespective of the boll weevil.
    d. At oat-planting time without regard to spring frosts.

5. The market class of cotton of highest quality is

    a. Middling fair.
    b. Strict good middling.
    c. Strict good ordinary.
    d. Strict middling.

6. How do you explain the tendency toward an excessive number of cotton varieties?

7. What effective steps can be taken to keep a cotton variety relatively pure?

8. Discuss cotton adaptation with respect to climate.

9. Discuss specifically the influence of cotton culture on soil productivity.

10. Why has the invention of successful cotton-harvesting machinery been extremely difficult?

References

BROWN, HARRY B.: "Cotton," McGraw-Hill Book Company, Inc., New York, 1938.

GABBARD, L. P., and F. R. JONES: Large-scale Cotton Production in Texas, *Tex. Agr. Expt. Sta. Bul.* 362, 1927.

HUTCHESON, T. B., T. K. WOLFE, and M. S. KIPPS: "The Production of Field Crops," McGraw-Hill Book Company, Inc., New York, 1936.

NEAL, D. C., and W. W. GILBERT: Cotton Diseases and Methods of Control, *U.S. Dept. Agr. Farmers' Bul.* 1745, 1935.

REYNOLDS, E. B., *et al.:* Fertilizer Experiments with Cotton, *Tex. Agr. Expt. Sta. Bul.* 469, 1932.

SHANKLIN, J. A., R. C. CAMPBELL, and W. C. JENSEN: Community Production of Cotton in Relation to Yield and Staple Length, *S.C. Agr. Expt. Sta. Cir.* 48, 1933

CHAPTER XXII

TOBACCO

The singsong chant of the tobacco auctioneer may be merely a novel radio feature to the average American, but it means dollars to over 400,000 tobacco growers. Four hundred thousand growers are not so many—more than ten times that number grow corn. But the $223,472,000 they take off 1,677,200 acres of land (1930–1939 average) makes tobacco a major cash crop excelled by none of the field crops in total acre returns.

Insofar as history can tell us, the use of tobacco has always been an American custom, long antedating that day in 1492 when Columbus found natives chewing it, in the West Indies, or the time a few years later when Cartier, the French explorer, observed the northern Indians "fill their bodies full of smoke, till it cometh out of their mouth and nostrils, even as out of the tunnel of a chimney."

Sir Walter Raleigh may not have been the first person to introduce the use of tobacco into the Old World; but certainly he was the most prominent, and it was he who gave the custom social standing. Despite violent controversies over the effects of tobacco, which originated then and which have never entirely ceased, the consumption of tobacco has steadily increased ever since.

In many Indian tribes the tobacco crop had a standing all its own, according to the historical researches of Carrier.[1] It was the one crop proud braves would take care of; usually only the men used it, though this was not universally true; and it was an important factor in their religious rites and tribal ceremonies.

Today almost everybody is affected by tobacco, either at first or second hand. Annual cigarette consumption is numbered in the billions; the smoking of cigars and pipes is likewise popular; plug tobacco and snuff take their share of the crop; industrial uses, particularly in insecticides, are important; and tobacco culture is an integral part of the agriculture of several regions extending from the Canadian border to the Gulf of Mexico. Its production is world-wide in scope in both temperate and tropical regions.

[1] CARRIER, LYMAN, "The Beginnings of Agriculture in America," McGraw-Hill Book Company, Inc., New York, 1923.

Tobacco growing is an enterprise for specialized areas of production and for specialized growers. Each environment exerts its own particular influence on the quality of the crop, as do the specialized curing methods for each type. The inexperienced grower in an untried area might produce a grade of tobacco that some hardy individual could smoke, but the chances are against his finding a profitable market for it. Tobacco growing in areas that produce an accepted quality could be greatly expanded in those same areas. However, economic conditions have not warranted such expansion, and tobacco is one of the crops not infrequently troubled with burdensome surpluses.

Size of Tobacco Enterprise.—For the most part the tobacco-growing enterprise utilizes a relatively small acreage on each tobacco-growing farm. According to the 1935 agricultural census, the average acreage of tobacco per farm reporting the crop was 3.9 in North Carolina and 2.5 in Kentucky, two states that have over 60 per cent of the tobacco-growing acreage of the country. The acreage per farm in Connecticut where special grades of cigar-binder and -wrapper tobacco are grown was 10.4. Some of this acreage is grown under artificial shade, more as a company rather than as an individual-farm enterprise.

The growing of tobacco requires considerable hand labor to produce the young plants and in transplanting, hoeing, topping, and removal of the suckers following topping. Further hand labor is necessary in harvesting, curing, and stripping of the leaves. This is the major reason why the acreage per farm is relatively small. On the other hand the income per acre is large in comparison with that from other field crops. For the United States as a whole, the average acre income from tobacco was $141.33 in 1939 and $166.08 in 1935, the years producing the two highest average acre yields on record up to 1940. The high-yielding and high-priced (as compared with that of other states) Connecticut crop of 1939 had an average acre value of $562.77.

Tobacco Types and Varieties.—The U.S. Department of Agriculture classifies tobacco according to numbered types, with symbol designations to indicate grades of different quality. The broad classification in accordance with use and methods of curing includes the following: cigar wrapper, cigar binder, cigar filler, flue-cured, fire-cured, light air-cured, and dark air-cured.

There are three important varietal groups of cigar tobaccos, as follows: the Broadleaf, or Seedleaf, group, the Havana-seed group, and the Cuban group. These are grown in the northern cigar-leaf states;

are used for filler, binder, and wrapper in cigar making; and are usually designated by the state producing them, *e.g.*, Pennsylvania Broadleaf, Ohio Broadleaf, Connecticut Havana, etc.

The Cuban group is composed of strains or selections obtained from the imported seed and certain disease-resistant selections from Cuban crosses. They are mainly used to produce cigar-wrapper leaf under artificial shade.[1]

One variety, the Orinoco, is basic in the production of flue-cured, fire-cured, and dark air-cured tobacco. For the most part the others are but strains of this one variety.

Fig. 120.—Finest grade of cigar wrapper being grown under shade in Connecticut. (*Courtesy of P. J. Anderson, Connecticut Agricultural Experiment Station.*)

Two special varieties are the White Burley, famed in Kentucky for the production of plug and cigarette tobacco, and the Maryland, used in cigarette blends. Both are light in color. The Maryland has particularly good burning qualities, and the White Burley has unusual absorptive capacity for the liquid materials used in flavoring plug tobacco.

Tobacco Soils and Their Management.—According to Garner[2] the best soils of the Connecticut Valley for the production of wrapper and binder tobacco are coarse sandy loam to very fine sandy loams with well-drained sandy-loam subsoils. Soils of similar texture are also favored for growing wrapper tobacco in Florida and Georgia. Somewhat heavier light clay loams and dark-loam prairie soils are used for

[1] Garner, W. W., Tobacco Culture, *U.S. Dept. Agr. Farmers' Bul.* 571 (revised), 1936.

[2] *Ibid.*

tobacco culture in Wisconsin. A moderately acid reaction is preferred, for it aids in the control of black-root rot; but should the soil reaction reach pH5 or below, light applications of lime high in magnesia are desirable (500 to 1,000 lb. an acre). Stable manure applied liberally every 2 or 3 years and applications of a ton or more per acre of complete fertilizer to each crop are used to ensure good tobacco yields. Organic nitrogens are preferred in the fertilizer for at least two-thirds of this constituent.

FIG. 121.—Cigar binder tobacco of the Havana seed variety. (*Courtesy of P. J. Anderson, Connecticut Agricultural Experiment Station.*)

As with wrapper and binder tobaccos, the lighter soils are preferred for the production of most other types. However, domestic cigar-filler leaf produced in Lancaster County, Pennsylvania, and the Miami Valley in Ohio is grown on heavier, richer soils. Under these conditions, tobacco is included in general crop rotations and produced by less intensive methods because of the lower price. The soil of the Piedmont Region in the South Atlantic states likewise tends to contain more clay. This region grows a bright flue-cured type of tobacco used in the manufacture of cigarettes and pipe and chewing tobacco and for export.

White Burley is grown on the limestone soils of Kentucky, eastern Tennessee, and southern Ohio. The crop sequence is simple. If virgin soils are not available, a bluegrass sod several years old is preferred. Fertilizer applications are much lighter than for wrapper and binder leaf, and 400 to 800 lb. of a 4-8-4 or comparable fertilizer are used, although the crops immediately following the bluegrass may receive no fertilizer. After two or three good crops of tobacco, the land is reseeded to bluegrass.

The Maryland, a distinctive type of tobacco grown in southern Maryland, is of best quality when produced following a growth of ragweed and such other weedy vegetation as usually springs up on land that is left idle. Fertilizers somewhat higher in potash are used than is the case in other areas although a high content of potash is also considered desirable in fertilizing for the flue-cured tobaccos of Virginia and the Carolinas.

Starting the Seed.—Tobacco seed is first started in specially prepared beds. In the North, cold frames are used, the soil preferably sterilized by a steam treatment, the frames frequently by other methods. The beds are enriched with manure and fertilizer, and the tiny seeds are scattered over the surface and covered very lightly by merely going over the bed with a roller or plank. The seed is started in late March or in April, depending on the variety and location, and the young plants are ready to be set out in the field in late May and June. Just prior to transplanting, the plants grown in a cold frame are hardened by removing the cover from the beds for several hours each day.

Flue-cured tobacco, a southern crop, is started in open beds having a southern or eastern exposure; or, if practicable, a spot in a wooded area is used. The beds are seeded in January, February, or March; and the seedlings are transplanted in April in the southern part of the region and in late May or June in North Carolina. The fire-cured types of tobacco in Kentucky, Tennessee, and Virginia and White Burley tobacco are started in essentially the same way as is flue-cured tobacco, the planting date depending on the location. Seedbeds for the 'Maryland types, preferably located in the woods, are handled similarly to cold frames, with only a cheesecloth rather than a glass cover.

Transplanting.—At the proper time of the season for the locality, the young tobacco plants, properly hardened by daily exposure to outside weather conditions, are removed from the plant beds and transplanted to the field. So-called *transplanting machines* regulate the spacing of jets of water for the transplants, which are actually set by hand by men riding close to the ground on the rear of the machine. When the job is done by hand, a hole is made with a dibble or similar tool, water is poured in, and the young plant is placed in the hole and the soil firmed around it before the water all escapes. Only healthy transplants are used, but even so a certain percentage usually fails to survive the transplanting process. These are replaced by hand with new plants from the bed as soon after the original transplanting date as possible.

Table 18, based on information presented by Garner, indicates the desirable row width and spacing for the different varietal groups.

TABLE 18.—ROW WIDTH AND SPACING FOR DIFFERENT KINDS OF TOBACCO*

Kind	Row width, inches	Spacing between plants in row, inches
Connecticut Havana seed................	39–42	16–20
Connecticut Broadleaf..................	40–45	20–25
Comstock Spanish and Wisconsin Havana seed.....................................	34–38	18–22
Shade-grown wrapper leaf:		
Connecticut.........................	40	10–15
Florida and Georgia..................	48–54	10–15
Pennsylvania Broadleaf.................	36–42	24–30
Zimmer Spanish........................	34–38	22–26
Flue-cured............................	48	20–28
Fire-cured............................	42	30–42
White Burley..........................	42	14–18
Maryland..............................	32–36	32–36

* GARNER, W. W., Tobacco Culture, *U.S. Dept. Agr. Farmers' Bul.* 571 (revised), 1936.

Topping and Suckering.—In order to induce the growing tobacco plant to produce large leaves of good quality, the top of the plant is broken off below the racemed or panicled inflorescence at about the time the first blossoms appear. The number of leaves left after topping depends on the variety, the vigor of the plants, and local custom. After the heads are broken off suckers or branches start development in the axils of the leaves. These must be removed by hand soon after they appear lest they retard leaf development. The topping of tobacco plants when properly managed helps to bring about a more uniform maturity of the crop.

Harvest.—Tobacco may be harvested by picking the leaves from the stem as they attain the proper stage of maturity or by cutting the whole plant when the middle leaves are mature. The handling details vary, but the object of subsequent procedure is to permit enough wilting in the field so that the leaves will not break easily; after wilting they are taken to the barn for curing. The picked leaves or cut plants are fastened to sticks or lath before being hung in the curing barn. This permits uniform air circulation around each leaf.

Curing.—The final curing of the leaves demands more in the way of skill and experienced judgment than any other procedure in tobacco culture. Air curing is a slow process in which natural weather conditions are used to develop the desired quality in the leaves. The plants are hung in well-ventilated barns in which temperatures and humidity are controlled insofar as possible by regulation of the ventilation.

Dark tobacco is partly air-cured, but curing is completed over slow-burning open fires that impart a dark color and special aroma and flavor to the leaf. Flue-cured tobacco is dried much more rapidly in closed barns provided with top ventilators. Furnaces or fireboxes provide the heat, and flues distribute it throughout the building. A light fire is used until the leaves have thoroughly yellowed, after which the temperature is gradually increased until curing is completed.

Fig. 122.—Tobacco barn in Falmouth, Kentucky, area showing the type of roof ventilator recommended for air curing. (*Courtesy of U.S. Department of Agriculture Soil Conservation Service.*)

When curing of the tobacco has been completed, arrangements are made so the leaves will reabsorb enough moisture either from the air or otherwise to keep them pliable. The leaves are then sorted and tied into bunches of uniform quality called *hands* and are ready for the market.

Tobacco Diseases.—Tobacco, like its relative the potato, is subject to attack by a number of disease organisms. Root rot, caused by a fungus, and mosaic, a virus disease, are illustrative of diseases controlled primarily by thorough seedbed sanitation. The soil itself may be sterilized by a steam treatment; and the frames and covers are disinfected with formaldehyde, corrosive sublimate, steam, or boiling water.

The mosaic disease is one of the most widespread. According to work done in Kentucky,[1] dark, fire-cured tobacco plants artificially infected with mosaic 3 weeks after setting were reduced in yield by 31 per cent and in quality by 48 per cent. When the mosaic was introduced at topping time, the yield was reduced 6.3 per cent and the value 25.8 per cent. Under field conditions, a 20 per cent infection prior to topping is not unusual.

Fig. 123.—Stripping air-cured Burley tobacco in Kentucky. (*Courtesy of U.S. Department of Agriculture Soil Conservation Service.*)

Incidentally, the tobacco mosaic virus provided the material used in studies that gave the first clues to the strange nature of these apparently complex protein chemicals that have the ability to grow and reproduce.

Tobacco wilt, a bacterial disease, and root knot, caused by a minute nematode, are controlled by rotation of tobacco with crops not susceptible to these ailments.

Potash hunger, evinced by a yellowing of the leaf surface followed by the appearance of small specks of dead tissue, and sand drown, or magnesia hunger, which shows symptoms similar but not identical to those of potash hunger, are deficiency diseases subject to correction by proper fertilization of the soil.

[1] Johnson, E. M., and W. D. Valleau, Effect of Tobacco Mosaic on Yield and Quality of Dark, Fire-cured Tobacco, *Ky. Agr. Expt. Sta. Bul.* 415, 1941.

Review Problems

1. Which of the following varieties is used for plug and cigarette tobacco?

    a. Cuban, shade-grown.
    b. White Burley.
    c. Wisconsin Havana seed.
    d. Pennsylvania Broadleaf.

2. A suitable rotation of crops is an effective control for

    a. Tobacco mosaic.
    b. Root knot.
    c. Sand drown.
    d. Root rot.

3. What are some of the fundamental difficulties that would be encountered in an attempt to start a tobacco-growing enterprise in a district not now growing the crop?

4. Why is the acreage of tobacco per farm relatively small in most cases?

5. Describe the preparation and planting of a tobacco seedbed as used for the starting of plants to produce flue-cured tobacco.

6. What is the function of magnesium in tobacco culture?

7. What is the purpose of growing certain kinds of tobacco under artificial shade?

8. Where can information be secured on the proper methods of curing tobacco?

References

GARNER, W. W.: Tobacco Culture, *U.S. Dept. Agr. Farmers' Bul.* 571 (revised), 1936.

HUTCHESON, T. B., T. K. WOLFE, and M. S. KIPPS: "The Production of Field Crops," McGraw-Hill Book Company, Inc., New York, 1936.

MORROW, J. V., and DUDLEY SMITH: Tobacco Shrinkages and Losses in Weight in Handling and Storage, *U.S. Dept. Agr. Cir.* 435, 1937.

CHAPTER XXIII

CROP IMPROVEMENT

What dissatisfied aborigine first started the art of plant breeding? Ancient and unlettered he must have been, for many of our crops were brought to a highly developed state before the beginning of recorded history. Dissatisfied, too, for he discarded many of nature's offerings and chose only the more thrifty, the more palatable, or that which most pleased his fancy. Whoever he may have been, we must relegate him and his methods to the realm of pure conjecture. He was not the first plant breeder, in any case. Nature herself, also dissatisfied with her own handiwork, had been constantly selecting, testing, discarding, inbreeding, crossing, retesting, and reselecting since the very dawn of plant life.

Heredity and Crop Improvement.—Man has stimulated and controlled many of these natural processes. Nature selected plants, each fitted to a peculiar environment. Man frequently changed environment to fit it for the plants he wished to grow. More than this, he augmented nature's plant-breeding program; he crossed species that normally are self-pollinated and inbred species that normally are crossed. He crossed remotely related species and has even caused mutations, those sudden heritable changes by which nature effects rapid, marked variations.

Modern man has used powerful microscopes to peer into germ cells, to see for himself and to count the chromosomes that carry the mysterious genes controlling the development of hereditary characteristics. He has watched the chromosomes unite, divide, and occasionally break and re-form in a new arrangement. He has mapped the theoretical alignment of genes along the chromosomes and observed how characters determined by genes carried on the same chromosome are linked or always associated in inheritance unless that linkage is broken by the breakage of the chromosome itself and its realignment in a new form.

It was Mendel, an obscure Austrian monk, who made the discovery that characters, inherited by offspring from their parents, were distributed among the offspring in definite mathematical ratios. This discovery passed unnoticed for over thirty years until Mendel's paper attracted the attention of three European botanists, Correns, De Vries,

417

and Tschermak, who were independently studying heredity. Mendel found dominant and recessive characters which segregated on a mathematical basis in the second generation after a cross. Dominant characters appeared to the exclusion of the contrasting (recessive) characters in the first hybrid generation whereas the recessive characters were not discernible, although present. It remained for later workers to establish the unit-factor basis of inheritance, certain complex character ratios becoming thus explainable. Mendel's work, however, inaugurated a great program of research that has helped to make plant breeding a science as well as an art.

Heredity and Environment.—The yield, appearance, quality, and other attributes of crop plants or for that matter the characteristics of living organisms in general are profoundly influenced by both environment and heredity, and often the effects of the two cannot be sharply differentiated. Surely such a factor as the color of a grain of wheat is heritable; yet genetically pure white wheat, if grown under certain environmental conditions, produces so many kernels of a dark amber color, similar to those of soft red wheat, that the resultant grain is commonly classed as mixed wheat on the market.

Even more striking is a certain type of corn, described by Emerson,[1] that ordinarily has white kernels. However, if the husks are removed before the kernels have hardened in ripening, the ears become red. In the case of this "sun-red" corn the red color of the kernels is not directly inherited; rather, the strain has the inherited characteristic of developing red-colored kernels in the presence of strong light but only white kernels under conditions of darkness. The strain is quite different, inherently, from other strains of corn that produce only red kernels and still others that produce only white ones, whether exposed to the light or not. The final color of the sun-red strain is determined by both heredity and environment.

Although the influence of heredity on the productivity of crops is important, there often is a tendency to overemphasize it. Let a farmer secure 50 bu. of wheat to the acre and he has a ready neighborhood seed market for much of his crop although seed from the identical lot may have been used in another less fertile field that produced but 20 bu. an acre.

A farmer purchased seed of a new variety of oats and became thoroughly convinced of the inherent stiffness of its straw because it stood up perfectly whereas his old variety, in a field "just over the fence," lodged badly. The new variety followed sugar beets; the old

[1] EMERSON, R. A., Heredity and Environment, Spragg Memorial Lectures on Plant Breeding, Michigan State College, 1932.

variety, field beans. The preceding crops had different fertilizer treatments, and there was a difference in crop residues. Actually, when tested repeatedly under environmental conditions as nearly identical for the two varieties as possible, the new oat the farmer grew showed no inherent superiority in lodging resistance.

Although the discussion in this chapter deals largely with varieties and the improvement of their hereditary properties, let it be understood at the outset that heredity and environment both are important. No

Fig. 124.—Plant breeders have done much to improve small-grain varieties. Left, Oderbrucker barley; right, Spartan barley. Note the difference in strength of straw. (*Courtesy of E. E. Down, Michigan Agricultural Experiment Station.*)

variety, however good, can overcome the detrimental influence of a low supply of available plant food, poor or indifferent cultural practices, or the damaging effects of bad weather. Conversely, a poor or unadapted variety cannot make the most of the advantages presented by a favorable productive environment.

How Better Varieties Are Developed.—The agriculture of a given area may acquire better crop varieties in the following ways:

1. Introduction.
2. Selection:
    a. Mass.
    b. Individual plant.
3. Crossing followed by selection.
4. Inbreeding followed by selection and the recombination of selected, inbred lines.

Introduction.—As has already been noted, a great many important United States crops are not native to this country but were brought in, some with the earliest colonial settlements. The introduction of special varieties has continued ever since. The Carolina White variety of rice is said to have been brought in by chance from Madagascar to South Carolina in 1694. Many introductions of very useful varieties have resulted from individual enterprise; many others have come through the highly organized plant-exploration service of the U.S. Department of Agriculture which cooperates with the various state agricultural experiment stations in the testing and proving of imported strains.

A few of the more noteworthy introductions are the following: Turkey wheat, brought by Russian settlers into central Kansas in 1873 to become the leading hard red winter wheat of the Southwest; Marquis spring wheat, introduced from Canada in 1913, the leading hard spring wheat for many years and a parent line for most of the newer spring-wheat varieties; Kubanka, the durum wheat, brought in from Russia by the U.S. Department of Agriculture, that has set the standard of merit by which other durum wheats are now judged.

Manchuria barley, a standard malting variety in the Middle West, was imported from Germany by a Wisconsin farmer in 1861; the Victory oat, an excellent midseason variety, came from Sweden; Ladak alfalfa was selected from material sent to the U.S. Department of Agriculture from northern India in 1910.

Mass Selection.—Strictly speaking, introduction of plant varieties as described above is not a method of plant breeding although introduced varieties have been very useful to plant breeders as well as to farmers. For example, Lion, the black barley introduced by the U.S. Department of Agriculture, has not been widely grown by farmers, but its smooth-bearded character has been transmitted to many of the newer white varieties in crosses made by plant breeders. Mass selection, however, is a form of plant breeding—probably the simplest form. It may consist in the selection of a large number of plants, heads, or seeds for propagation; or it may be accomplished by discarding that which is off-type, poor in vigor, or otherwise undesirable. Nature has been the great mass selector—and to good purpose. The local or regional adaptation of strains of red clover, for example, has resulted largely from natural mass selection and the elimination to an appreciable extent of the unhardy, the disease susceptible, or the otherwise unfit strains.

One of the most noteworthy illustrations of mass selection is the development of Grimm alfalfa. Wendelin Grimm, a German settler in

Carver County, Minnesota, seeded 15 or 20 lb. of alfalfa that he had brought with him in 1858. With severe Minnesota winters acting as the selecting agent, Grimm's alfalfa gradually became outstanding in winter hardiness, a character that it probably had to a considerable degree when Grimm first seeded it. Though it remained obscure for almost fifty years, Grimm alfalfa eventually became one of the most important factors in the development of alfalfa culture in the northern United States. The Minnesota Agricultural Experiment Station aided greatly in giving this variety prominence.

For many years, mass selection was almost the only method of corn improvement. The ear-to-row method of breeding, by which the progeny of individual ears was tested and the remnants of the better ears were used for seed, was merely a modified form of mass selection.

The Pure-line Theory.—Johannsen, a Dane, working with self-fertilized crops, found that if the line was homozygous, *i.e.*, pure as to its hereditary properties, further selection within such a line was of no avail. True, the progeny of a single, self-fertilized plant varied widely, but these variations were not inherited. Thus, selection might effect marked changes in such open-pollinated crops as corn, clover, rye, and alfalfa, but it could not be expected to change a pure line of wheat, oats, or barley which are normally self-pollinated. Mechanical mixtures might be sorted out by selection, or a mutation might occur in a pure line; but the latter takes place so rarely as to be of little interest other than scientific.

Individual-plant Selection in Self-pollinated Crops.—Because many of the early varieties of self-pollinated crops were mechanically impure and because of a certain amount of natural crossing, the application of the pure-line theory by a process of individual-plant selection has been an effective method of breeding new varieties. The fact that the Kherson oat, as originally introduced into this country, was not pure gave the Iowa Agricultural Experiment Station the opportunity to select, by the individual-plant or pure-line method, such valuable distinct varieties as Richland, Iogold, and Iowar. The Richland and Iogold have shown high resistance to stem rust, a fact that gives them added value as parent material to be used in crosses.

Red Rock wheat is an important soft-red-winter variety developed by selection of a single kernel in Michigan. Years after its introduction, there appeared in fields of the bearded Red Rock a trace of beardless heads on plants that showed many of the other characteristics of Red Rock. The plants were still segregating for the beardless characteristic, it being thus indicated that they came from some natural cross.

By individual-plant selection a pure line of beardless soft red winter wheat was developed from this natural cross. This newer variety, Baldrock, has largely replaced Red Rock in Michigan.

Crossing Followed by Selection.—Most varieties of self-pollinated crops have been selected to a high state of purity, and the possibilities of finding good naturally crossed material or the more rare valuable mutation are limited. In order to secure new combinations of desirable characters, plant breeders are constantly making large numbers of crosses by controlled technique.

Fig. 125.—Using overhead irrigation in order to subject bean crosses to environmental conditions conducive to mosaic and blight to aid in finding disease-resistant strains. (*Michigan Agricultural Experiment Station.*)

For example, the Michigan Agricultural Experiment Station crossed two varieties of barley. One of the parent lines was a Hanna selection, a white, two-rowed, rough-bearded barley, moderately late in maturity, and with a fairly weak brittle straw. The other parent, Lion, was black, six-rowed, short- but stiff-strawed, and smooth-bearded; but the beards clung persistently to the kernels, and so clean threshing was difficult. Out of the great number of strains that segregated from this cross, one was selected and purified that was white, two-rowed, and smooth-bearded; the beards threshed off easily, and the straw, of moderate length, proved unusually stiff. Thus was secured a new variety, Spartan barley, which combined many of the desirable attributes of its parents.

Crossing followed by selection has resulted in many useful varieties. Following are but a few that have attained some importance:

Variety	Parent material	State
Marquillo wheat............	Marquis × Iumillo	Minnesota
Ceres wheat...............	Marquis × Kota	North Dakota
Rex wheat................	White Odessa × Hard Federation	Oregon
Hope wheat...............	Marquis × Yaroslav (emmer)	South Dakota
Ridit wheat...............	Turkey × Florence	Washington
Barbless barley............	Oderbrucker × Lion	Wisconsin
Velvet barley.............	Manchuria × Lion	Minnesota
Hero barley...............	Lion × Club Mariout	California
Velvon barley.............	Colorado Sel. 3063 × Trebi	Utah
Huron oats...............	Markton × Victory	Michigan
Michelite beans............	Robust × Early Prolific	Michigan

The U.S. Department of Agriculture has played a part in the development of most of the above varieties. In addition, the work of the department and cooperating state agricultural experiment stations in oat hybridization should be mentioned. These workers have in process of development many strains that should prove highly useful in combating the more important oat diseases. Several Markton × Iogold crosses have shown marked resistance to stem rust and smut, and certain progenies from Victoria × Richland crosses are resistant to crown rust, stem rust, and smut.

Backcrossing.—Backcrossing consists in remating a hybrid with one of its parents. If a variety is highly satisfactory in all but one or two characters and it is desirable to supplant these with superior characters from another variety, backcrossing is particularly effective. Several successive backcrosses between hybrids (carrying the characters that are to be added to the new variety) and the most desirable original parent line are necessary. The California Agricultural Experiment Station has used the backcrossing method to add a factor for bunt resistance to commercial wheat varieties that were otherwise very satisfactory.[1]

HYBRID CORN

The story of inbreeding, followed by selection within inbred lines and the recombination by crossing of selected inbred lines, is the story of hybrid corn. This method of breeding has been used with sugar beets and may prove useful with other open-pollinated species, but the progress already made with corn is one of the outstanding achievements in the field of plant breeding.

[1] SUNESON, C. A., O. C. RIDDLE, and F. N. BRIGGS, Yields of Varieties of Wheat Derived by Back-crossing, *Jour. Amer. Soc. Agron.*, Vol. 33, No. 9, 1941.

In 1881, William J. Beal, botanist of the Michigan Agricultural Experiment Station, crossed two distinct varieties of corn, and the seed

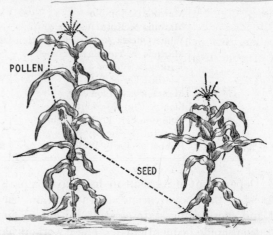

Fig. 126.—Normal open-pollinated corn plant (left) if self-pollinated for several generations produces the inbred (right). Inbreds are small and lack vigor but they become increasingly pure with each successive generation of inbreeding and selection.

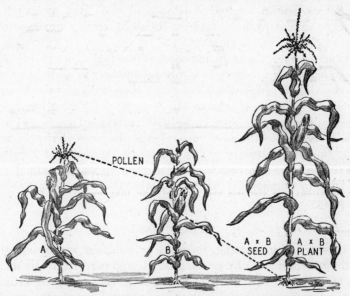

Fig. 127.—Pollen from the tassel of inbred (*A*) pollinates the silks of the detasseled inbred (*B*), resulting in the single-crossed seed (*A* × *B*). This seed produces the single crossed line (*A* × *B*).

thus obtained produced a crop of unusual thrift and vigor. The results that Dr. Beal obtained when he repeated his crossing experiments were variable, doubtless owing to the mixed heritage of the parent lines with which he worked. Hybridization as a method of corn improvement owes much to the early work of two men whose original interest lay in the study of purely theoretical principles. G. H. Shull began inbreeding corn in 1905 at the Station for Experimental Evolution of the Carnegie Institution of Washington at Cold Spring Harbor, N.Y. That same year, E. M. East started inbreeding corn in Illinois

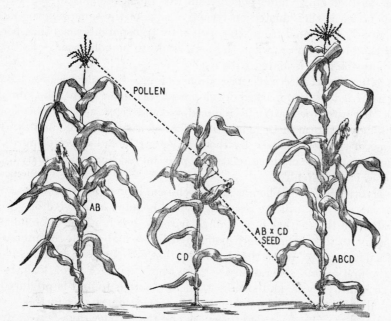

Fig. 128.—Pollen from the tassel of the single-cross (*AB*) pollinates the silks of the single-cross (*CD*) resulting in the production of double-crossed hybrid seed (*AB* × *CD*). This is the seed that corn growers plant to produce a vigorous high-yielding crop for feed or market. The grain produced by the hybrid line (*ABCD*), if used for seed, yields a crop materially less vigorous and uniform than that grown from first-generation hybrid seed.

and continued it at the Connecticut Agricultural Experiment Station. The work of these men suggested the possibilities of improving corn by (1) selecting desirable inbred lines the plants of which were uniform in appearance and hereditary characters and (2) testing the crosses to determine which inbred lines produced vigorous hybrids when crossed together. Dr. D. F. Jones of the Connecticut Agricultural Experiment Station suggested the mating of two single crosses to produce a double-crossed hybrid as a feasible means of utilizing superior crosses in the commercial production of corn.

What Is Hybrid Corn?—The term *hybrid corn* as employed with respect to modern methods of corn improvement is used to designate the first generation of a cross involving inbred lines. Inbred lines eliminate much of the uncertainty found in the mixed heritage of ordinary corn. Inbreeding is really a means of genetic purification, and very close inbreeding is readily possible with corn. Pollen is carefully gathered in a paper sack placed over a tassel for a long enough time so that only viable pollen from this tassel remains in the sack. This pollen is then dusted on receptive silks of the same plant—silks previously protected from stray pollen by transparent sacks that permit the breeder to see when they are ready to be pollinated. In this manner the corn is mated with itself.

After several successive generations of inbreeding and selection have been carried on, two marked developments become evident: the inbred lines of corn show materially reduced size and vigor, and they become strikingly uniform in their inherited characteristics. This uniformity is one of the goals sought by the breeder. It is indicative of purity. The performance of these relatively pure inbred lines when mated in crosses is consistent.

Hybrid Vigor.—When two well-chosen inbred lines of corn are crossed, not only will the resulting hybrid be much more vigorous and productive than either of its inbred parents, but it will also be much superior to the original open-pollinated lines from which the inbreds were developed. When the characters that are expressed (dominants) in the first hybrid generation are those which make for vigor, leafiness, large healthy roots, and strong stalks, a vigorous hybrid is produced. Not all inbreds carry a large number of superior inheritance factors. A thousand may be discarded for every one the breeder saves. Nor are all possible combinations of good inbred lines satisfactory. Only by developing large numbers of inbred lines, making a great many crosses, and repeatedly testing the crosses in comparison with corn lines of known value and adaptation is it possible to obtain hybrids suitable for commercial production.

Kinds of Hybrids.—Hybrids made by crossing two inbred lines are called *single crosses*. These may be entirely satisfactory from the standpoint of vigor and productivity, and they usually are very uniform in appearance. The seed to produce a single-cross hybrid is grown on an inbred parent, which, as a rule, is low in yield and produces small ears and kernels. Thus seed production is expensive. Breeders have found that hybrid vigor can be obtained for one generation by mating two single crosses. This is called a *four-way*, or *double-crossed*, hybrid. In the case of a double-crossed hybrid the seed is produced on a vigorous single-cross plant, seed yields are good, and commercial production of hybrid seed is entirely practical.

Other crosses are *three-way crosses*, in which an inbred is mated with a single cross, and *top crosses*, in which an inbred is mated with an ordinary, nonhybrid variety. The chief advantage of these types is that it is easier to find one inbred to use in a top cross or three inbreds to use in a three-way cross than it is to find four inbreds that mate well in a double cross. Most of the best hybrids in use in the United States are double crosses, with one vigorous single cross producing the pollen and another the seed, which is used the following year for the commercial corn crop.

Finding Desirable Hybrid Combinations.—Corn breeding, as carried on by state agricultural experiment stations and the U.S. Department of Agriculture, is a cooperative undertaking. With their work coordinated under the direction of M. S. Jenkins of the U.S. Department of Agriculture and by annual conferences, the various state agricultural experiment stations pool their best inbred lines for testing purposes. Fortunately, a reliable index of the value of a double cross can be had from the performance of its four component single crosses.[1] Thus, the double cross

$$(A \times B) \times (C \times D)$$

is influenced in equal proportions by the single crosses

$$A \times C,$$
$$A \times D,$$
$$B \times C,$$
$$B \times D.$$

The average yield, average maturity, and average of other characteristics of these single crosses can be used to predict the performance of the double cross $(A \times B) \times (C \times D)$. By testing a number of inbred lines in all possible combinations the corn breeder can know in advance which combinations are likely to make the best double crosses.

Many of the better double crosses are made up of inbreds originating in two, three, or four different states.

Hybrid Seed Superior for One Generation Only.—One of the important considerations in corn improvement by the hybridization method is that a hybrid maintains its uniformity and superior vigor for one generation only. Segregation and recombination of characters occur in the second and subsequent generations, resulting in variations

[1] ANDERSON, D. C., The Relation between Single and Double-cross Yields in Corn, *Jour. Amer. Soc. Agron.*, Vol. 30, No. 3, 1938.

in type, size of plant, maturity, and other characters and in a reduction in productivity. The amount of reduction in yield depends on the kind of cross made, the average productivity of the inbred lines involved, and the vigor of the first-generation hybrid.[1] Reduction in productivity and general desirability is great enough so that the use of second- and subsequent-generation seed is inadvisable.

How Hybrids Are Produced Commercially.—The production of experimental hybrids is carried on by a process of hand-pollination, a procedure entirely too expensive for commercial production.

Fig. 129.—Left, pollen producing rows; right, detasseled rows, for the commercial production of double-crossed hybrid seed corn in Indiana. (*Courtesy of J. C. Allen and Son.*)

However, the field production of hybrid seed is feasible and can be accomplished at a reasonable cost. The grower who is to produce double-crossed seed first obtains seed of the two single-crossed parents. One satisfactory planting method is to plant four rows of the single cross from which the seed ears are to be harvested to one row of the single cross which is to be used as the male, or pollinating, parent. As soon as the first tassels appear and before they shed any pollen, the female, or seed-producing, parent is detasseled. The detasseling work must be kept up for a 10-day to 2-week period or as long as new tassels appear, the object being to prevent the seed-producing parent from shedding any pollen. Thus, all its ears will be pollinated from the

[1] For a genetic rule on decrease in yielding capacity of advanced-generation corn hybrids, see N. P. Neal, The Decrease in Yielding Capacity in Advanced Generations of Hybrid Corn, *Jour. Amer. Soc. Agron.*, Vol. 27, No. 8, 1935.

plants in the male rows, double-cross hybrid seed being thus produced. The corn produced by the male parent is used for feed.

Single crosses are produced on a field scale in a similar manner; inbred lines are used as parent stock, and a somewhat higher proportion of male rows is grown to ensure good pollination. The inbred lines are produced by various methods of controlled pollination designed to secure seed in adequate quantities for the production of parent-stock single crosses without material change in the hereditary properties of the inbred lines.[1]

Characteristics of Good Hybrids.—The corn breeder, in making his selection within inbred lines, discards those with inferior hereditary characteristics and saves those that are superior. By combining inbred lines capable of transmitting desirable characters, he has been able to produce hybrids that are very much superior to the best lines previously developed by the mass selection of open-pollinated corn. Characteristics that have been developed in the better hybrid lines include the following:

Uniformity.—A well-bred hybrid line will show a much higher degree of uniformity than an open-pollinated variety. Such uniformity makes for evenness in maturity, a smaller proportion of nubbins and off-grade ears, and greater ease of harvest, especially with mechanical equipment.

Strength of Stalk.—Corn breeders have been able to produce strong-stalked hybrids very resistant to lodging or breaking over. Growers using stiff-stalked hybrids have reported that this feature alone warranted the extra expenditure for hybrid seed because of greater ease of harvest.

Large Roots.—Vigorous hybrids generally have a much larger root system than the usual standard open-pollinated varieties.

Disease Resistance.—Resistance to seedling, stalk, root, and ear diseases is one of the objectives of the corn breeder. The stronger stalks and roots of some of the hybrids are due in part to inherent disease resistance.

Insect Resistance.—It appears possible to develop corn hybrids resistant to damage by certain insects. Although no lines have been found that are in any sense immune to infestation by the European corn borer, some of the stronger stalked lines are certainly able to withstand borer attack with less breakage and secondary damage than are suffered by other types.

[1] BORGESON, CARL, and H. K. HAYES, The Minnesota Method of Seed Increase and Seed Registration for Hybrid Corn, *Jour. Amer. Soc. Agron.*, Vol. 33, No. 1, 1941.

Adaptation.—No one corn hybrid is universal in adaptation. Hybrids have already been bred to meet the different requirements of growing seasons of various lengths; some show their greatest advantage where growing conditions are most favorable; others where productivity of the soil is lower. Some have shown evidence of being better able to withstand drought than others or than open-pollinated varieties. The development of hybrids of particular value to the feeding or milling industries is an opportunity offered by this method of corn improvement.

Yield.—The major advantage in the use of corn hybrids is that the good ones are substantially more productive than the good open-pollinated corns of similar maturity. Most of the hybrids in commercial production are at least 10 to 15 per cent more productive than comparable open-pollinated varieties, and increases in productivity of more than 20 per cent are not unusual.

Many of the state agricultural experiment stations conduct trials of the adaptation and comparative productivity of corn hybrids in several localities, such trials providing unbiased information as an aid to farmers in making well-advised choices for commercial corn production.

OTHER APPLICATIONS OF BREEDING METHODS

Using Hybrid Vigor in Sugar Beets.—The improvement of corn by selection within self-pollinated lines and the recombination, by crossing, of selected inbred lines to secure hybrid vigor is particularly feasible because the pollination of corn is easily controlled, seed production per plant is large, and the amount of seed required per acre is small. The same method, in principle, has been used for the development of new sugar-beet varieties. Inbreeding of sugar beets, as with corn, results in a reduction in the vigor of the inbred lines. Because, in sugar beets, the male and female organs are parts of the same flower, the crossing of all flowers is not secured under field conditions. However, a large percentage of hybridization is secured by mixing the seed of two inbred lines in proper proportion and allowing natural open-pollination to take place. The U.S. Department of Agriculture has developed inbred lines that, when crossed together in this manner, have produced first-generation hybrids of good productivity showing marked resistance to Cercospora leaf spot.

Hybrid vigor has been evinced in first-generation crosses of other open-pollinated crops. The difficulty, thus far, has been in finding a practical way to make the crosses on a field scale.

Strain Building.—Strain building is a method of crop improvement, used with open-pollinated species, that aims at the development of better strains by intercrossing unrelated selected plants similar with respect to any desired agronomic qualities. It attempts to maintain vigor by bringing into the strain a large range of desirable inherited characters. Strain building is described by Kirk[1] as any system of mating by which a strain is built up by the crossing of carefully selected plants. It differs from selfed-line breeding in that the latter presupposes several generations of inbreeding until the parent lines are reasonably pure, followed by the commercial production of first-generation hybrid seed. Strain building involves the synthesis of parent lines from carefully selected open-pollinated material or inbred lines. It has been used with timothy, brome grass, alfalfa, clover, and other open-pollinated species and appears to be merely a form of mass selection.

MAINTAINING IMPROVED VARIETIES

Crop improvement does not stop with the development of superior varieties. Such varieties are of no use to agriculture until pure seed is made available to farmers in large quantities and at reasonable prices. Very often the seed of two varieties cannot be differentiated though the varieties themselves may be vastly different in agronomic value and adaptation. Therefore, assurance must be provided the farmer that the seed he purchases is genuine as to variety. Good seed must also be pure and of strong germination. These requirements have led to a system of seed certification now practiced in 35 states and the Dominion of Canada and correlated through the International Crop Improvement Association.

Foundation Seed.—In the United States, where so much of the plant-breeding work is carried on by public agencies, the Federal and state agricultural experiment stations have generally assumed the task of purifying a new variety and increasing the seed to such quantities that it can be released to farmers for production on a large enough scale to be handled with ordinary equipment and, with reasonable caution, kept pure. If unusually large quantities of parent stock are required, as in the case of hybrid corn, special organizations may be designated to produce such seed under supervision. Inbred lines are increased and parent single crosses are produced in Ohio by the Ohio Hybrid Seed Corn Producers Association which cooperates closely with the Ohio Agricultural Experiment Station in this work. An interesting instance of the production of foundation-seed stocks under conditions

[1] Kirk, L. E., Improvement of Pasture Grasses and Legumes, Spragg Memorial Lectures on Plant Breeding, Michigan State College, 1937.

that make the avoidance of mixtures easy is the growing of pure seed of
Rosen rye and Michelite beans in perfect isolation on South Manitou
Island in northern Lake Michigan.   In the case of rye, cross-pollination is avoided; with the beans, the problem is to keep seed stocks free
from mechanical mixtures that cannot readily be identified.

Such foundation-seed stocks provide the basis for the large-scale
production of certified seed.

Certified Seed.—"Seed certification is intended to preserve the
purity, increase the supply, and hasten the distribution of pure seed of
new and improved varieties of crops to the farmers in order that the

Fig. 130.—A field of certified seed tobacco in North Carolina.   (*Courtesy of E. R.
Collins, North Carolina Agricultural Experiment Station.*)

business of farming may be made more profitable."[1]   It is usually
carried on by organizations of farmers cooperating very closely with
the extension services and experiment stations of the various colleges of
agriculture.   To a large extent, though not wholly, it is limited to
varieties that, after thorough test, have proved to be of special merit in
the state carrying on the certification.   In some instances the certifying agency is the state department of agriculture; but for the most part
the work is more educational than regulatory, and it is therefore associated with educational institutions.

Ordinarily the work consists in the maintenance of an adequate
supply of seed of a superior variety from which farmers may renew their
seed stocks at reasonable intervals, for such crops as wheat, oats, and
barley.   With hybrid corn, however, new seed must be secured each
year, and so certification implies the provision of great quantities of
seed of known pedigree, produced under inspection to ensure proper

[1] *The Official Handbook of Seed Certification,* Illinois Crop Improvement Association, Urbana, Ill., 1941.

isolation of the seed fields, prompt and complete detasseling of the seed-bearing parent lines, adequate storage conditions, careful grading, and high quality and germination. Likewise, in the case of potatoes, certification is carried on with large supplies of seed that are superior in productivity not only because of varietal vigor but also because of freedom from serious seed-borne diseases.

Certification involves inspection of both the growing crop and the seed as it is finally cleaned and made ready for the market. The tag of the certifying agency attests to variety, purity, germination, and other matters concerning the merit of the seed. Skillful specialized seed growers with acreages large and small constitute the producing membership of crop-improvement associations. In some associations, seed lots of special merit for further seed production are designated as *registered seed*.

The Rapid Spread of a New Variety.—The story of the Michelite bean provides an illustration of how crop improvement functions, from breeding to the widespread commercial use of a variety—a story that has been duplicated in principle with many crops and in many states. The Robust and Early Prolific varieties of beans were crossed in a Michigan State College greenhouse in 1926. After years of selection, purification, and testing at East Lansing, Mich., two of the most promising strains were put into a series of state-wide trials to make sure of their adaptation and merit. One of these strains proved most acceptable to the bean trade as well as to farmers, and sufficient seed of this strain was produced on the college farm in 1936 to plant 20 acres in 1937. All the production from this 20 acres grown on eight farms was distributed to certified-seed growers in the spring of 1938 under an agreement preventing price exploitation of the seed while the supply was limited, because the variety was developed with public funds. Two chains of privately owned elevators and certain cooperatives in Michigan's most important bean district bought practically all the certified seed produced in 1938, 1939, and 1940 and distributed it to their farmer clients. (These agencies, incidentally, continue the distribution of certified seed of well-established varieties.) From less than a bushel of seed in the spring of 1936, this variety was expanded to over 300,000 acres in 1941, and its merit is such that it promises to make up 80 to 90 per cent of Michigan's production until an even better variety is developed by the continuing efforts of plant breeders.

Private Plant-breeding Agencies.—For the most part, plant breeding with field crops has been carried on as a public service by Federal and state agricultural experiment stations. However, privately owned **seed companies** frequently maintain plant-breeding programs which have made noteworthy contributions particularly in cotton and hybrid-corn breeding. The activities of private plant breeders have, on the whole, been centered more in horticultural than in field crops.

Review Problems

1. Discuss the interactions of heredity and environment.
2. What is the significance of mutations in crop improvement?
3. What was Mendel's contribution to plant improvement?
4. A pure line of wheat was planted under conditions where winterkilling was severe. About 15 per cent of the plants survived and produced seed. Discuss the selection of this seed from the standpoint of improving the winter hardiness of the wheat.
5. Would your conclusions be the same if the crop mentioned in the preceding problem were red clover? Why?
6. Why do plant breeders make crosses between different strains or varieties of self-pollinated crops?
7. What is the usual function of the cross made to produce hybrid corn?
8. What is the purpose of seed-certification work in your state, and how is it carried on?
9. Most regional strains of red clover were developed by

    a. Natural selection.
    b. Pure-line selection.
    c. Strain building.
    d. Selection within inbred lines.

10. Double-crossed corn hybrids are generally used commercially, rather than single crosses because

    a. They are twice as vigorous.
    b. They are more uniform.
    c. Seed production is cheaper.
    d. The breeding problem is less complex.

11. Name four varieties of self-pollinated crops developed by crossing, followed by selection.

    1. _____
    2. _____
    3. _____
    4. _____

12. Four inbred lines A, B, C, and D were crossed in all possible combinations, and the single crosses were tested, with the following yield results:

$$A \times B = 72 \text{ bu.}$$
$$A \times C = 69 \text{ bu.}$$
$$A \times D = 64 \text{ bu.}$$
$$B \times C = 67 \text{ bu.}$$
$$B \times D = 69 \text{ bu.}$$
$$C \times D = 71 \text{ bu.}$$

How should these inbreds be mated to produce the most productive double cross?

References

Better Plants and Animals, Vols. I and II, *U.S. Dept. Agr. Yearbook of Agriculture*, 1936, 1937.

FAIRCHILD, DAVID: "The World Was My Garden. Travels of a Plant Explorer," Charles Scribner's Sons, New York, 1938.

HAYES, H. K., and R. J. GARBER: "Breeding Crop Plants," McGraw-Hill Book Company, Inc., New York, 1927.

LOVE, H. H., *et al.*: Spragg Memorial Lectures on Plant Breeding (1st ser.), Michigan State College, East Lansing, Mich., 1930–1936.

RICHIE, F. D.: The What and How of Hybrid Corn, *U.S. Dept. Agr. Farmers' Bul.* 1744, 1935.

WALLACE, HENRY A.: Corn Breeding Experience and Its Probable Eventual Effect on the Technique of Livestock Breeding, Spragg Memorial Lectures on Plant Breeding, Michigan State College, East Lansing, Mich., 1938.

APPENDIX

The following table of weights and measures, covering a partial list of the more important field-crop products, is taken from *U.S. Department of Agriculture Agricultural Statistics*, 1940. With respect to the table from which this material comes, the U.S. Department of Agriculture states:

"The approximate or average weights, as given in this table, do not (necessarily) have official standing as a basis for packing or as grounds for settling disputes. Not all of them are recognized as legal weights. The table was prepared chiefly for use of workers in the Department of Agriculture, who have need of conversion factors in statistical computations. The figures are subject to revision."

TABLE 19.—SOME WEIGHTS AND MEASURES USED IN THE U. S. DEPARTMENT
OF AGRICULTURE

Commodity	Unit[a]	Approximate net weight, pounds
Alfalfa seed...................................	Bushel	60
Barley..	Bushel	48
Beans:		
Lima, dry.................................	Bushel	56
Other, dry................................	Bushel	60
	Bag	100
Bluegrass seed.............................	Bushel	14–30
Broomcorn (6 bales per ton)...................	Bale	333
Broomcorn seed.............................	Bushel	44–50
Buckwheat..................................	Bushel	48–52
Clover seed.................................	Bushel	60
Corn:		
Ear, husked...............................	Bushel	70[b]
Shelled...................................	Bushel	56
Cotton......................................	Bale, gross	500
	Bale, net	478[c]
Cottonseed..................................	Bushel	32[d]
Cottonseed oil..............................	Gallon	7.5[e]
Cowpeas....................................	Bushel	60
Flaxseed....................................	Bushel	56
Grain sorghums.............................	Bushel	56 and 50
Hempseed..................................	Bushel	44
Hops.......................................	Bale, gross	200
Kaffir......................................	Bushel	56 and 50
Linseed oil.................................	Gallon	7.5[e]
Malt.......................................	Bushel	34
Millet......................................	Bushel	48–50
Molasses...................................	Gallon	11.75
Oats.......................................	Bushel	32
Orchard-grass seed..........................	Bushel	14
Peanuts, unshelled:		
Virginia type.............................	Bushel	22
Runners, southeastern.....................	Bushel	28
Spanish..................................	Bushel	30
Peas, dry...................................	Bushel	60
Popcorn:		
On ear...................................	Bushel	70[b]
Shelled...................................	Bushel	56
Potatoes....................................	Bushel	60
	Barrel	165
Rapeseed...................................	Bushel	50 and 60
Redtop seed................................	Bushel	14–40

TABLE 19.—SOME WEIGHTS AND MEASURES USED IN THE U. S. DEPARTMENT OF AGRICULTURE.—(*Continued*)

Commodity	Unit[a]	Approximate net weight, pounds
Rice:		
Rough	Bushel	45
	Bag	100
	Barrel	162
Milled	Pocket or bag	100
Rye	Bushel	56
Sorgo:		
Seed	Bushel	50
Sirup	Gallon	11.4
Soybeans	Bushel	60
Soybean oil	Gallon	7.5[e]
Spelt	Bushel	40
Sudan-grass seed	Bushel	40
Sugar-cane sirup	Gallon	11.25
Sunflower seed	Bushel	24 and 32
Sweet potatoes	Bushel	55[f]
Timothy seed	Bushel	45
Tobacco:		
Maryland	Hogshead	600– 800
Flue-cured	Hogshead	900–1,100
Burley	Hogshead	1,000–1,200
Dark air-cured	Hogshead	1,000–1,250
Virginia fire-cured	Hogshead	1,050–1,350
Kentucky and Tennessee fire-cured	Hogshead	1,350–1,650
Velvet beans (hulled)	Bushel	60
Vetch	Bushel	60
Water, 60°F	Gallon	8.33
Wheat	Bushel	60
Various commodities	Short ton	2,000
	Long ton	2,240

[a] The standard bushel used in the United States contains 2,150.42 cu. in.; the gallon, 231 cu. in.; and the standard fruit and vegetable barrel, 7,056 cu. in. Such large-sized products as apples and potatoes sometimes are sold on the basis of a heaped bushel, which would exceed somewhat the 2,150.42 cu. in. of a bushel basket level full.

[b] The standard weight of 70 lb. is usually recognized as being about 2 measured bushels of corn, husked, on the ear, because it requires 70 lb. to yield 1 bu., or 56 lb. of shelled corn.

[c] For statistical purposes the bale of cotton is 500 lb. gross or 478 lb. net weight. Actual bale weights vary considerably, and the customary average weights of bales of foreign cotton differ from that of the American square bale.

[d] This is the average weight of cottonseed, although the legal weight in some states varies from this figure of 32 lb.

[e] This is the weight commonly used in trade practice, the actual weight varying according to temperature conditions.

[f] This average of 55 lb. indicates the usual weight of sweet potatoes when harvested. Much weight is lost in curing or drying, and the net weight when sold in terminal markets may be far below 55 lb.

INDEX

A

B

441

56
.30
————
16.80

5.6
.4
————
22.4

3.
7.5 | 22.4
     225

2.25
2.0 | 16.8
      150
      ————
      180
      150
      ————
      300